Practical Analog, Digital Embedded Electronics Scientists

Practical Analog, Digital, and Embedded Electronics for Scientists

Brett D DePaola

Department of Physics, Kansas State University, Manhattan, Kansas, USA

IOP Publishing, Bristol, UK

Permission to make use of IOP Publishing content other than as set out above may be sought at permissions@ioppublishing.org.

Brett D DePaola has asserted his right to be identified as the author of this work in accordance with sections 77 and 78 of the Copyright, Designs and Patents Act 1988.

ISBN   978-0-7503-3491-4 (ebook)
ISBN   978-0-7503-3489-1 (print)
ISBN   978-0-7503-3492-1 (myPrint)
ISBN   978-0-7503-3490-7 (mobi)

DOI   10.1088/978-0-7503-3491-4

Version: 20210101

IOP ebooks

British Library Cataloguing-in-Publication Data: A catalogue record for this book is available from the British Library.

Published by IOP Publishing, wholly owned by The Institute of Physics, London

IOP Publishing, Temple Circus, Temple Way, Bristol, BS1 6HG, UK

US Office: IOP Publishing, Inc., 190 North Independence Mall West, Suite 601, Philadelphia, PA 19106, USA

I dedicate this book to my father, Anthony Joseph DePaola,
who gave me my love of science.

Contents

Preface

There are few really good texts available for a lecture/lab-based electronics course that teaches analog, digital, and embedded electronics. And yet there is a crying need. Virtually all science and engineering programs would benefit from their students having familiarity with these topics. Most existing texts seem designed for multi-semester courses that are geared toward training electrical engineers. Other texts fall short in that they are either hopelessly out of date or are overly focused on a narrow range of topics.

This book is different. First of all, it is short. We cover only a subset of topics covered by the classic by P Horowitz & W Hill (now in its third edition) and we cover those topics only as deeply as needed in order to understand the material in the accompanying labs. This allows us to cover all the material in a single semester course. This text/lab manual was created for a one-semester course taken by physics students, both undergraduate and graduate. But unlike many electronics texts for physics students, this one does *not* delve into the physics of, say, a transistor. Devices are largely treated as black boxes having certain properties that are important to know for designing circuits. The physics comes when the students use their acquired electronics instrumentation knowledge to construct apparatus to make measurements. But since the physics has been left out, this book should be equally useful for students in any of the physical or life sciences.

Furthermore, right from the beginning, this was written as an integrated text and lab manual combination. I find in my classes that the students have largely eschewed the Internet for further explanation, and instead flip to the appropriate lecture.

A third feature of this book is that much of the analog and digital electronics know-how that is learned in the early sections are put to use in the section on embedded electronics. To our knowledge, there are no electronics textbooks, geared for the non-electrical engineering student, that has both the generality on analog and digital electronics circuits, coupled to the very timely technology of embedded electronics.

Brett DePaola
Department of Physics
Kansas State University
March 2020

Acknowledgements

I would like to acknowledge all of my past students, both undergraduate and graduate, who through their enthusiasm and hard work have taught me so much.

Author biography

Brett D DePaola

 **Brett D DePaola** is a professor of Physics at Kansas State University. He is an experimentalist in the field of atomic, molecular, and optical physics. Born in Ohio, he received his BS in Physics at Miami University, and his MS in Physics at Miami university, for research done at The University of Paris in Orsay, France. He then received his PhD in Physics from The University of Texas, Dallas. DePaola has taught analog, digital, and embedded electronics at Kansas State University for roughly 30 years and, in the course of his research efforts has designed countless pieces of electronics, both for his own use and for the use of his colleagues.

Part I

Lectures

IOP Publishing

Practical Analog, Digital, and Embedded Electronics for Scientists

Brett D DePaola

Chapter 1

Introduction

In this chapter we review the basics, some of which have probably already been learned, but may have been forgotten by now. We start with a review of the basic math that we will need to use. We next review Ohm's law and Kirchhoff's rules. We apply basic electronics analysis tools to the most fundamental non-trivial circuit: the voltage divider. After covering these basics, we introduce Thévenin's theorem, which will be invaluable in our analysis of input and output impedances. Finally, we discuss input and output impedances in a general way.

1.1 Laws of the land

1.1.1 Logs and decibels

In many fields, for example acoustics and, of course, electronics, we find that we must compare quantities that differ or change over many orders of magnitude. In order to discuss such large ranges it is often convenient to take the logarithms of the quantities of interest. But because the argument of a logarithm must be dimensionless, we often take the log of a ratio of like objects. For example, the healthy human ear can detect sound over the range of $10\,000\,000\,000$ in power. To work with this large range, we use the decibel (dB) system.

For powers, the decibel is defined as:

$$\text{Number of dBs} = 10\,\log(P_1/P_2), \tag{1.1}$$

where P_1 and P_2 are two powers being compared and the log is base-10. Note that if $P_1 = 2P_2$, then the result, to a very good approximation, is 3 dB. Conversely, if $P_2 = 2P_1$, then the result is -3 dB. You should remember this.

Generally speaking, power is proportional to the square of amplitude. For example, $P = V^2/R$, where V voltage and R is resistance. Then the algebra of logarithms shows that for amplitudes,

doi:10.1088/978-0-7503-3491-4ch1

$$\text{Number of dBs} = 20 \log(V_1/V_2). \tag{1.2}$$

For amplitudes the 2× condition gives ±6 dB. (Remember this as well. It's important!) Furthermore, if the ratio $V_1/V_2 = \sqrt{2}$, the result of equation (1.2) is 3 dB. (This is also well worth remembering!)

1.1.2 Complex arithmetic (Complex, yes. Difficult, no!)

Especially in lecture 2, we'll find it essential to manipulate complex variables. Let's suppose z is a complex number. Then we can express z as a combination of a pure real and pure imaginary number:

$$z = a + jb, \tag{1.3}$$

where a and b are pure real and $j \equiv \sqrt{-1}$. Note that in the electronics world we use a j instead of an i for the square root of -1. The reason is that in electronics the symbol i is generally used to designate a current. The complex conjugate of a complex number is defined as replacing j by $-j$. Notationally, the complex conjugate of z is expressed as z^*. Then,

$$\text{Re}(z) = \frac{(z + z^*)}{2}, \tag{1.4a}$$

$$\text{Im}(z) = \frac{(z - z^*)}{2}, \tag{1.4b}$$

where Re (z) and Im (z) are the real and imaginary parts of z, respectively.

Complex numbers can also be expressed in terms of a magnitude and a phase. The magnitude of complex number z is given by

$$|z| = \sqrt{z^*z} \tag{1.5a}$$

$$= \sqrt{(a - jb)(a + jb)} \tag{1.5b}$$

$$= \sqrt{a^2 + b^2}. \tag{1.5c}$$

It is often useful to think of complex numbers graphically as lying in the complex $x - jy$ plane. For example, consider the number z in the complex plane, as shown in figure 1.1.

If, as in equation (1.3), the real and imaginary parts of z are a and b, respectively, then from Pythagoras' theorem, we obtain equation (1.5c). Furthermore, the angle ϕ is given by

$$\phi = \tan^{-1}(b/a), \tag{1.6}$$

and is referred to as the phase. We can then express z as

$$z = |z|e^{j\phi}. \tag{1.7}$$

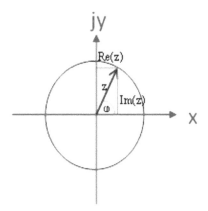

Figure 1.1. Graphical representation of the complex number z.

This is reasonable because by Euler's theorem, $|z|e^{j\phi} = |z|\cos\phi + j|z|\sin\phi$. But from figure 1.1, $a = |z|\cos\phi$ and $b = |z|\sin\phi$, leading us back to equation (1.3).

Generally speaking, equation (1.3) is a more useful representation for manipulating complex numbers, while equation (1.7) is more useful in their interpretation. We'll see examples of this in lecture section 2.2 when we discuss RC circuits.

1.1.3 Ohm's law and Kirchhoff's rules

Ohm's law relates the current, i, flowing through a resistance R, the voltage drop, v, across that resistance, and the value of that resistance:

$$i = v/R. \tag{1.8}$$

We will use Ohm's law over and over in this course.

Kirchhoff has two rules:
1. Loop rule: The directed sum of voltage drops and emfs (for example, batteries) around any closed network is zero.
2. Junction rule: The directed sum of currents into/out of any junction in a network is zero.

1.2 The voltage divider (You can't believe how important this is!)

Consider the circuit in figure 1.2. V_1 is the voltage drop across the 'input' terminals and V_2 is the voltage drop across the 'output' terminals. R_1 and R_2 are resistors. It is assumed that whatever is connected to the output side has 'infinite' impedance. The funny symbol at the bottom means 'ground' or electrical potential of zero. It is not actually needed in this example, but often appears in circuits so get used to it.

From Ohm's law, the current flowing through R_1 and R_2 is

$$I_{tot} = \frac{V_1}{R_1 + R_2}. \tag{1.9}$$

Then, again by Ohm's law, V_2, the voltage drop across R_2, is given by

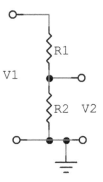

Figure 1.2. Typical voltage divider circuit.

$$V_2 = I_{tot}R_2. \tag{1.10}$$

This is true because all of the current that passes through R_1, also passes through R_2 since it is assumed that the outputs feed a device with infinite impedance. Combining equations (1.9) and (1.10) gives

$$V_2 = \frac{R_2}{R_1 + R_2}V_1. \tag{1.11}$$

Equation (1.11) is incredibly useful. And, while trivial to derive, should be memorized. The voltage divider appears over and over again in circuits and even simple derivations take time. I strongly suggest you first make sure you can do the derivation and then memorize the result. As we will see in lecture section 2.2, the voltage divider equation can be applied to general impedances, not just Ohmic resistors.

1.3 Mr Thévenin and his amazing equivalent circuit

In 1853 Hermann von Helmholtz made a startling deduction, one that was independently discovered by Léon Charles Thévenin in 1883. That is, that any combination of emfs (e.g. batteries) and resistors could be replaced by a single battery in series with a single resistor, and that the new circuit would be a functional copy of the original one.

The new circuit is called the Thévenin-equivalent circuit, and the new battery and resistor are called the Thévenin-equivalent battery (or voltage) and Thévenin-equivalent resistor, respectively. The principal value of the Thévenin theorem, as it is called (perhaps Helmholtz already had too many things named after him?) is that it simplifies analysis of complicated circuits.

As an example, let's consider the circuit of figure 1.2, explicitly replacing V_1 by a battery having an emf of V_{Th}. The Thévenin-equivalent circuit is shown in figure 1.3.

Well, that was easy, but not too useful—unless we can give a value to R_{Th} and V_{Th}, based on the values of the components in figure 1.2. To do this, look at figure 1.2 and imagine two limiting cases, the first for the circuit as drawn, namely leaving the V_2 terminals 'open', and the second for those terminals shorted

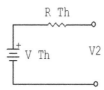

Figure 1.3. Thevenin equivalent circuit of that in figure 1.2.

(connected to each other). In the first case, in order for the circuit of figure 1.3 to be equivalent to that of figure 1.2, it *must* be the case that $V_{Th} = V_2$. The proof is simple: no current flows through R_{Th}. (Where would it go?!) Therefore, according to Ohm's law, the voltage drop across R_{Th} is 0. Therefore $V_2 = V_{Th}$. QED.

Now consider the second case. If the output is shorted, then the current flowing through the shorting wire is V_1/R_1. But for the circuit in figure 1.3, the current flowing through the shorting wire is V_{Th}/R_{Th}. According to the Thévenin theorem, these currents must be equal. That is,

$$\frac{V_1}{R_1} = \frac{V_{Th}}{R_{Th}} = \frac{V_2}{R_{Th}}, \tag{1.12}$$

or, combining equations (1.11) and (1.12),

$$R_{Th} = \frac{R_1 R_2}{R_1 + R_2}. \tag{1.13}$$

This is a remarkable result: equation (1.13) is saying that the Thévenin-equivalent resistance of a voltage divider is equal to the two resistors in the divider added in parallel. This is *not* intuitive because those resistors are definitely *not* in parallel! Among other things, we will use Thévenin analysis to deduce the input and output impedances of circuits.

1.4 Input and output impedances

1.4.1 Theoretical determination of impedance

At first glance, circuits seem pretty complicated. Part of the skill set one develops in learning electronics is the ability to break up a circuit into its constituent sub-circuits, and then separately analyze those sub-circuits. This divide-and-conquer approach is only possible when one sub-component does not change the behavior of the other sub-components.

As an example, consider the extremely simple circuit of figure 1.4, consisting of just two sub-components: a voltage divider and a resistive load. Let's suppose $V_1 = 10$ V, and $R_1 = R_2 = 100k$. If R_{load} were infinite, then you'd expect the potential at the top of the load resistance to be 5 V. But what if $R_{load} = 0$ Ω. Then the potential at the 'top' of the load should be 0 (by definition). What is the correct answer? Clearly the choice of R_{load} affects how the voltage divider functions—and this is a very undesirable situation! So what to do? With only a few exceptions, when you have one sub-circuit (call it circuit 'A') 'feeding' another (that we'll call 'B'), you

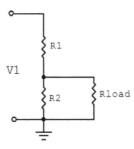

Figure 1.4. Compound circuit consisting of a voltage divider and a load resistor.

want the output impedance of circuit A to be much less than the input impedance of circuit B.

In the case of the circuit in figure 1.4, we need the output impedance of the voltage divider part, given by equation (1.13), to be much less than R_{load}. For example, suppose $R_1 = R_2 = 100k$. Then the output impedance is $50k$, and we would like R_{load} to be very large compared to that. What if, for example, $R_{\mathrm{load}} = 50k$? Then, replacing the voltage divider by its Thévenin-equivalent resistance, we obtain a new voltage divider, with R_{Th} as the 'upper resistor' and R_{load} as the 'lower resistor'. Using the voltage divider equation, we can now see that the voltage at the top of R_{load} has 'sagged' from 5 V to 2.5 V. In fact, using the new voltage divider equation, for which $R_1 \rightarrow R_{VD}$, and $R_2 \rightarrow R_{\mathrm{load}}$ we see that for $V_1 \approx V_2$, (the equivalent of saying very little sag) we need

$$\frac{R_{\mathrm{load}}}{R_{VD} + R_{\mathrm{load}}} \approx 1, \tag{1.14}$$

or,

$$R_{VD} \ll R_{\mathrm{load}}. \tag{1.15}$$

That is, we need the output impedance of the voltage divider to be much less than the input impedance of the load. As a rule of thumb, we can usually replace the $\gg$ symbol with $\times 10$. For the example of equation (1.15), we only need to choose our voltage divider components such that $R_{VD} \lesssim R_{\mathrm{load}}/10$.

Choosing component values in a voltage divider such that hanging the next sub-circuit on it does not change its output, is called making the divider 'stiff'.

In general we need to design each of our sub-components such that its output impedance is low compared to the input impedance of the downstream sub-circuit, and its input impedance is high compared to the module immediately upstream.

There are two significant exceptions to this rule. The first is that when you are dealing with high frequencies, you want to match input and output impedances. Failure to do this will result in reflections as the high frequency signal encounters an impedance mismatch. Note that because the Fourier transform of a short pulse contains high frequencies, this note of caution applies to short pulses as well.

The second exception is when the signal is a current rather than a voltage. For example, you may have a signal from a photodiode; this is a photocurrent. In the case of current signals, the impedance rule is flipped: you want $Z_{\text{in}} \ll Z_{\text{out}}$. Fortunately, this is usually not difficult to achieve because for a perfect current source, $Z_{\text{out}} = \infty$.

1.4.2 Experimental determination of impedance

It is not always possible to determine theoretically the input or output impedance of a device. For example, suppose you are given a function generator and that device has no documentation. How would you determine its output impedance? How would we even model what we mean by output impedance?

Consider figure 1.5 where we have represented a realistic function generator by an ideal ($R_{\text{out}} = 0$) function generator in series with an internal non-zero R_{int}. If you measure the output signal without a load resistor attached, then the measured signal is the ideal signal, S_{ideal}. Now, if you attach a (known) load resistor and re-measure the output signal (S_L) you can deduce R_{int} simply by using the voltage divider equation:

$$S_L = \frac{R_{\text{load}}}{R_{\text{load}} + R_{\text{int}}} S_{\text{ideal}},\tag{1.16}$$

or

$$R_{\text{int}} = \frac{S_{\text{ideal}} - S_L}{S_L} R_{\text{load}}.\tag{1.17}$$

From equation (1.16), it's easy to see that your 'best' measurement would be if you choose $R_{\text{load}} \sim R_{\text{int}}$, because for that choice of load resistor, your measured S_L would lie halfway between S_{ideal} and ground.

How about input impedance? For example, suppose you are given an analog–digital converter (ADC) to use, but no information about its input impedance. One uses an ADC by feeding it an analog signal and the ADC outputs the digital equivalence of that signal. But if the input impedance of the ADC is not much higher than the output impedance of the source of your analog signal, the ADC will 'load down' that signal and your digital output would not be correct. So, how should you measure the input impedance of the ADC?

One way would be to place a test resistor of known value in series with the input signal, as shown in figure 1.6. Then after putting the test resistor in place measure the signal at both V_1 and V_2. Once again using the voltage divider equation, we obtain

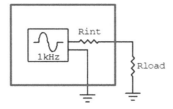

Figure 1.5. Function generator, drawn as an ideal function generator having an internal output impedance.

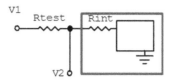

Figure 1.6. ADC represented as an ideal ADC in series with an internal input impedance.

$$V_2 = \frac{R_{\text{int}}}{R_{\text{int}} + R_{\text{test}}} V_1, \tag{1.18}$$

which gives

$$R_{\text{int}} = \frac{V_2}{V_1 - V_2} R_{\text{test}}. \tag{1.19}$$

And once again the best quality measurement will be obtained for the choice of $R_{\text{test}} \approx R_{\text{int}}$.

1.5 Error propagation

In the process of testing and debugging a circuit, you make measurements. You may measure gain, you may measure an RC time constant, you may be probing a signal at various points in your circuit. But in any case, these are measurements. When comparing your measured values to what you'd expect to see, you need to estimate your uncertainties. In particular, you have to estimate how uncertainties in various quantities will combine to give an overall uncertainty. General measurement theory and error analysis are beyond the scope of this text. However, we will briefly derive the most important and useful results of error propagation theory. As an aside, we use the terms 'error' and 'uncertainty' interchangeably.

Suppose you make a great deal of measurements of a certain quantity. Because of statistical error in your measurement, you should expect a range of results. For example, if you were measuring the height of a small child, you might expect to obtain a range of values, perhaps due to the resolution of the measuring device, perhaps due to the fidgeting of the child. Suppose we call the quantity you are measuring x. Then, perhaps the best estimate of the quantity's true value is the average or mean:

$$\bar{x} \equiv \lim_{N \to \infty} \frac{1}{N} \sum_i^N x_i. \tag{1.20}$$

But how to estimate your uncertainty? You could imagine just taking the average of how much each measurement differs from the average:

$$\text{Possible Error Estimate} = \frac{1}{N} \sum_i^N (\bar{x} - x_i). \tag{1.21}$$

But for a large enough number of measurements, the left-hand side of equation (1.21) will be zero:

$$\lim_{N\to\infty} \frac{1}{N}\sum_i^N (\bar{x} - x_i) = \lim_{N\to\infty} \frac{1}{N}\left[\sum_i^N \bar{x} - \sum_i^N x_i\right] \tag{1.22a}$$

$$= \bar{x} - \bar{x} = 0. \tag{1.22b}$$

Therefore, instead of summing the error, we sum the squares of the errors:

$$\sigma_x^2 \equiv \frac{1}{N}\sum_i^N (\bar{x} - x_i)^2. \tag{1.23}$$

We refer to σ_x^2 as the *variance* of x, and the quantity σ_x as the *standard deviation* of x.

Now suppose you have a derived quantity f that depends on two or more measured quantities. That is

$$f = f(u, v). \tag{1.24}$$

From differential calculus we know that

$$df = \frac{\partial f}{\partial u}\, du + \frac{\partial f}{\partial v}\, dv. \tag{1.25}$$

Equation (1.25) relates infinitesimal variations in u and v to the infinitesimal variation in f. Furthermore, equation (1.25) can be extended to any number of variables. If we replace the differential by Δ, we can use equation (1.25) to approximate combined error:

$$\Delta f = \frac{\partial f}{\partial u}\, \Delta u + \frac{\partial f}{\partial v}\, \Delta v, \tag{1.26}$$

where now, Δu and Δv are some measure of the uncertainties in u and v, respectively.

If we associate $(\Delta f)^2$ with a variance, then squaring equation (1.26) gives an expression for the measured variance in f:

$$(\Delta f)^2 = \left(\frac{\partial f}{\partial u}\, \Delta u\right)^2 + \left(\frac{\partial f}{\partial v}\, \Delta v\right)^2 + 2\left(\frac{\partial f}{\partial u}\frac{\partial f}{\partial v}\, \Delta u\, \Delta v\right). \tag{1.27}$$

Now if the error in u and the error in v are completely uncorrelated, then the right-most term in equation (1.27) goes to 0. Taking the square root of equation (1.27) gives us an expression for the standard deviation of f in terms of the standard deviations of u and v:

$$\sigma_f = \sqrt{\left(\frac{\partial f}{\partial u}\, \sigma_u\right)^2 + \left(\frac{\partial f}{\partial v}\, \sigma_v\right)^2}, \tag{1.28}$$

where we have replaced Δu and Δv by the standard deviations σ_u and σ_v, respectively.

Equation (1.28) is extraordinarily useful! So long as the error in the measured parameters are uncorrelated, you can apply equation (1.28) to just about any derived quantity, regardless of how many measurement parameters there are, or how they are combined to give the derived quantity.

1.5.1 Example 1: the product of two parameters

Suppose

$$f = auv, \qquad (1.29)$$

where a is a constant. Then

$$\frac{\partial f}{\partial u} = av \qquad (1.30a)$$

$$\frac{\partial f}{\partial v} = au, \qquad (1.30b)$$

and equation (1.28) becomes

$$\sigma_f = \sqrt{(av\sigma_u)^2 + (au\sigma_v)^2} . \qquad (1.31)$$

Equation (1.31) can be expressed more simply by dividing both sides by equation (1.29):

$$\frac{\sigma_f}{f} = \sqrt{\left(\frac{\sigma_u}{u}\right)^2 + \left(\frac{\sigma_v}{v}\right)^2} , \qquad (1.32)$$

where now the uncertainties are expressed as *relative errors*. Equation (1.32) is the familiar result that the relative error of a product equals the relative errors of the factors, added in quadrature.

1.5.2 Example 2: the quotient of two parameters

Consider

$$f(u, v) = \frac{au}{v} . \qquad (1.33)$$

What is the uncertainty in f in terms of the uncertainty in u and v? Taking the partials,

$$\frac{\partial f}{\partial u} = \frac{a}{v} = \frac{f}{u} \qquad (1.34a)$$

$$\frac{\partial f}{\partial v} = -\frac{au}{v^2} = -\frac{f}{v} . \qquad (1.34b)$$

Then, from equation (1.28) we obtain

$$\frac{\sigma_f}{f} = \sqrt{\left(\frac{\sigma_u}{u}\right)^2 + \left(\frac{\sigma_v}{v}\right)^2}, \tag{1.35}$$

the exact same result as for multiplication.

1.5.3 Example 3: an exponential

Just to show the generality of equation (1.28), let's consider the function

$$f(u, v) = au \exp(bv). \tag{1.36}$$

The partials are

$$\frac{\partial f}{\partial u} = a \exp(bv) = \frac{f}{u} \tag{1.37a}$$

$$\frac{\partial f}{\partial v} = aub \exp(bv) = bf. \tag{1.37b}$$

Then,

$$\frac{\sigma_f}{f} = \sqrt{\left(\frac{du}{u}\right)^2 + (b\ dv)^2}. \tag{1.38}$$

With the brief introduction given in this lecture/chapter, you should now have all the basics needed to understand and apply the circuits covered in the rest of this manual. Let's have at it!

IOP Publishing

Practical Analog, Digital, and Embedded Electronics for Scientists

Brett D DePaola

Chapter 2

RC circuits

2.1 R and C

2.1.1 Resistors

Resistors are simple devices, but they do not always behave the way you might expect. Ideally, resistor values are constant, but in fact all resistors have a resistance that is a function of temperature. Thus, when you design a circuit, you want it to be 'robust' against slight variations in resistance due to temperature.

In general, resistors come in seemingly strange values. Table 2.1 shows the values resistors commonly have. The components in boldface are the 'standard' values, which are readily available for all tolerance resistors; the non-boldface only exist for resistors having tolerance of 5% or better. The values in this table do not include factors of 10.

For example, one can obtain resistors having the values 6.8 Ω, 68 Ω, 680 Ω, 6.8k Ω, etc.

A word about notation: in circuit schematics, it is traditional to leave off the Ω. Thus instead of 68 Ω, a schematic's value might read just 68. Instead of 6.8k Ω, the schematic would read just 6.8k.

In our lab we use 5% resistors. The reasons are as follows: first, that tolerance is good enough, particularly if the circuit has been designed to be 'robust'. Second, 1% resistors typically have their color coding overlaid on a blue background, making it difficult to determine the true colors of the stripes. (We'll get to color coding shortly.) The final reason is cost: why buy a more expensive component than you actually need? Even in my research lab I rarely use resistors having a tolerance better than 5%.

As just mentioned, resistors typically have their values marked using colored bands. Resistors have 3, 4, or 5 bands. For resistors having 3 or 4 bands, the colors of the first 3 bands give the resistor value and the last band (if it exists) indicates the

Table 2.1. Common resistor values.

10	16	**27**	43	**68**
11	**18**	30	**47**	75
12	20	**33**	51	**82**
13	**22**	36	**56**	91
15	24	**39**	62	**100**

Table 2.2. Resistor color code.

Color	Digit	Multiplier	Tolerance	Mnemonic
Black	0	10^0	—	**B**ad
Brown	1	10^1	1%	**B**ooze
Red	2	10^2	2%	**R**ots
Orange	3	10^3	—	**O**ur
Yellow	4	10^4	—	**Y**oung
Green	5	10^5	0.5%	**G**uts
Blue	6	10^6	0.25%	**B**ut
Violet	7	10^7	0.1%	**V**odka
Gray	8	10^8	—	**G**oes
White	9	10^9	—	**W**ell
Gold	—	10^{-1}	5%	—
Silver	—	10^{-2}	10%	—
(none)	—	—	20%	—

precision of the resistor. Three-banded resistors do not explicitly show the tolerance, but by convention the are 20%. The way the bands tell a value is that each band color is associated with a number, as shown in table 2.2. The first 2 colors give the basic value and the 3rd band gives the power of 10:

$$\text{Resistance} = xy \times 10^z. \tag{2.1}$$

For example, a resistor having colors Yellow–Violet–Red, corresponding to numbers 4–7–2 has a resistance of $47 \times 10^2 \Omega$, or 4.7k. Don't make the mistake of thinking the value is $4.7 \times 10^2 \Omega$ or 470 Ohms! There is no implied decimal point between the first two colors. For four-banded resistors, the first three bands are used just as in the three-band case, with the 4th band indicating tolerance, with the colors indicated in table 2.2.

For resistors having five bands the first four bands give the resistance value:

$$\text{Resistor value} = xyz \times 10^q, \tag{2.2}$$

where now x, y, z, and q are the numbers corresponding to the first four colors, respectively. The mnemonic shown in column five of table 2.2 was created by Texas Instruments many years ago. It replaced a very commonly used, but extremely disturbing one. Although you can readily look up the color codes, you should memorize them. You will find it worth the effort.

2.1.2 Capacitors

Unlike the case for a resistor, current does not actually flow through a capacitor. However, for time-varying signals, it can seem as if current really does flow through. What is going on? Consider an initially discharged capacitor, by which we mean that both capacitor plates have no net charge. Now allow a current to flow into the capacitor. What this means is that charges are flowing onto the near plate. But through Coulomb repulsion, these charges that are accumulating on the near plate 'push' like charges off of the far plate, causing a current to flow out of the far side of the capacitor. Current flows in and current flows out. Thus it does appear that current flows through the capacitor, and we will talk about it as if it actually does. The flow can only happen while the near plate can accommodate further charges, and the amount of charge that can be forced onto the plate depends on the voltage.

Now recall the fundamental capacitor equation

$$q = Cv, \tag{2.3}$$

where q is charge, C is the capacitance, and v is the voltage drop across the capacitor. The greater the voltage drop across the capacitor, the more charge can be deposited on it. Also the greater the capacitance, which is proportional to the area of the capacitor plates and inversely proportional to the distance between the plates, the more charge can be deposited on the capacitor, consistent with the above model of charge flow on a capacitor. Taking the derivative of equation (2.3) gives

$$i = \frac{dq}{dt} = C\frac{dv}{dt}, \tag{2.4}$$

where i is the current flowing through the capacitor. This looks a bit like Ohm's law except that it relates the current to the *derivative* of the voltage drop. Let's compare equation (2.4) to a generalized form of Ohm's law,

$$i = v/Z_C, \tag{2.5}$$

where Z_C is the presumed impedance of a capacitor. ('Impedance' is a sort of generalized resistance. The impedance of a resistor is just its resistance.) Let's assume $v(t)$ is of the form

$$v(t) = v_0\, e^{j\omega t}, \tag{2.6}$$

where $\omega = 2\pi f$, and f is the frequency. Then, comparing equations (2.4) and (2.5), and using equation (2.6), we find that

$$Z_C = \frac{1}{j\omega C}. \tag{2.7}$$

Note that the impedance of a capacitor is proportional to the reciprocal of the capacitance, but also is proportional to the reciprocal of the frequency, unlike a resistor whose resistance is frequency-independent.

Capacitor values are usually not as well labeled as resistors. Furthermore, capacitors come in a bewildering assortment of packages. Even worse, some capacitors are polarized, meaning that the '+' side of the capacitor must be kept at a higher electrical potential than the '−' side, or you risk damaging the capacitor.

2.2 RC filters

Now let's examine the circuit of figure 2.1 that uses only one resistor and one capacitor. If that capacitor were a resistor, then the circuit would be a simple voltage divider. Treating it as one, but using R and Z_C instead of R_1 and R_2 of equation (1.11), we find

$$V_{out} = \frac{Z_C}{R + Z_C} V_{in}.$$
(2.8)

Using equation (2.7), after a bit of algebra, we get

$$\frac{V_{out}}{V_{in}} = |S| e^{j\phi},$$
(2.9)

where

$$|S| \equiv \left| \frac{V_{out}}{V_{in}} \right| = \frac{1}{\sqrt{1 + \omega^2 R^2 C^2}}, \quad \text{and } \phi = -\tan^{-1} \omega RC.$$
(2.10)

Let's think a minute about what equations (2.9) and (2.10) are telling us. First of all, they are telling us that the *higher* the frequency, the *smaller* the output signal is. Furthermore, they are saying that if $\omega RC \gg 1$, then the output signal drops roughly as $1/\omega$. Is this reasonable? Think about it: remember that according to equation (2.7), the higher the frequency, the *smaller* the impedance of the capacitor. The smaller the impedance, the smaller the voltage drop (Ohm's law), so this does make sense.

Now examine figure 2.2 in which I've plotted $|S|$ (in blue) and the phase ϕ (in red) versus frequency, for the RC product $=10^{-3}$ s. (Note the log scale on f.)

From our discussion on decibels, the −3 dB point occurs when $\frac{V_{out}}{V_{in}} = \frac{1}{\sqrt{2}}$. From equations (2.10),

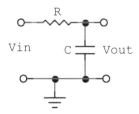

Figure 2.1. A simple RC circuit.

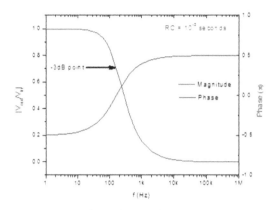

Figure 2.2. Plot of magnitude and phase versus frequency.

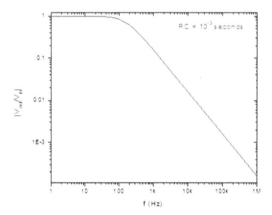

Figure 2.3. Same as figure 2.2 but on a log–log graph.

$$\sqrt{2} = \sqrt{1 + \omega_{3\,\mathrm{dB}}^2 R^2 C^2}, \quad \text{and} \tag{2.11a}$$

$$f_{3\,\mathrm{dB}} = \frac{1}{2\pi RC}. \tag{2.11b}$$

Note, by the way, that it's really negative 3 dB because the output is smaller than the input. Nevertheless, virtually nobody refers to this as the −3 dB point, just 'the 3 dB point'.

Let's go back to equations (2.10). As already pointed out, if $\omega RC \gg 1$, then $|S| \approx \frac{1}{\omega RC}$. That is, if the frequency increases by a factor of 2 (an octave), then the magnitude of the output/input ratio drops by a factor of 2.

In other words, the 'gain' is −6 dB/octave or, as usually expressed, 6 dB/octave. (Remember, in engineer-speak, we drop the minus sign, though we technically need it.) You can better see the 6 dB/octave trend if the first of equations (2.10) is plotted in log–log form, as in figure 2.3. The straight line portion of the plot, which starts at $f \sim 400\text{–}500$ Hz, has a slope of −1, as expected. The condition that $\omega RC \gg 1$ is

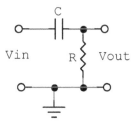

Figure 2.4. Another simple RC circuit.

equivalent to saying that the frequency must be well above the 3 dB point. For the example of figure 2.3, the 3 dB point is about 160 Hz, and thus the condition is satisfied.

Now consider swapping the positions of the capacitor and resistor in Figure 2.1, resulting in the circuit of figure 2.4.

Homework 2.1:

   Following the procedure used above, show that for the circuit in figure 2.4,

$$\frac{V_{\text{out}}}{V_{\text{in}}} = |S|e^{j\phi}, \tag{2.12}$$

where

$$|S| = \frac{\omega RC}{\sqrt{1 + \omega^2 R^2 C^2}} \quad \text{and} \tag{2.13}$$
$$\phi = \tan^{-1}(\omega RC)^{-1}.$$

Also show that the 3 dB point remains

$$f = \frac{1}{2\pi RC}. \tag{2.14}$$

What sort of frequency response would you expect for this circuit? I leave the answer to this question to the reader:

Equations (2.13) seem significantly different from equations (2.10). In fact they are very nearly reciprocal functions, as can be seen in the plots of figure 2.5. In figure 2.2 we saw attenuation at the higher frequencies, meaning that the circuit of figure 2.1 is a **low-pass filter**.

But figure 2.5 shows attenuation at lower frequencies, meaning that the circuit of figure 2.4 is a **high-pass filter**. Both low- and high-pass filters have the same expression for the 3 dB point (remarkably!). Furthermore, for $f \ll f_{3\,\text{dB}}$, the output voltage rise is proportional to f. That is, we see the same 6 dB per octave, but rising with increasing frequency, rather than dropping as in the low-pass filter case.

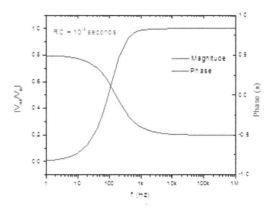

Figure 2.5. Plots of equations (2.13).

2.3 Doing calculus with R and C

Let's revisit the circuit of figure 2.4, but now let's do our analysis from first principles rather than applying the voltage divider equation. From equation (2.4), the current flowing 'through' the capacitor is

$$i = C\frac{d(V_{in} - V_{out})}{dt} = \frac{V_{out}}{R}, \tag{2.15}$$

or

$$V_{out} = RC\frac{dV_{in}}{dt} - RC\frac{dV_{out}}{dt}, \tag{2.16}$$

where the right-most term in equation (2.15) is from Ohm's law. If RC is chosen to be small enough then

$$\frac{dV_{out}}{dt} \ll \frac{dV_{in}}{dt}, \tag{2.17}$$

giving us

$$V_{out}(t) \approx RC\frac{dV_{in}(t)}{dt}. \tag{2.18}$$

In other words, with judicious choice of the RC product, the circuit of figure 2.4 is not just a high-pass filter, but also a differentiator! For example, if $V_{in}(t)$ is a triangle wave, then $V_{out}(t)$ would be a square wave. Cool.

Handwaving the requirement of equation (2.17)
   If C is small, Z_C is large, which means not much signal gets past the capacitor. So the V_{out} of the left-hand side of equation (2.15) is small compared to V_{in}.

How about the circuit of figure 2.1? Using a similar analysis,

$$i = C\frac{dV_{out}}{dt} = \frac{V_{in} - V_{out}}{R}. \tag{2.19}$$

Now, keeping $V_{out} \ll V_{in}$ by keeping RC large, we get

$$C\frac{dV_{out}}{dt} \approx \frac{V_{in}}{R}, \tag{2.20}$$

or

$$V_{out} \approx \frac{1}{RC}\int V_{in}\,dt. \tag{2.21}$$

Thus, the circuit of figure 2.1 is not just a low-pass filter, but also an integrator. For example if $V_{in}(t)$ is a square wave, then $V_{out}(t)$ would be a triangle wave. Very cool!

Let's re-examine equation (2.19), but this time let's not make the assumption that $V_{out} \ll V_{in}$. Then,

$$\frac{dV_{out}}{V_{out} - V_{in}} = -\frac{dt}{RC}. \tag{2.22}$$

Now if V_{in} is a constant, then integrating equation (2.22) gives

$$V_{out} = V_{in} + Ae^{-t/RC}, \tag{2.23}$$

where A is a constant that is determined by boundary conditions. Consider, for example, the case where $V_{in}(t)$ is a square wave, having values of 0 and V_{in}, and having a period that is very long compared to the RC product. Suppose we examine the portion of V_{in} where its value has been 0 for a very long time (compared to RC) and we choose $t = 0$ to be at the point of the low to high transition. Because the capacitor has seen a potential of 0 for a very long time before $t = 0$, $V_{out}(t = 0) = 0$. That is,

$$0 = V_{in} + Ae^{-0}, \tag{2.24}$$

or $A = -V_{in}$. Then equation (2.23) becomes

$$V_{out} = V_{in}(1 - e^{-t/RC}). \tag{2.25}$$

We see from equation (2.25) that the output starts at 0 and then grows exponentially with a time constant of RC before rolling over and asymptotically approaching the value V_{in}.

Going back to equation (2.23), now consider the case where V_{in} has been 'on' for a time that is long compared to RC, and at $t = 0$ the input makes the transition $V_{in} \to 0$. Before the transition, $V_{out} = V_{in}$, but afterwards, $V_{in} = 0$. So,

$$V_{out}(t = 0) = V_{in}(t = 0) + A\,e^0 \tag{2.26}$$

Or

$$V_{in} = 0 + A. \tag{2.27}$$

And $A = V_{in}$, giving us,

$$V_{out} = V_{in}e^{-t/RC}. \tag{2.28}$$

This is the equation of a *falling* exponential but with the same RC time constant as the *rising* exponential of equation (2.25). Note that, as a rule of thumb, at $t = 5RC$, the rising (or falling) exponential is within 1% of its asymptotic value.

IOP Publishing

Practical Analog, Digital, and Embedded Electronics for Scientists

Brett D DePaola

Chapter 3

Diodes and transistors

In this chapter, we will not discuss the fascinating physics of semiconductors. Rather, we will discuss how to use semiconductor devices, specifically, diodes and transistors.

All solid state diodes are constructed of two doped blocks of semiconductors placed back to back, as shown in figure 3.1. Application of bias potentials to the anode and cathode moves mobile electrons into the region where the two semiconductor blocks come into contact. This has the effect of shifting energy levels in a spatially-dependent way and gives rise to the properties of the diode (and transistor) that we will exploit.

3.1 Signal diodes

Loosely speaking, diodes can be classified as belonging to one of two distinct types: signal diodes, and Zener diodes. While the properties of these different diode classes differ only slightly, their functions in a circuit are usually quite different.

First, look at the schematic symbol of a diode, shown in the lower portion of figure 3.1. The left side of the diode, corresponding to the p-type semiconductor, is called the anode, while the side of the diode, with the bar on the schematic, is called the cathode. We say that a diode is forward biased when the potential on the anode is greater than that on the cathode. The diode is said to be reverse biased when potential on the cathode exceeds that on the anode.

Figure 3.2 shows an idealized plot of a typical signal diode 'I–V plot', that is, a plot of the current passing through a diode versus the voltage drop across the diode. A diode's I–V curve consists of three distinct regions. In the forward biased region, the current starts off nearly flat as a function of bias voltage. But it then takes off, roughly exponentially near some critical voltage, V_d. Recalling that for an Ohmic device (like a resistor) the inverse of the slope of an I–V curve is the impedance, this

doi:10.1088/978-0-7503-3491-4ch3

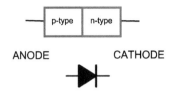

Figure 3.1. Configuration of semiconductor material and schematic symbol for a solid state diode.

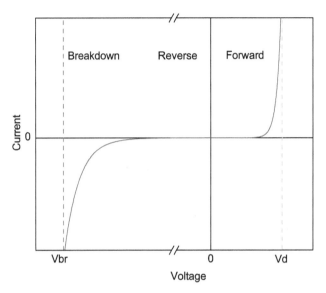

Figure 3.2. Idealized plot of a typical signal diode output.

means that for low forward voltages, the impedance of a diode is nearly infinite and the impedance near V_d is essentially 0. Furthermore, in the region near V_d, the impedance passes almost instantaneously from infinite to 0. Diodes are typically fabricated from either doped germanium or doped silicon. For germanium diodes, $V_d \approx 0.3$ V, while for silicon diodes, $V_d \approx 0.6$ V. You need to know these numbers.

Now look at the region of the I–V curve labeled 'Reverse'. We can see that when the diode is reverse biased there is a small leakage current. Furthermore, when reverse biased, the diode acts nearly Ohmic—that is until the reverse bias voltage is in the vicinity of V_{br}, at which point the diode's impedance drops to nearly 0, much like the region near V_d. V_{br} varies from diode to diode, but is typically much larger in magnitude than V_d.

3.1.1 Diodes as 'one-way valves'

If we ignore the region of the I–V curve in the vicinity of V_{br}, we can think of the diode acting as a one-way valve: current can flow in the forward direction essentially with no impedance (when the applied voltage exceeds V_d) but, except for some small leakage, does not flow at all in the reverse direction. We can take advantage of this property to *rectify* an ac signal.

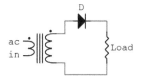

Figure 3.3. Simple half-wave rectifier.

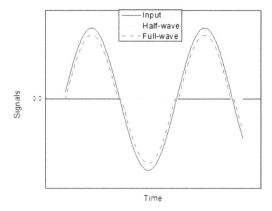

Figure 3.4. Input and outputs for the half-wave rectifier circuits of figure 3.3 and 3.5.

Examine figure 3.3. An ac signal flows through a transformer which either raises or lowers the voltage amplitude, depending upon how it is connected. When the ac current is in the phase that forward-biases the diode, current can flow through the diode, through the load, and then back to the transformer. When the ac current attempts to flow in the other direction, the diode blocks it.

Figure 3.4 shows a plot of input (red), and output (green) signals versus time for the circuit of figure 3.3. Because only half of the input signal is passed, this circuit is referred to as a half-wave bridge. Notice that the half-wave output is lower than the input, due to conduction not commencing until $V_{\text{input}} \simeq V_d$, but does not drop below 0.

Half-wave bridges are useful if all you want to do is chop out the negative signals, but they are wasteful if your goal is to take the absolute value of a signal. For that purpose, you'd be better off with a full wave bridge, for example the one shown in figure 3.5.

In this case, we put a diode on both sides of the transformer output. However, we still need to provide a return path for the circuit. But unlike the circuit of figure 3.3, the return path is blocked by a diode. Therefore, for this full-wave bridge circuit we must use a 'center-tap' transformer, and then reference that center tap to ground, as shown in the schematic.

3.1.2 Diodes as non-ohmic devices

Besides their use as rectifiers, signal diodes are often used as *clamps*. Suppose you have an application in which, to avoid damage to a piece of equipment, you absolutely cannot exceed some particular voltage, say, 6 V.

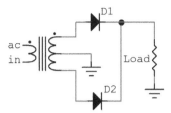

Figure 3.5. One kind of full wave bridge circuit.

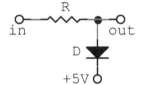

Figure 3.6. Simple clamp circuit.

The circuit of figure 3.6 might be what you need. Because the diode is back-biased by 5 V, the diode will not conduct until the input signal exceeds 5 V + 0.6 V = 5.6 V, which is still in the safe range. The resistor is required because if the input signal exceeds 5.6 V, 'infinite' current will flow through the diode in order that it maintain $V_d \leqslant 0.6$ V. Of course this really means that you'll fry the diode.

3.2 Zener diodes

In general, the V_d point of a diode is not precisely defined, but is usually close enough to 0.6 or 0.3 V (depending if the semiconductor is silicon or germanium based) that slight tweaking of the other components can get you where you need to be. However, the V_{br} point of a diode is usually a terrible parameter to base your circuit design on. But there is an exception: the Zener diode. This is a special kind of signal diode that has been engineered to have a fairly precise reverse-bias breakdown voltage. Even better, that portion of the I–V curve has been designed to be extremely steep. The principle uses of Zeners is in clamping and signal smoothing.

Look at the circuit in figure 3.7. Here the output signal will not exceed the Zener breakdown voltage, so we don't need an extra power supply in order to clamp. Note in figure 3.6 we made use of the 'fairly good' parameter V_b, while in figure 3.7 we made use of the 'very good' parameter (for Zeners), namely V_{br}. Zener diodes are available with a very large range of reverse breakdown voltage values.

3.3 Bipolar junction transistors

Sometimes referred to as bjt, the bipolar junction transistor is what many people mean by just 'transistor'. You could think of a bjt as being three blocks of alternating types of semiconductor materials stuck together. The npn transistor consists of n-type material on either end with a p-type block sandwiched in between.

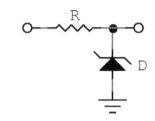

Figure 3.7. Clamp using a Zener diode.

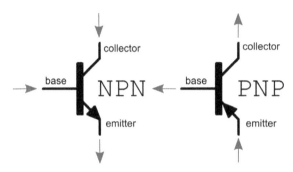

Figure 3.8. Schematic symbols of the npn and pnp transistors. Observe the direction of current flow.

The pnp transistor consists of p-type material on either end, with n-type sandwiched in between. In both cases, the 'base' of the transistor is the middle block of material, with the 'collector' and 'emitter' being the two outer blocks. Figure 3.8 shows the schematic symbols for these two types of bjt's. Note the directions of the current flow in the two cases. For both types of transistors, the base-collector acts like a diode operating in reverse-bias mode, while the base-emitter junction acts like a diode operating in forward bias mode. For example, in the case of the npn silicon transistor, when the base-emitter is forward biased,

$$v_e \approx v_b - 0.6 \text{ V, while for the pnp case,} \qquad (3.1a)$$

$$v_e \approx v_b + 0.6 \text{ V.} \qquad (3.1b)$$

Also, through conservation of current, in both the npn and the pnp transistor,

$$i_e = i_b + i_c. \qquad (3.2)$$

So what does a transistor actually do? It amplifies current. That is, to a very good approximation,

$$i_c = h_{FE} i_b, \qquad (3.3)$$

where $h_{FE} \approx 100$. (In older texts, h_{FE} is also known as β.) Combining equations (3.2) and (3.3), we obtain

$$i_e = i_b(1 + h_{FE}) \approx i_b h_{FE}. \qquad (3.4)$$

From equation (3.4) we see that a transistor is simply a current amplifier, with h_{FE} as gain. While it is tempting to use equation (3.4) as a design property, you should never do so because h_{FE} is not a value you can count on. Even for transistors of the same type, h_{FE} can vary quite a bit. The only thing about h_{FE} that you can count on is that it is on the order of 100. It is very important to note that equations (3.3) and (3.4) only hold when $v_c > v_e$, in the case of the npn, or $v_e > v_c$, in the case of the pnp. That is, in order for collector–emitter current to flow, the collector–emitter must be biased in the direction that the current can flow.

3.3.1 Transistors as a switch

For our first example, consider an application where you'd like to turn a light on and off using the 3.3 V output of a 'credit card computer' like the Raspberry Pi or the Beaglebone Black. Like most computers, the Pi or BBB can only source about 4–6 mA, at 3.3 V, from its signal pins. For the purposes of this example, though, suppose the lamp you'd like to turn on and off is a 10 V, 100 mA device. What to do? You could try the circuit of figure 3.9. But how do we choose the resistor value? First, recall that when the transistor is 'on', v_b is 1 diode drop above v_e, in this case $v_b \cong 0.6$ V. (We assume a silicon-based transistor.) Then, when the computer's output is 3.3 V, the drop across R is about 2.7 V. We want the computer's output current to be limited to no more than, say, 4 mA. Then,

$$\frac{2.7\,\text{V}}{R} \leqslant 4\,\text{mA}, \tag{3.5}$$

or $R \geqslant 675\,\Omega$. Let's be safe and choose $R = 1k$. Then when the computer output is 'high' (3.3 V) we have a base current $i_b = \frac{3.3\,\text{V} - 0.6\,\text{V}}{1k} = 2.7$ mA, which is well within the safety margin for not burning up our computer. According to equation (3.4), we should now have a collector current $i_c \approx 100 \times 2.7$ mA $= 270$ mA. Oops, not so fast! The lamp we chose draws 0.1 A at 10 V, implying a resistance of about 100 Ω. So if we had 270 mA flowing through the lamp, the voltage drop across the lamp would be 27 V. But this is impossible! Our voltage drop is limited to just 5 V because, in order for the transistor to 'conduct', $v_c \geqslant v_e$, or in this case, $v_c \geqslant 0$, and we are only supplying our lamp with 5 V. Therefore the maximum current we can push through the lamp is 5 V/100 Ω = 50 mA. What this circuit actually does is to allow no

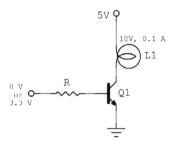

Figure 3.9. Using an npn transistor as a switch.

current flow through the lamp when the computer output is 'off' and to allow 50 mA to flow through the lamp when the computer is 'on'. But, and this is the key, the computer only has to source 2.7 mA to accomplish this. (Of course something has to be able to supply the current to the lamp. Often, though, devices like the Pi or **BBB** has a separate 'power pin' for just this purpose.)

3.3.2 The emitter follower

Transistors make great switches because they enable large currents to flow, with only a small control current requirement. But transistors have greater utility than this; they are more than just on-off devices. Let's examine the simple emitter follower circuit. The whole point of an emitter follower is to act as a high input impedance, low output impedance buffer between two circuit elements. So let's look at the input and output impedances of the simple emitter follower circuit of figure 3.10. From equations (3.1) we see that a change in the base voltage gives rise to an equal change in the emitter voltage. That is,

$$\Delta v_b = \Delta v_e. \tag{3.6}$$

By Ohm's law, the change in the emitter current is

$$\Delta i_e = \frac{\Delta v_e}{R_e}. \tag{3.7}$$

Combining equations (3.6) and (3.7) gives

$$\Delta i_e = \frac{\Delta v_b}{R_e}. \tag{3.8}$$

But from equation (3.4),

$$\Delta i_b = \frac{\Delta i_e}{h_{FE} + 1}. \tag{3.9}$$

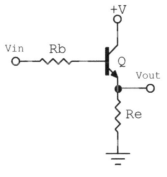

Figure 3.10. Simple emitter follower.

Combining equations (3.8) and (3.9), we obtain

$$\Delta i_b = \frac{\Delta v_b}{R_e(h_{FE} + 1)}. \tag{3.10}$$

The impedance 'looking into' the base is $\Delta v_b / \Delta i_b$, or

$$Z_{in} = (h_{FE} + 1)R_e. \tag{3.11}$$

Equation (3.11) is very important. It says that whatever sub-circuit is 'feeding' the emitter follower sees an impedance that is about $100 \times R_e$. (Recall that $h_{FE} \sim 100$.)

Since for the circuit of figure 3.10, the 'load' is R_e, we can say that the output impedance is

$$Z_{out} = \frac{Z_{in}}{h_{FE} + 1}. \tag{3.12}$$

The circuit of figure 3.10 is useful because of the favorable Z_{in} and Z_{out} relationships.

However, because of the directions currents are constrained to flow in a transistor, it will only work for a positive signal. In contrast, the circuit of figure 3.11 will work for a bipolar signal. In this circuit the capacitor C_1 passes the ac signal. The voltage divider made up of R_1 and R_2 adds a dc offset to the signal. The voltage source, transistor and R_e act as the emitter follower, just as in figure 3.10. Finally, the capacitor C_2 blocks the dc component. The tricky part is to figure out what values to give to all the components. But to do this we first need some design constraints. First of all, let's assume that we need this circuit to work over the 'audio frequency range'. This means that the signal frequency could be anything from 20 Hz to 20 kHz. Second, we need to have what is referred to as a 'quiescent current'. This is the emitter current that will flow even when $V_{in} = 0$. You need to have a non-zero quiescent current because otherwise, when V_{in} goes negative, your circuit would shut off. In general, the larger the quiescent current, the better your circuit will perform. However, the larger the quiescent current, the more power you waste. A typical compromise is to have the quiescent current $i_e^{(q)} = 1$ mA. Finally, let's suppose that $+V = 10$ V.

With the design parameters spelled out, it is now a simple step by step procedure to deduce the values of the circuit elements. Here's the plan:

1. Choose the quiescent emitter voltage, $v_e^{(q)}$, to be halfway between $+V$ and ground. Because after blocking the dc component, your signal will be symmetric about the quiescent point, this will give you the greatest signal range.
2. At this value of $v_e^{(q)}$, compute the value for R_e such that the emitter current is equal to the design parameter value of the quiescent current.
3. Recognize that the base voltage is 1 diode drop above the emitter voltage. Thus, $v_b^{(q)} = v_e^{(q)} + 0.6$ V.

4. Using this value of $v_b^{(q)}$ and the constraint that the output impedance of the voltage divider must be much less than the impedance 'looking into' the base of the transistor, compute the required values of R_1 and R_2.
5. Given the input impedance of the voltage divider and considering the constraints on the signal frequency, deduce a value for C_1.
6. Given the output impedance of the circuit and the signal frequency, deduce a value for C_2.

That's it! Let's go through this list and see what we can do.
1. For $+V = 10$ V, we will have $v_e^{(q)} = \frac{10 \text{ V}}{2} = 5$ V.

2. For $v_e^{(q)} = 5$ V and $i_e^{(q)} = 1$ mA, we have $R_e = \frac{5 \text{ V}}{1 \text{ mA}} = 5k$. Now a quick inspection of table 2.1 shows that the closest convenient resistor value to $5k$ is $5.1k$, so that's what we will use. We still want the quiescent voltage to be 5 V to give us the maximum signal range, so this value of R_e only just slightly compromises our value of the quiescent current.

3. If $v_e^{(q)} = 5$ V, then $v_b^{(q)} = 5.6$ V.

4. The two equations we need to simultaneously solve are

$$5.6 \text{ V} = \frac{R_2}{R_1 + R_2} \times 10 \text{ V}, \tag{3.13}$$

and

$$\frac{R_1 R_2}{R_1 + R_2} \leqslant \frac{100}{10} R_e. \tag{3.14}$$

In equation (3.14), the ratio on the left-hand side is the output impedance of the voltage divider, the factor of 100 is the estimated value of h_{FE}, and the 10 in the denominator means '$\ll$'. Simultaneously solving equations (3.13) and (3.14) gives $R_1 = 91k$ and $R_2 = 115.8k$. Comparing these values to table 2.1, we see that while the value for R_1 is commonly available, the value for R_2 lies between the two common values of $110k$ and $120k$. Re-inserting these values into equation (3.13) shows that $R_2 = 120k$ comes closer to our desired value of 5.6 V, missing it by only 0.09 V. However, we have only been approximating the value of our 'diode drop' anyhow. And any slight 'error' in getting the voltage divider value correct only slightly reduces the 'perfect' range of our signal swings. Bottom line: Don't put too fine a point on these calculations!

5. Looking into the voltage divider, the signal 'sees' an impedance of $51k$ in parallel with $510k$, that is, the impedance of the voltage divider in parallel with h_{FE} times R_e. This comes out to $46k$. So we want to construct a high pass filter that has its 3 dB point at the low value of the desired frequency range. That is, we want to be able to pass everything above 20 Hz. Rearranging equation (2.14), we obtain

$$C_1 = [(2\pi)(46k)(20 \text{ Hz})]^{-1} = 0.17 \text{ } \mu\text{F}. \tag{3.15}$$

6. We do not know the load impedance, but most likely it will be much larger than R_e. So we can use equation (2.14) again to compute C_2, but use a resistance of $5.1k$, giving us $C_2 = 1.56\,\mu\text{F}$.

Now to deduce our values for C_1 and C_2, we used the 3 dB points. But this means that our signal will be reduced by 6 dB because it will see two consecutive attenuations. So when it comes time to choose our capacitors, we could increase their values to, say, $0.56\,\mu\text{F}$ and $4.7\,\mu\text{F}$ for C_1 and C_2, respectively. (To get these values, I multiplied the computed values by 3 and then looked at the web page of an electronics components supplier to see what the commonly offered values were.) A summary of the component values is given in table 3.1.

Coming up with component values for the emitter follower seems really complicated, but it isn't really. Actually, it's rather cook-book. One aspect that is a bit confusing at first is that we sort of work backwards. For example, we know that we want a maximum voltage swing and so we know we want the quiescent emitter voltage to be $+V/2$. And this implies that we want the quiescent base voltage to be $0.6\,\text{V} + V/2$. Then this implies that we must build a voltage divider that gives us this voltage. In reality, the voltage divider gives us a voltage, the transistor drops this by 1 diode drop, and we end up with some emitter voltage when the signal input is zero. The bottom line is that the best way to learn how to figure out component values is to practice doing it. So,

---

Homework 3.1:

Compute the values of the components in the circuit of figure 3.11 subject to the following design constraints:
- The supply voltage is +15 V.
- The quiescent current is 2 mA.
- The signal frequency is in the 'audio range'.

Table 3.1. Summary of component values for the circuit of figure 3.11, given the specified design parameters.

Component	Value
R_1	$91k$
R_2	$120k$
R_e	$5.1k$
C_1	$0.56\,\mu\text{F}$
C_1	$4.7\,\mu\text{F}$

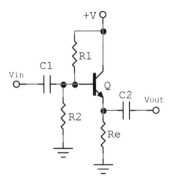

Figure 3.11. Single supply emitter follower for bipolar input.

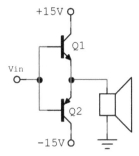

Figure 3.12. Classic 'push–pull' emitter follower.

In the circuit of figure 3.11 we had to provide a dc offset to our signal using a voltage divider. But to make the divider 'stiff' we had to choose resistor values that allowed more than 75 μA to constantly flow through them to ground. This 'wastes' nearly a mW of power. Furthermore, we had to capacitively couple our signal into and out of the emitter follower, which could degrade our frequency fidelity. Perhaps these limitations are not a problem for some particular application, but if you have a bipolar power supply available, you may try the 'push–pull' circuit of figure 3.12. The idea of the push–pull is that when the signal is positive, current will flow into the base of Q1 which amplifies it. And when the signal is negative, the current will flow out of the base of *Q2* (remember the flow directions for a pnp are opposite that for an npn) which amplifies it. Either way, an amplified signal current drives the load, in this example, a speaker.

Unfortunately, for a signal input like the blue curve in figure 3.13, the signal that the speaker sees looks like the red curve in the same figure. On the positive swing the output lies a diode drop below the input, while on the negative swing, the output lies a diode drop above the input. This results in what is called cross-over distortion and gives a high frequency hiss to the audio signal. One solution is to modify the basic-push as in figure 3.14.

The trick is to pre-compensate for the base-emitter voltage drops with diodes. The diodes are put into forward conduction by biasing them with the supply voltages, current-limited, of course with resistors. You need to select resistor values that will

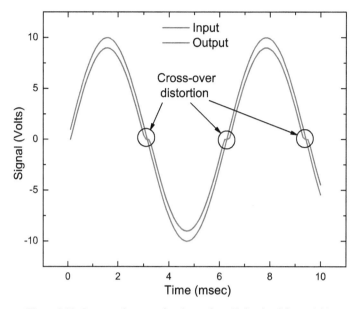

Figure 3.13. Input and output for the push–pull circuit of figure 3.12.

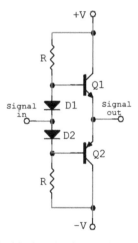

Figure 3.14. Push–pull with diode biasing to eliminate cross-over distortion.

keep the base current high enough to allow the emitter to source adequate current to drive your load. For example, suppose you are using ± 15 V supplies and you are driving an 8 Ω, 10 W (rms) speaker. Then the peak power is $\sqrt{2} \times 10$ W $= 14.14$ W. This means that the peak emitter voltage would have to be $\sqrt{(14.14 \text{ W})(8 \text{ }\Omega)} = 10.6$ V, making the peak emitter current 1.33 A. For this emitter voltage, the base voltage would be 11.2 V.

Now for power transistors, the h_{FE} is only about 50, so the required base current would be about 26.6 mA, requiring $R \leqslant (15 \text{ V} - 11.2 \text{ V})/26.6 \text{ mA} \approx 150 \text{ }\Omega$.

3.3.3 Common emitter amplifier

Thus far, we've been using the bjt as a current amplifier, which in a sense is the natural way to use it. But often we need to amplify signal voltages. The most basic single supply signal amplifier is the so-called common emitter amplifier shown in figure 3.15. The 'common' used in the name does not mean 'simple' or 'ordinary'. It actually means that the emitter is attached to the 'common', another term for ground. Notice how similar this circuit is to the single supply emitter follower of figure 3.11. Here's how it works. As in the emitter follower, C_1 'floats' the signal input, allowing the voltage divider of R_1 and R_2 to shift the transistor input to an appropriate level. The emitter voltage, which follows base voltage, is 1 diode drop below it, and the emitter current is given by the emitter voltage divided by the R_e. All of this is as in the emitter follower. But now we have a new twist: because $i_e = i_c + i_b \approx i_c$, due to the large value of h_{FE}, as i_e changes, so does i_c. But because of R_c, as i_c changes, so does v_c since

$$v_c = +V - i_c R_c \approx +V - i_e R_c. \tag{3.16}$$

But

$$\Delta i_e = \frac{\Delta v_e}{R_e}. \tag{3.17}$$

Therefore,

$$\Delta v_c = -\frac{R_c}{R_e} \Delta v_b, \tag{3.18}$$

giving us

$$\text{Gain} \equiv \frac{\text{Signal out}}{\text{Signal in}} = -\frac{R_c}{R_e}. \tag{3.19}$$

The minus sign in equation (3.19) comes from equation (3.16) and means that the output signal will be inverted with respect to the input signal.

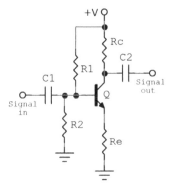

Figure 3.15. Single supply common emitter amplifier.

To determine the values of the components in the common emitter amplifier, we follow much of the same procedure as we used with the single supply emitter follower. First let's list the parameters for this example design exercise:

- $V_{cc} = 20$ V (the supply voltage);
- frequency-range: audio (20 Hz–20 kHz);
- $i_c^{(q)} = 1$ mA;
- Gain = 4 (actually −4!).

We would like our $v_c^{(q)}$ to be in the middle of the possible range, that is, $Vcc/2$, here, 10 V. Therefore, with a 10 V drop across R_c, and $i_c^{(q)} = 1$ mA, using Ohm's law we get $R_c = 10k$. Now using the gain relation of equation (3.18) or (3.19), we obtain $R_e = 2.5k$. Because $i_e \approx i_c$, we see that $i_e^{(q)} \approx 1$ mA, which, through Ohm's law, means that $v_e^{(q)} = i_e^{(q)} R_e \approx (1 \ \text{mA})(2.5k) = 2.5$ V. Because v_b lies a diode drop above v_e, $v_b^{(q)} \approx 3.1$ V.

Now that we have the quiescent base voltage, we can follow exactly the same procedure as in the single supply emitter follower to obtain values for R_1, R_2, and C_1. Recall that we used the voltage divider equation as well as the condition that the voltage divider's output impedance be much less than the impedance looking into the transistor base. That is,

$$v_b = \frac{R_2}{R_1 + R_2} v_{cc}, \tag{3.20a}$$

$$\frac{R_1 R_2}{R_1 + R_2} \leqslant \frac{100}{10} R_e. \tag{3.20b}$$

Solving these two equations simultaneously, with the values already determined for v_b, v_{cc}, and R_e, and using readily available resistors (table 2.1) we obtain $R_1 = 160k$, $R_2 = 30k$. To obtain C_1 we use equation (2.14), but with R the impedance looking into the voltage divider, in parallel with the impedance looking into the base, altogether about $24k$. This gives us $C_1 \sim 0.33$ μF. To determine C_2, we need to use equation (2.14), but with R equal to R_c in parallel with the impedance looking into the collector. In the next section we will show that the collector is essentially a current sink, which means that the impedance looking into the collector is essentially infinity. Therefore for equation (2.14), we can safely use $R = R_c$. This gives us $C_2 \sim 0.8$ μF. But as in the emitter follower, we have 2 high pass filters in series. To avoid too much signal attenuation, we can simply double each of the capacitor values (and match them with values that are readily available). This gives us $C_1 = 0.68$ μF, and $C_2 = 1.5$ μF.

3.3.4 Transistor current sources/sinks

Thus far, we've mainly dealt with signal voltages. But sometimes we need a source (or sink) of current. For example, suppose you are trying to build a voltage ramp. Using equation (2.4) we see that if the current i is a constant, then so is dv/dt. So how do you make a constant current source or sink? And what's the difference between a source and a sink? Answering the second question first, a current source *supplies* a constant current to some load, in principle, independent of the size of the load. A current sink lies between a load and ground and 'extracts' a constant current from the load, delivering it to ground. Look at figure 3.16.

We show three constant current devices, all of which are nearly the same design but with slightly different biasing schemes. The two on the left are current sinks, while the one on the right is a current source. All three were designed to pass 1 mA through the load resistor.

Consider the left-most circuit. If, as desired, the collector current is 1 mA then, within about 1%, the emitter current will also be 1 mA. If so, then $v_e = 1$ V, making $v_b \approx 1.6$ V. Thus all we have to do is bias the base such that $v_b = 1.6$ V. Of course we'd like the voltage divider to be stiff and therefore want its $Z_{out} \leqslant 10R_e$ or $\leqslant 10k$. For the values shown, $v_b = 1.6$ V and $Z_{out} = 10.7k$.

In the center circuit, we use an appropriate Zener diode to bias the base to 5.6 V, making $v_e \approx 5.0$ V. A $5k$ emitter resister then guarantees an emitter (and therefore collector) current of 1 mA. We use a similar scheme to bias the base in the right-most circuit. Here we use three diodes in series to bring v_b to 1.6 V below the supply voltage. The emitter–base junction brings v_e back up to two diode drops below the supply. An emitter resistor of $1.2k$ then guarantees a current of 1 mA.

Each of the circuits has advantages and disadvantages. The voltage divider of the first circuit is not as stiff as the use of either a Zener or stack of ordinary diodes. To make it more stiff by lowering the resister values means wasting more current in the bias path. Diode biasing has another advantage as well. In the Zener biasing scheme, v_b is referenced to the ground. Thus even if the supply voltage has ripples, the current passing through the load should be constant. In the right-most circuit, v_b is referenced to the supply, but so is R_e, and therefore supply ripples cancel out as well. If desired, you can modify any of the three circuits to make your current

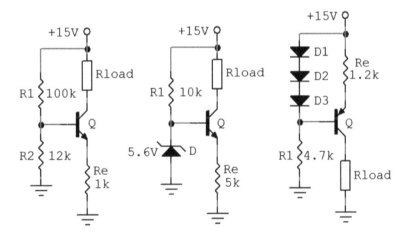

Figure 3.16. Three examples of constant current devices showing different biasing schemes. The first two are current sinks, while the third is a current source. All three devices are designed to have a constant current of 1 mA passing through the load resistor.

source/sink variable: just replace R_e by a pot. There are many other ways to construct current sources, but the circuits in figure 3.16 are probably the simplest.

Compliance

We claim that the circuits in figure 3.16 source or drain a constant current, but this is clearly not the case for all choices of R_{load}: suppose we choose $R_{load} = 1M\ \Omega$. Then to achieve a current of 1 mA, we'd have to have a voltage drop across the load of 1000 V—which is clearly impossible to achieve with a 15 V power supply. The limitations on R_{load} for which a current supply/sink will correctly operate is called the circuit's *compliance*. Let's look more closely at the left-most circuit of figure 3.16 to see if we can determine its compliance. Analysis of the other two circuits will follow the same basic logic.

First we note that for the transistor to function, $v_c \geqslant v_e$, and v_e must be at 1 V so that the sink is at 1 mA. Then the drop across R_{load} must be less than 14 V. For a 1 mA sink, the means that $R_{load} \leqslant 14k$. We can expand the compliance by using a larger supply voltage or we can redesign the circuit to have a smaller R_e, with the appropriate adjustment to the bias resistors. Note that the smaller R_e, the greater the compliance. But, the lower R_e, the lower the values for R_1 and R_2, resulting in more current being dumped through the voltage divider. As always, circuit design is all about compromise.

Homework 3.2:

Design a 2 mA current *source* using a 20 V supply. You are free to use any biasing scheme you like.

Homework 3.3:

Derive an equation that gives the upper limit on R_{load} for the left-most circuit in figure 3.16. That is, find an expression for R_{load} as a function of V_{cc}, R_e, and i_{design} where i_{design} is the current that the circuit is designed to sink.

3.3.5 Common emitter amplifier re-visited

When we analyzed the common emitter amplifier we came up with equation (3.19), the expression for gain. Something was fishy about this expression: it seems we can get infinite gain by letting R_e go to zero. Clearly this can't happen. So what's going on? To answer this we have to go to the Ebers–Moll equation, which is a better model for how diodes and transistors operate.

$$I_C \approx I_S\left[\exp\left(\frac{V_{BE}}{V_T}\right) - 1\right], \tag{3.21}$$

Here,

- I_S is the reverse saturation current of the particular transistor. It is a function of temperature, but is on the order of 10^{-15} to 10^{-12} A.
- V_{BE} is the base–emitter voltage drop.
- The *thermal voltage* $V_T \equiv k_B T / q$, where T is the temperature in Kelvin, q is the magnitude of the electron charge, and k_B is Boltzmann's constant. $V_T \approx 25.3$ mV at $T = 20$ °C = 293.16 K.
- In the 'active' region, $I_C \gg I_S$ and the -1 term can be neglected in comparison with the exponential.

As in the simple transistor model, $I_B = I_C/h_{FE}$, but now the 'constant' h_{FE} is a function of transistor type, I_C, V_{CE}, and T.

We can solve equation (3.21) for V_{BE}, giving us

$$V_{BE} = \frac{k_B T}{q} \ln\left(\frac{I_C}{I_S} + 1\right). \tag{3.22}$$

Equation (3.22) is a more accurate description of a 'diode voltage drop' than equations (3.1), and sometimes we need to turn to it rather than the simplistic model. For example, equation (3.22) gives us the *steepness* of the diode curve. That is, we can see that to raise I_C by a factor of 10, we have to increase V_{BE} by $V_T \ln 10$ or about 60 mV at room temperature. This gives us a handy rule of thumb: Base voltage increases by 60 mV for every decade of collector current increase.

Another way to think about this is to take the derivative of equation (3.22) with respect to I_C:

$$r_e \equiv \frac{dV_{BE}}{dI_C} = \frac{k_B T}{q} \frac{1}{I_C + I_S} \tag{3.23a}$$

$$\approx \frac{k_B T}{q} \frac{1}{I_C} \quad \text{for } I_C \gg I_S \tag{3.23b}$$

$$\approx \frac{25\,\Omega}{I_C}, \tag{3.23c}$$

when I_C is measured in mA. That is, it is like having a small resistor, r_e in series with the emitter, and the value of that resistor varies with collector current.

So, if, in a common emitter amplifier, you try to get high gain by reducing the value of R_e, you will start to get a nonlinear response when $R_e \lesssim r_e$.

Transistor amplifying circuits can thus be a bit tricky, especially when you are in the high gain regime. But there are a couple ways to avoid this. First of all, instead of a single stage amplifier with high gain, you could cascade several amplifiers, each with a more modest gain. Another strategy is to use op-amp-based amplifier circuits. Op-amps, discussed in lecture 4, can be used to give high gain, and can even be combined with transistors to supply high circuits. But op-amps do suffer from not being as fast as transistors. As with all engineering applications, circuit design is all about compromise.

IOP Publishing

Practical Analog, Digital, and Embedded Electronics for Scientists

Brett DePaola

Chapter 4

Op amps I

4.1 Op amp basics

Operational amplifiers, or op amps for short, are powerful devices. Remember in chapter 3 we saw from the Ebers–Moll model, that there are practical limits on the possible gain from a common emitter amplifier. Effectively, op amps do not have this limitation. Their typical open loop gain is 10^5–10^6 and their output impedance is typically very low. While op amps are not the right device for every application, they certainly come close. Furthermore, as we will soon see, they are very easy to use. First let's look at figure 4.1, a typical op amp schematic, so that we can consistently discuss the device.

An op amp has two signal inputs, V_+ and V_-. In general, these signal inputs can be positive or negative voltages; the signs on the schematic refer to how the amplifier uses the signals. I strongly suggest that you refer to these inputs as the 'non-inverting' and 'inverting inputs', respectively, rather than 'V-plus' and 'V-minus', which can lead to confusion. The single output is labeled in figure 4.1 as V_{out}. Also shown are the inputs for the supply voltages, conventionally labeled V_{cc} and V_{ee} for the positive and negative supplies, respectively. Note that the power inputs are usually left off of schematics but you must always supply power, whether or not the inputs are shown.

All an op amp does is to amplify the difference between the two signal inputs:

$$V_{out} = \text{Gain} \times (V_+ - V_-), \tag{4.1}$$

where, as already stated, the gain is 10^5–10^6 and, as we will see in chapter 5, can depend on the signal frequency.

In most cases, it is not useful to employ such a large gain. After all, with a gain of 10^6, even an input difference of 100 μV would cause the output to 'hit the rails' (go to the maximum voltage output allowed by the supply voltages). We will see how

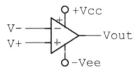

Figure 4.1. Generic schematic symbol for an op amp.

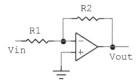

Figure 4.2. Circuit of a simple inverting amplifier.

to tame this monster gain to give us circuits with very desirable output characteristics.

To understand or to design op amp circuits, you only have to use two golden rules:

1. An op amp will do everything it can to insure that $V_+ = V_-$.
2. A op amp's signal inputs have infinite impedance. That is, no current can flow into the op amp via V_+ or V_-.

Golden rule 1 assumes the op amp has been correctly wired up in the circuit, and golden rule 2 is an approximation. Though the input impedance is extremely high, it is not infinite. For example the signal inputs of the LF411 draw about 50 pA. In the following examples, we will demonstrate how to use these rules.

4.2 Examples

4.2.1 Inverting amplifier

Consider the circuit of figure 4.2. Assume that the current, i_1 from the signal input flows through R_1 towards the op amp. (The choice of current flow direction is arbitrary as it will cancel out.) Then from Ohm's law,

$$i_1 = \frac{V_{in} - V_-}{R_1}. \tag{4.2}$$

But for this circuit, golden rule 1 says that $V_- = 0$ because V_+ is connected to ground. Now suppose the current flowing through R_2 is flowing towards V_{out} (once again, an arbitrary choice). Then

$$i_2 = \frac{V_- - V_{out}}{R_2} \tag{4.3a}$$

$$= \frac{-V_{out}}{R_2}. \tag{4.3b}$$

Golden rule 2 says that no current flows into or out of the op amp signal inputs. Therefore, using Kirchhoff's junction rule for the chosen current directions,

$$i_1 - i_2 = 0, \tag{4.4}$$

or, using equations (4.2) and (4.3b),

$$\frac{V_{in}}{R_1} - \frac{-V_{out}}{R_2} = 0,$$

or

$$V_{out} = -\frac{R_2}{R_1} V_{in}. \tag{4.5}$$

Equation (4.5) tells us that the amplifier has a gain of R_2/R_1 and the minus sign says that the signal is inverted.

What do you think the input impedance of this circuit is? That's actually easy to see: looking into the input, what is the impedance to ground? It's R_1. Don't forget that V_- is a virtual ground!

How about the output impedance? With it's virtually infinite gain capabilities, the op amp's output impedance is essentially zero, or as close to zero as one can imagine coming. In reality, it's a fraction of an Ohm.

Let's see if we can figure out why the circuit did what it did, without the anthropomorphism of golden rule 1. Suppose that initially $V_+ = V_-$. Now we slightly increase V_{in} by ΔV, making V_- more positive than it had been. From equation (4.1), we see that V_{out} will take the value $-G \times \Delta V$. This is fed back to the inverting input, V_-, reducing it back towards 0 V. Suppose now that ΔV is negative. Now equation (4.1) says that V_{out} will take the value $+G \times \Delta V$, once again driving V_- back towards 0 V.

Suppose we wanted to make a non-inverting amplifier. Couldn't we just use the circuit of figure 4.2, but swap the inverting and non-inverting inputs? Let's see.

If we apply a negative ΔV to V_{in}, this will lower V_+. Equation (4.1) now says that $V_{out} = +G \times \Delta V$. But this makes V_+ even *more positive*, driving it *farther* from 0 V. Applying a negative ΔV has the same problem so, no, you can't make a non-inverting amplifier simply by swapping the inverting and non-inverting inputs.

The idea of bringing a system back into equilibrium by feeding back a signal that is opposite in polarity to the initial change is called *negative feedback* and is an important concept in any sort of control system, whether it is electrical or mechanical. The opposite situation, called *positive feedback*, is usually not a good thing. We will see a few exceptions to this in chapter 5.

Homework 4.1:
Design an inverting amplifier having the following properties:
- A gain of −5.
- An input impedance of 10k.

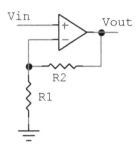

Figure 4.3. Circuit for a simple non-inverting amplifier.

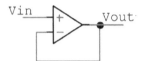

Figure 4.4. Circuit of a follower.

4.2.2 Non-inverting amplifier

In the previous section we saw that we could not make a non-inverting amplifier just by swapping the inputs to an inverting amplifier. But it is still easy to build a non-inverting amplifier. Figure 4.3 shows one way to do this. The analysis is quite simple if we recognize V_{out}, V_-, R_1 and R_2 to all be components of a voltage divider. Then,

$$V_- = V_{in} = \frac{R_1}{R_1 + R_2} V_{out},$$

or

$$V_{out} = \left(\frac{R_2}{R_1} + 1\right) V_{in}. \tag{4.6}$$

Homework 4.2:
   Design a non-inverting amplifier having a gain of +5.

Now look at figure 4.4. With the direct connection between V_{out} and V_-, it is clear that $V_{out} = V_{in}$. What is the point of such a circuit?! Remember that golden rule 2 says that the input impedance of an op amp is infinite. Practically speaking, this means that it can be in the GΩ range. But in order for golden rule 1 to work, the output impedance of an op amp must be low. And it is, typically in the mΩ range. Thus the circuit of figure 4.4 works wonderfully as a device to insert between two other elements in order to guarantee that a signal always moves from a device having low output impedance into a device having high input impedance. Such a circuit is called a *follower* or *buffer*.

4.2.3 Summing amplifier

The basic idea of the inverting amplifier can be extended to the extremely useful circuit shown in figure 4.5. The analysis of this circuit is exactly like that of the inverting amplifier of figure 4.2. That is, the current flowing through R_1 *plus* the current flowing through R_2 equals the current flowing through R. And since the voltage drops across R_1, R_2 and R are, respectively, V_1, V_2 and V_{out} (since $V_- = 0$) then

$$V_{out} = -\left(\frac{R}{R_1}V_1 + \frac{R}{R_2}V_2\right), \tag{4.7}$$

which, for the special case of $R_1 = R_2 = R$ becomes

$$V_{out} = -(V_1 + V_2).$$

Note the minus sign!

A special case of equation (4.7) is shown in figure 4.6. Notice that the input resistors increase in multiples of 2. Using the logic that was employed in deriving equation (4.7), we obtain

$$V_{out} = -(Bit_0 + 2 \times Bit_1 + 4 \times Bit_2 + 8 \times Bit_3). \tag{4.8}$$

To see why this could be useful, consider the 4-bit binary number $xxxx$ where each of the x is either a 0 or a 1. For example, consider the specific case of $N_2 = 1011$,

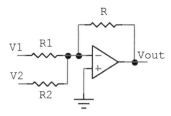

Figure 4.5. Basic circuit for summing two signals.

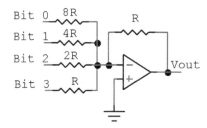

Figure 4.6. Circuit for a digital–analog converter or DAQ.

where the subscript on the N refers to the base. Convert this to base-10: multiply the nth digit by 2^n, where n starts with zero in the right-most column. Then,

$$N_{10} = 1 \times 2^0 + 1 \times 2^1 + 0 \times 2^2 + 1 \times 2^3 = 11_{10}. \tag{4.9}$$

Now imagine that the inputs Bit_0, Bit_1, etc are either 0 V or 5 V, depending on whether the binary numbers they represent are 0 or 1. Then it is easy to see that $V_{out} = -5$ $V \times N_2$. This is so because we have *weighted* the sum by the same amounts that we weighted the binary digits in equation (4.9) when we converted them to the decimal base. Thus, the circuit of figure 4.6 is a digital (i.e. base-2) to analog (i.e. base-10) converter, or DAQ. This DAQ is subject to error because it relies on uniformly applied voltages for 'Hi' and 'low' signals. Furthermore, you may need to worry about temperature effects on the resistor values. You can purchase a much better quality DAQ, but the simple circuit of figure 4.6 can be a convenient substitute, especially for a small number of bits.

4.2.4 Current source

Recall that in section 3.3.4, we described current sources/sinks based on transistors. Those circuits are simple and easy to design and build, but they do suffer from one defect: you have to supply your transistor base with a stiff voltage, and this usually means wasting current by having it flow to ground through the biasing network. Now consider the circuit of figure 4.7 which is an op-amp based current sink.

You set the desired current with R_3 and V_+. Now, because of the incredibly high input impedance of the op amp, you can use very large resistor values in the voltage divider of R_1 and R_2 without fear of droop. The feedback to V_- guarantees that the potential downstream of the load is constant, regardless of the value of R_{load}, at least until the output of the op amp reaches its maximum (often the supply voltage of the op amp). The programmed current is just V_+ $(=V_-)$ divided by R_3. If you replaced any of R_1, R_2, or R_3 with a pot, you'd have a variable current sink.

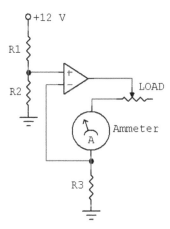

Figure 4.7. Circuit of an op-amp-based current sink.

Homework 4.3:
  Design a current sink having the following properties:
  • Supply voltages are ±15 V.
  • The circuit sinks 3.0 mA.

What is the compliance of your sink?

4.2.5 Peak finder

Sometimes you need to find the peak value of a time-varying signal. Figure 4.8 shows a simple way to do this.

Here's how it works. Suppose your signal, which is brought to U_1's V_+, initially has the same potential as V_-. Now as your signal increases in potential, so does the output of U_1, bringing the top of the capacitor and V_- to the same value. If your signal potential is reduced, the op amp output will go negative, but the diode prevents the capacitor from discharging. (Recall that V_- has 'infinite' input impedance and so the cap cannot discharge through the op amp.) This means that you can raise the potential at the top of the cap, but once raised, it can never go down. The second op amp is just a buffer. This is usually necessary because you don't want any downstream circuitry to discharge your cap. This circuit works pretty well, but there are several problems. The first flaw in this circuit is that you may occasionally want to reset so you can find a new maximum signal value, but this circuit has no way to allow a reset. This is easily fixed by putting a switch across the capacitor. This will allow you to reset whenever you like. Second, recall from figure 3.2 that a reverse-biased diode has a non-zero current. That is, a diode is a 'leaky' one-way valve. This means that when your input signal drops below its peak, the capacitor will slowly discharge *backwards* through the diode. The fix to this problem is to replace D_1 with a pair of diodes in series, and then feed back from the output of U_2, through a resistor, to a point between the two diodes. The idea is that when the input signal drops, forcing U_2 to go negative, the point after the first diode will still stay at the peak value. It is 'protected' by the second diode as well as the feedback from U_2. The other flaws with the circuit have to do with the finite response

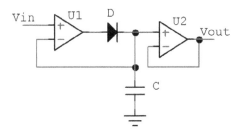

Figure 4.8. Peak detector.

time of an op amp, reducing its ability to respond to rapid changes in the input. We will discuss op amp 'slew rate' limitations later.

4.2.6 Sample and hold

Related to the peak detector is the sample-and-hold circuit. In this case, we want to sample a signal, outputting the signal value as it comes—until a switch is hit. At that point on, the circuit outputs the value the signal had at the time the switch had been hit. Once the switch has been reset, the circuit outputs the time-varying signal again. Look at the simple sample-and-hold circuit shown in figure 4.9. The signal passes through the buffer made from the follower of U_1 before arriving at the solid state switch, Q. When the switch is 'open' the input signal is seen at V_+ of U_2 which forms a second buffer. The first buffer of U_1 is necessary because you need a very low output impedance so that the capacitor doesn't cause the signal to droop. (You want U_1 to be able to source all the current it needs to keep C at the signal potential.) But you can also think of Z_{out} and C as forming a low-pass filter, with

$$f_{3\,\mathrm{dB}} = \frac{1}{2\pi Z_{out} C}.$$

Then, you'd like the ZC product to be as small as possible so as to push the 3 dB point up to as high a frequency as possible, another reason to keep Z_{out} (as well as C) small. On the other hand, you'd like to keep C as large as possible to minimize the 'droop rate': $dv/dt = I_{leakage}/C$, where $I_{leakage}$ is from the small currents leakages of Q_1 and U_2. While the circuit of figure 4.9 works very well for most applications, you may wish to purchase a specialized chip that contains all the ingredients of figure 4.9, excepting the capacitor, with is externally supplied.

4.2.7 Push–pull follower

Recall in section 3.3.2 we discussed the push–pull follower. In the circuit of figure 3.12 we used a pair of npn and pnp transistors, the first to handle the positive portion of the ac signal, and the second to handle the negative portion. The problem was that the circuit caused the cross-over distortion of figure 3.13, which was caused by the base–emitter diode drop being in opposite directions for the two transistors.

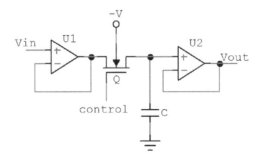

Figure 4.9. A simple sample-and-hold circuit.

Figure 4.10 is an improvement over figure 3.12. The feedback from V_{out} 'precompensates' the input to the op amp to correct for the diode drops. The major problem with the circuit of figure 4.10 is that cross-over has 'sharp edges', and to create—or compensate for—sharp edges takes high response speed, and this is the op amp's big weakness, as we will discuss in chapter 5. Nevertheless, the circuit of Figure 4.10 is a vast improvement over that of figure 3.12. Furthermore, it demonstrates a very important theme: using the flexibility of an op amp with the current capacity of power transistors.

4.2.8 Integrator

In section 2.3 we found that we could integrate with simple RC circuits. However, in those circuits, integration was only approximate; we had to select components and operate in a frequency range such that equation (2.20) holds. Figure 4.11 shows a circuit that integrates *exactly*.

Ignoring R_2 for the moment, we analyze the circuit in the usual way: The current passing through R_1 is V_{in}/R_1. This is equal to the current passing 'through' the capacitor, $-CdV_{out}/dt$. That is,

$$dV_{out} = -\frac{V_{in}}{R_1 C} \, dt.$$

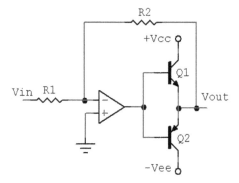

Figure 4.10. An improved push–pull emitter follower that uses feedback to correct cross-over distortion.

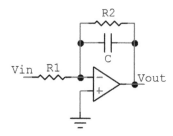

Figure 4.11. An improved integrator circuit.

or

$$V_{out} = -\frac{1}{R_1 C} \int V_{in}\, dt + \text{a constant.} \qquad (4.10)$$

The problem is that there is no dc path to ground for V_{out} and this can lead to a gradual charge build-up on the capacitor until V_{out} eventually goes to the rails of the op amp. By putting R_2 in the feedback, we allow a dc path to discharge C. You typically want R_2 to be large, such that the feedback is a filter to all but the lowest frequencies,

$$f < \frac{1}{R_2 C}.$$

4.2.9 Differentiator

Using op amps, we can also differentiate without the approximation of equation (2.18). The circuit of figure 4.12 shows us how. The analysis is virtually identical to that for the integrator, but with the terms reversed:

$$C\frac{dV_{in}}{dt} = -V_{out}\Big/ R,$$

or

$$V_{out} = -RC\frac{dV_{in}}{dt}. \qquad (4.11)$$

The problem with a differentiator is that it can dramatically emphasize noise. That is, tiny noise spikes in V_{in}, when differentiated, become large features in V_{out}. This is not a defect in the circuit, it's just calculus! But we can tweak the circuit of figure 4.12 by placing a small capacitor in parallel with R. The idea is that for very high frequency components (i.e. spikes) the feedback impedance, and therefore the gain, is nearly zero.

4.2.10 Active rectifier

In section 3.1.1 we described diodes as 'one-way valves' and used them to rectify signals. But this model of a diode assumes that the signal levels are much greater than a diode drop, ~0.6 V for silicon diodes. How do you rectify small signals?

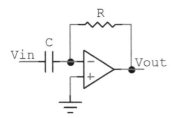

Figure 4.12. An improved differentiator circuit.

Look at the circuit of figure 4.13. When V_{in} is positive, feeding the diode output back to V_- forces U_1 output to compensate for the diode drop. When V_{in} is negative, the diode blocks the feedback, forcing the op amp to hit the negative rail, and the input to U_2 is at zero. The second op amp is optional, but allows you to use a large value of R (which reduces the current that U_2 would have to output) and without raising the output impedance of the rectifier.

But there is still a problem with this circuit. It takes time for the op amp to recover from going to the negative rail and if your signal is too fast, this can give rise to undesirable distortion. For example, the op amp used in our labs, the LF411, has a maximum *slew rate* (rate of change of voltage output) of 15 V per microsecond. If the negative rail is -15 V, then the op amp will take at least a microsecond to recover from a negative signal.

A solution to this is shown in figure 4.14—and all it takes is one extra diode and one extra resistor. Here's how it works: when V_{in} is negative, the combination of D_1, and the two resistors makes U_1 an amplifier with a gain of -1. (It's a simple inverting amplifier.) U_1 output will be one diode drop above V_{in}, but $U_2 V_+$ sees $-V_{in}$ because this is an *inverting* amplifier. When V_{in} goes positive, the feedback is through D_2 and once again the gain is -1 (positive this time). This time, U_1 output is a diode drop below V_{in}. Also, $U_2 V_+$ sees 0. This circuit is an improvement over figure 4.13 because instead of U_1 output going from $V_{in} + 0.6$ V to the negative rail, it only goes between ± 0.6 V, a huge improvement. We point out that U_2 output is inverted; if you want a positive signal, you'll need to add a unity-gain inverting amplifier.

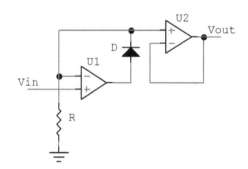

Figure 4.13. An active rectifier.

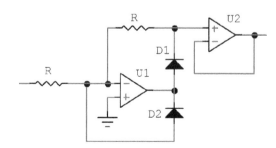

Figure 4.14. An improved active rectifier.

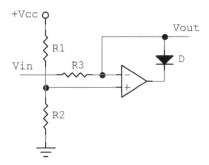

Figure 4.15. Circuit of an active clamp.

4.2.11 Active clamp

In section 3.1.2, we described using a diode in a clamp; that is, a circuit that prevents the output voltage from exceeding some designed amount. In that circuit, shown in figure 3.6, a 5 V power supply was used to set the clamping voltage at one diode drop above the supply voltage. But what if you want to be able to vary your clamping voltage? Whatever supply you use must be stiff because the diode will pass to it whatever current is required to maintain one diode drop across it.

With this in mind, consider the circuit of figure 4.15. The resistors R_1 and R_2 form a voltage divider, the output of which is 'protected' by the op amp. When $V_{in} < V_{VD}$, the op amp output goes to the positive rails, but V_{out} is just V_{in} because of the diode. When $V_{in} \geqslant V_{VD}$, the op amp output goes just negative enough to bring V_- (and V_{out}) to V_{VD}. The circuit works great, with the usual limitations of finite op amp slew rates as the op amp tries to recover from the positive rail.

IOP Publishing

Practical Analog, Digital, and Embedded Electronics for Scientists

Brett D DePaola

Chapter 5

Op amps II: non-ideal behavior and positive feedback

5.1 Non-ideal behavior

5.1.1 Finite slew rate

In the previous chapter we used op amps to correct some aberrant behavior of p–n junctions. Those circuits were certainly improvements, but still came up short of expectations at higher frequencies. The problem is the finite *slew rate* of op amps.

Figure 5.1 shows the log of the open (dashed line) and closed (solid line) loop gain versus the log of frequency. The first thing we should notice in both curves is the 6 dB per octave roll-off that is characteristic of a low-pass filter. This is not an accident: op amps are deliberately slowed down to help with stability. We can also see that the higher the gain, the lower the bandwidth of the op amp. The low bandwidth, essentially equivalent to saying 'the low speed' or 'low slew rate' of op amps, is one reason we still have to know how to use transistors. The LF411 has a maximum slew rate of about 15 V μs^{-1}. Generally speaking, op amps with bjt transistor inputs have faster slew rates than those having FET-inputs.

5.1.2 Finite input impedance

One of the golden rules that we used in helping us with op amp design is that their input impedance is infinite. While certainly high, the impedance is not infinite, and this can cause problems under certain circumstances.

Input bias current
Finite input impedance means non-zero current at the inputs. The *input bias current*, or I_B is defined as the average current that leaks into the op amp when the two inputs are tied together. The op amp's inputs are either the bases of bipolar transistors, e.g.

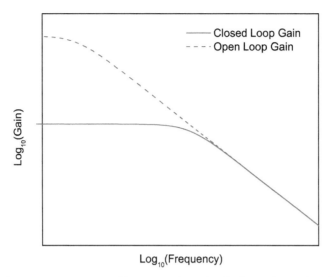

Figure 5.1. Log of op amp gain versus log of frequency. The dashed line is open loop gain while the solid line is closed loop gain.

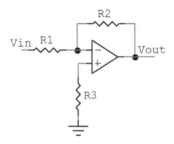

Figure 5.2. Inverting amplifier with a resistor on V_+ to compensate for non-zero I_B.

for the 741, or the gate of a JFET or MOSFET, e.g. for the LF411. In the former case, $I_B \sim 80$ nA; in the latter case, $I_B \sim 50$ pA, though in both cases the I_B is temperature-dependent. Still, that's a pretty small current, so why should we care?

Consider the inverting amplifier circuit of figure 4.2. The small leakage into the inverting input causes a small additional voltage drop across R_1, which for sufficiently high gain or sufficiently high values of R_1, will give us an offset voltage error.

A fix is shown in figure 5.2. At first glance, R_3 looks superfluous: why would we need a resistor here if no current can flow into V_+? But it is precisely because a current *does* flow that sometimes makes R_3 necessary. To battle I_B, we would make $R_3 = R_1 \parallel R_2$, where this notation means R_1 in parallel with R_2. In practice, we rarely use R_3 (or its equivalent in other circuits) if we are using FET-input op amps like the LF411, but nearly always balance our input impedances if we are using BJT-input op amps like the 741.

Differential input currents

Not only is the current to the inputs non-zero, but the currents to V_- and V_+ are not even equal. Typically, this *input offset current* is 1/2 to 1/10 of I_B, and is typically better matched for BJT-input op amps than for the FET-input types. In the case of the LF411, the input offset current is typically about 25 pA. Depending on your application, you may have to tweak your input resistor values, or even the voltage offset adjustment (if one exists) as described in the next section.

5.1.3 Voltage offset

Another reason for a non-zero output voltage, even when the op amp's inputs are tied together is due to *input offset voltage*. This is caused by imbalances in the circuitry within the op amp itself. The input offset voltage can be problematic in many cases. For example, suppose you are integrating over long times. Then even a small V_{offset} can accumulate and give you substantial error. Many op amps have pins that allow you to compensate for V_{offset}. In figure 5.3 we show how to do this on the LF411 using a pot and the negative supply voltage.

5.1.4 Voltage limitations

We have not yet discussed how high a voltage you can apply to an op amp, but those limits do exist—and the cost of ignoring those limits could well be a fried chip. The data sheets give you this information. When we speak of voltage limits, we can refer to three different ones: (1) the *supply* limits, (2) the *differential mode* limits, and (3) the *common mode* limits. For the supply limits, there are both maximum and minimum values. In the case of the LF411, the minimum supply voltage is 10 V; the maximum is 36 V. 'Differential mode' refers to the voltage difference between the inputs. In the case of the LF411, this is about 30 V. Anything more than this and you can fry the op amp. Common mode input refers to the maximum voltage you can put on either input, even if you keep the differential mode voltages equal. It is always unwise to exceed the supply voltages, and is even risky to come too close to the supply values   unless the op amp is specifically advertised to operate 'rail-to-rail'.

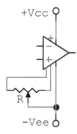

Figure 5.3. Using a potentiometer to compensate for V_{offset}. Compensation pins are not always available.

5.1.5 Output current limitations

When we used an emitter follower to boost the output of an op amp we said something about op amps not being able to source a great deal of current. (This is another reason that we still have to learn about transistors.) But we didn't talk about how small a current we were limited to. In the case of the LF411, the maximum output current is 20 mA. This is typical of op amps and rarely, if ever, exceeds 100 mA.

5.1.6 Output phase shift

The low-pass filters that are used to stabilize op amps also give rise to a frequency-dependent phase shift. We will talk more about this in section 5.2.3.

5.1.7 Temperature dependence

Unfortunately, *everything* depends on temperature. In the case of the output voltage offset, for example, not only does V_{offset} depend on temperature, but so does the resistance of the pot you may use to compensate it. I have seen extreme cases where the entire circuit board had to be placed in a controlled temperature environment just to keep it working within specs. Fortunately, this is usually not necessary but trying to design your circuit to be *relatively* temperature independent will save you many a headache in later trying to fix the problem.

5.2 Positive feedback

Thus far, in every circuit we've examined, we've fed a portion of the output back to the inverting input, resulting in negative feedback. Negative feedback gives stability to the circuit, but sometimes you don't want stability. In this section we examine a handful of circuits where positive feedback is used.

5.2.1 Comparators

Basic comparator
Consider the circuit of figure 5.4. As already discussed in chapter 4, $V_{out} = \text{Gain} \times (V_{ref} - V_{sig})$, with Gain $\gtrsim 10^5$. We pointed out earlier how singularly useless such a circuit is because the crazy high gain of op amps means that, effectively, your output would always sit at one rail or the other. But sometimes this is exactly what you want.

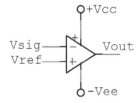

Figure 5.4. Circuit of a basic comparator.

Suppose, for example, you want to trip a relay that turns on a heater whenever the temperature in your room drops below some particular temperature. You could connect a temperature sensor to V_{sig} and connect a voltage divider to V_{ref} such that when the sensor output drops below the reference voltage, V_{out} goes to the positive rail. It can then drive a transistor emitter follower circuit to drive a relay, turning on the heater. You wouldn't need to worry about your op amp output going negative when the temperature sensor output exceeds V_{ref} because for $V_{out} < 0$ your follower would not output anything. In this configuration, you are using the op amp as a *comparator*.

The circuit of figure 5.4 will do the job. But what if you are trying for faster control? As we learned in section 5.1, op amps have finite slew rates—for purposes of stability—and going from rail to rail costs time. Furthermore, you have to choose V_{cc} and V_{ee} to be compatible with whatever your op amp is going to drive. In the above application this was easy because we were just driving an emitter follower, but in general this is an additional hassle.

More serious is the problem that no signal is 100% clean. For example in figure 5.5 we see a 'typical' signal (in blue) and a rock-stable reference (in green). While the signal is less than the reference, the output (in red) is 'high', for example, at the positive rail; and when the signal goes above the reference, the output goes 'low', for example, to the negative rail. But look what happens to the output when the signal is close to the reference. Because of the 'noise' on the signal, the op amp output jumps up and down multiple times. This could be inconsequential—or it could be disastrous, depending on your application.

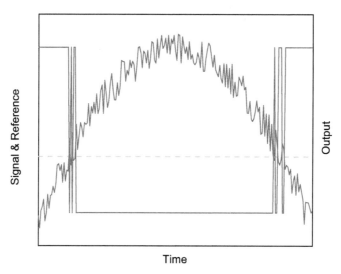

Figure 5.5. Possible inputs and output of the circuit of figure 5.4. Note how the output (red) jumps between the two rails when the signal (blue) comes close to the reference (green).

Special purpose comparator op amps

What we need is a comparator with *hysteresis*. Hysteresis, in general, implies a path-dependance. In this case we mean that the voltage at which the output changes depends on whether the signal is approaching the reference from below or from above. We illustrate this with the circuit of figure 5.6. Compared to figure 5.4 we've changed quite a few things. First of all we used a special chip, an op amp specifically designed to be used as a comparator. A comparator op amp has a much higher slew rate than a normal op amp because the 3 dB per octave RC filter has been removed. This makes the comparator chip much less stable for ordinary op amp functions, but much faster for switching between high and low. Second, this particular comparator chip has an *open-collector* output. What this means is that you can think of the 'output' of the op amp to be the collector of an internal transistor. Thus it cannot source a signal, but can only serve as a signal drain. That is, when the internal output transistor is 'on', an externally supplied voltage, here from a +5 V source, will flow through the transistor to ground (or wherever the transistor's emitter is connected to).

Note the use of R_3. Without it you'd have a short-circuit from the +5 V supply to ground whenever the transistor is active. Thus when the transistor is active, V_{out} will be at ground but when the transistor is inactive, V_{out} will be at +5 V. A resistor used as R_3 is called a *pull-up resistor*. The advantages of the open-collector output are two-fold: First, you can control the voltage levels of the output independent of the op amp's supply voltages. Second, you can drive higher current loads with a power supply than with the usual op amp, obviating the need for an emitter follower.

All of this is a change in op amp type from the circuit in figure 5.4. This makes the circuit faster and more convenient to use, but does not address the problem illustrated in figure 5.5. For that we need feedback—and please note that in figure 5.6 we used *positive* feedback.

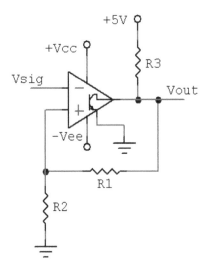

Figure 5.6. Comparator circuit that has hysteresis.

Here's how to analyze the circuit. First suppose that $V_{sig} < V_+$. Then V_{out} will be 'high'; in this case it will be pulled up to +5 V. Then the voltage divider resistors R_1 and R_2 will cause V_+ to be at

$$V_+ = \frac{R_2}{R_1 + R_2}\, 5\text{ V}.$$

For example, if $R_1 = R_2 = 1$ k, then when V_{out} is high, $V_+ = 2.5$ V. Therefore, 2.5 V is the reference voltage. But once $V_{sig} > 2.5$ V, V_{out} drops to zero and so does the reference at V_+. Now in order for V_{out} to switch back to +5 V, V_{in} will have to drop all the way to just below 0 V. Once it does, the reference voltage will jump back to 2.5 V. Thus, we have a hysteresis of 2.5 V because that is the difference between the switching point when the signal is coming from below, compared to when it is coming from above. Of course we are not constrained to operate between +5 V and 0 V. We could insert another resistor between V_+ and, say, $+V_{cc}$, and replace the ground connection on R_2 with a connection to $-V_{ee}$.

Figure 5.7 shows a characteristic output from a comparator with feedback. The signal is the same as in figure 5.5 but now there are two references, a higher one for when the signal approaches from below, and a lower one for when the signal approaches from above. The hysteresis, i.e. the separation between the two references, was chosen to be slightly larger than the expected noise on the signal.

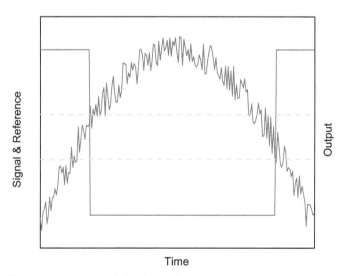

Figure 5.7. Possible inputs and output of the circuit of figure 5.4. There are now two references (shown in green), the upper one when the input approaches from below, and the lower one when the input approaches from above.

Homework 5.1:

Design a comparator using the open-collector output op amp of this discussion, and having the following characteristics:

- $V_{cc} = +15$ V,
- $V_{ee} = -15$ V,
- $V_{TTL} = +5$ V,
- $V_{threshold} = 3.0$ V,
- $V_{hyst} = 0.1$ V,

where V_{TTL} is the supply labeled $+5$ V in figure 5.6, $V_{threshold}$ is the lower voltage threshold, and V_{hyst} is the hysteresis (2.5 V in the circuit of figure 5.6).

Hints:
- Your references are between 0 V and $+5$ V,
  so you can connect your voltage divider between these two points.
  That is, you can connect R_2 to ground,
  but you need to add another resistor between V_+ and $+5$ V.
- If you have two resistors connected to each other on one side,
  with the other sides both going to, say, $+5$ V, then those resistors are in parallel,
  even if the two 5 V sources are different ones.
- Choose your resistors to have values that are large compared to the pull–up resistor.
  This allows you to neglect the pull–up in your analysis.

5.2.2 Oscillators

In this section we show how positive feedback works well with circuits intended to oscillate. We will start with op amp-based oscillators and then we will introduce a chip that was specifically designed with oscillators in mind.

Basic relaxation oscillators

Many oscillator circuits are in the category of the *relaxation oscillator*. The essential idea is that you charge capacitor and, once the cap has reached a set point, a comparator switches and the capacitor begins to discharge. Figure 5.8 shows a simple 'RC Oscillator'. Notice that V_{out} will oscillate between $\pm V_{cc}$ (for $V_{ee} = -V_{cc}$), and that the reference at V_+ will therefore oscillate between $\pm \frac{R_2}{R_3 + R_3} V_{cc}$. Furthermore, as V_{out} oscillates between $\pm V_{cc}$, the capacitor will alternatively charge and discharge. While $V_{out} = +V_{cc}$ the capacitor will charge through R_1, with the characteristic RC time constant (see equation (2.25)) until $V_- = V_+$, that is until the voltage on the capacitor, V_C is

$$V_C = \frac{R_2}{R_2 + R_3} V_{cc}.$$

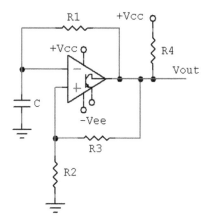

Figure 5.8. The classic RC relaxation oscillator circuit.

At this point V_{out} and V_+ change sign and the capacitor discharges through R_1 until

$$V_C = -\frac{R_2}{R_2 + R_3} V_{cc}.$$

Then V_{out} and V_+ change sign again and the process is repeated.

Homework 5.2:
Derive an expression for the oscillation period of the circuit in figure 5.8.
- Assume that $V_{ee} = -V_{cc}$.
- Your expression should be a function of R_1, R_2, R_3 and C.
- Assume that you've made R_4 small enough that there is negligible voltage drop across it.
- Your expression should be *independent* of V_{cc}.

Wien-bridge oscillator
It is very easy to make an oscillator for square and rectangular waves. But it is not so easy to make an oscillator for sine waves. Figure 5.9 shows a circuit that actually does this. It is called a Wien-bridge oscillator and it is a bit tricky to understand—but let's try!

First of all, notice that there is both positive and negative feedback. Let's tackle them separately, starting with the positive. We can think of this as a voltage divider made up of reactive components. Let's define the impedance of the RC parallel combination as Z_1 and the RC series combination as Z_2. Then,

$$\frac{V_+}{V_{\text{out}}} = \frac{Z_1}{Z_1 + Z_2},$$

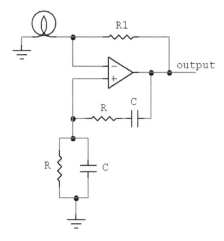

Figure 5.9. The Wien-bridge oscillator.

where

$$Z_1 = \frac{RZ_C}{R + Z_C} = \frac{R}{1 + j\omega RC}$$

and

$$Z_2 = R + Z_C = \frac{-j + \omega RC}{\omega C}.$$

After a bit of algebra, we can show

$$\left| \frac{V_+}{V_{out}} \right| = \frac{\omega RC}{\sqrt{\omega^4 R^4 C^4 + 7\omega^2 R^2 C^2 + 1}} \tag{5.1a}$$

$$\tan \phi = \frac{1 - \omega^2 R^2 C^2}{3\omega RC}. \tag{5.1b}$$

I've plotted equations (5.1a) and (5.1b) in figure 5.10.

Homework 5.3:
- Derive equations (5.1).
- Show that equation (5.1a) leads to oscillation at $\omega = (RC)^{-1}$.
- Show that at resonance, the phase of the feedback is 0.

As you can see in figure 5.10, the positive feedback peaks at $\omega = (RC)^{-1}$. But feedback is a non-linear effect that is reinforced with every feedback iteration. Thus, very quickly the frequency for which the feedback is greatest quickly dominates—to the exclusion of all other frequencies.

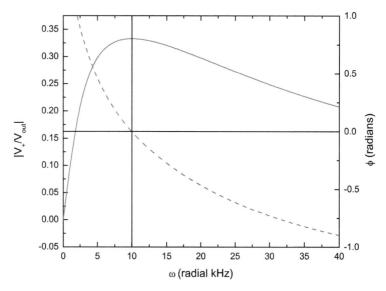

Figure 5.10. The amplitude (solid blue) and phase (dashed red) of the positive feedback leg in a Wien-bridge oscillator circuit. The RC product was taken to be 0.1 ms.

A quick examination of equation (5.1a) shows that at $\omega = (RC)^{-1}$,

$$\left| \frac{V_+}{V_{out}} \right| = \frac{1}{3},$$

and equation (5.1b) shows that $\phi = 0$. If we don't want the output to go to the rails, we need to counter the positive feedback of 1/3 with negative feedback of exactly 3. If we think of the lamp as being a resistor having resistivity R_L, then we see that the negative feedback in the Wien-bridge looks just like that of the non-inverting amplifier. That is, the gain is $(1 + R_1/R_L)$. Therefore, we must have $R_1/R_L = 2$, exactly. That is, if R_1/R_L is just slightly greater than 2, the negative feedback will kill the oscillations; and if the ratio is just slightly less than 2, the positive feedback will force the output to go to the rails. What to do? Here's where the lamp comes in. If the gain from the negative feedback is slightly too large, forcing the output to head toward either the positive or negative rails, the current flowing through the lamp will increase. This will cause the filament to heat up a bit, thereby increasing its resistance and lowering the gain. If the gain is slightly too low, which could cause the oscillator to stop oscillating, the current flowing through the lamp will be reduced, causing R_L to become smaller, increasing the gain and increasing the output. You can see that the purpose of using the lamp as a resistor is to stabilize the oscillator, both keeping it going and preventing it from going to the rails.

But why do we get a sine wave output instead of a square wave? Not going to the rails is important, but doesn't guarantee a sine. Going back to the frequency dependance of the positive feedback, we see the answer. Any periodic signal can be expressed as a weighted sum of frequencies (the Fourier series) starting with the overall fundamental frequency of the oscillator, and including harmonics of that fundamental. But because the filters on the positive feedback kill all frequencies but the fundamental, we get only the leading term in the Fourier series, namely the sine wave at the frequency of the oscillator. The fact that the phase shift of the feedback is zero at the fundamental frequency helps as well since a phase shift could look like a frequency shift under certain circumstances. (We'll see more of that when we start discussing phase-locked loops.)

The 7555 oscillator chip

Using either a conventional op amp or a comparator, it is simple to build an oscillator circuit that is usually good enough for your application. However, it is often more convenient to use a special purpose (and inexpensive) chip that does much of the design work for you.

An example of such a chip is the 7555 timer chip (the CMOS descendant of the venerable 555 timer chip). The 7555 is a veritable toolbox of a chip and should be in every electronics tinkerer's collection of essential circuit building blocks. A schematic representation of the 7555 wired up as a simple relaxation oscillator is shown in figure 5.11. Before explaining the circuit, let's go over the inputs and outputs of the 7555 itself.

The supply and ground inputs, V_{cc} and G, respectively, are self-explanatory. The output goes from rail to rail. The input labeled R is the reset. To reset this chip, you must hold R to ground until you are ready for it to function. Upon connecting R to V_{cc}, the 7555 will start to 'do its thing'. Notice the use of the circle on the R input. This is a logic symbol that we will see quite a bit when we move on to digital electronics. It indicates 'negative true' logic. In this case, instead of activating R with a positive (or TRUE) signal, we activate it with a 'negative' (0 V or FALSE) signal; hence the circle. The input labeled D is the 'drain'. When activated, the drain is essentially a short-circuit to ground. When not activated, the drain floats. The drain pin is effectively the same as the open-collector output that we saw on the

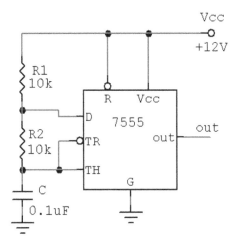

Figure 5.11. The classic 7555 timer chip wired up as a relaxation oscillator.

comparator. The last two inputs are what make the 7555 interesting. The *TH* or 'threshold' pin is activated when it sees a signal $\geqslant 2/3\ V_{cc}$. Once the threshold has been activated, two things happen: (1) The drain is activated, and (2) the output goes low. These stay this way until the trigger is activated, which occurs when $TR \leqslant 1/3\ V_{cc}$. When the trigger is activated, two things happen: (1) the drain is deactivated, and (2) the output goes high. They stay this way until the threshold is hit.

All of this sounds complicated, but an example will make things more clear. Look at how the 7555 has been wired up in figure 5.11.

When the power is switched on, the capacitor has a potential of 0 V on it and the trigger is activated. This causes the output to go high, and the drain is disabled. The capacitor then begins to charge with an RC time constant of $(R_1 + R_2)C$. But once $V_C = 2/3\ V_{cc}$, here 8 V, the threshold is hit, the output goes low, and the drain is turned on. With the drain on, the capacitor begins to discharge through R_2 with an RC time constant of $R_2 C$. The cap continues to discharge until $V_C = 1/3\ V_{cc}$ at which time the drain turns off, the output goes high again and the process repeats.

The output of the 7555 for the circuit in figure 5.11 is shown along with V_C in figure 5.12. The red dashed line shows V_C and the blue solid line shows the output from the 7555. Initially, V_C starts from 0 V but after that, both V_C and V_{out} settle into a periodic pattern. Notice that V_{out} is HIGH longer that it is LOW. This is because C is charging through 20k of resistance but discharging through 10k of resistance.

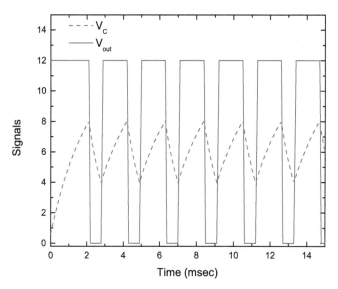

Figure 5.12. Sample outputs from the circuit in figure 5.11. The red dashed line is the voltage on the top of the capacitor and the blue solid line is the output from the 7555.

Homework 5.4:
   Derive an expression for the period of the basic 555 relaxation oscillator of figure 5.11.

There are many other ways to use the 7555 as the basis of an oscillator. For example, instead of charging the capacitor with a voltage source, you could charge it through a current source. Then, from equation (2.4), V_C will rise linearly in time until V_C hits V_{TH}, at which time V_C would be shunted to ground via the drain. So now, taking V_C as the output you've made a sawtooth wave. These applications just scratch the surface of what you can do with the 7555 timer chip. Best to keep several on hand.

5.2.3 Positive feedback gone bad

Even though most of our circuits will—and should—use negative feedback, we've seen a number of cases where positive feedback is useful. However, you may also run into confusing situations where you *think* you have negative feedback, but are seeing the results of positive feedback. For example, in figure 5.13, we see a trivial circuit: a buffer followed by a capacitor to ground. First of all, why would we do this? Well, we already have! Re-examine figure 4.8 and 4.9. In both of these we have a buffer followed by a capacitor. Furthermore, even if you use a buffer simply to push a signal through a long cable, you could have built the equivalent of the circuit in figure 5.13 because of the capacitance of the cable itself. Ok, so what's wrong with this circuit?

We'll come back to this, but first, let's consider a more straight-forward circuit, like the one in figure 5.14. In this circuit, we see that we are driving the base of a common-emitter amplifier with the output of an op amp. We then feed the output of the common-emitter back to the inverting input of the op amp, much as we did with 'the improved push–pull' of figure 4.10. In this case, however, the circuit will definitely not work. Why? Recall that the common-emitter amplifier has a negative gain. That is, the phase of the output has been shifted by 180° from the input. Going to the inverting input, effectively, shifts it by another 180°, putting it back in phase with the input—and hence positive feedback.

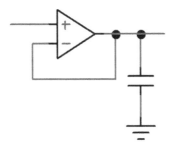

Figure 5.13. Simple circuit that could go bad!

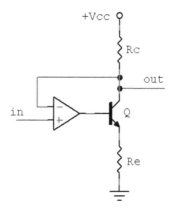

Figure 5.14. Op amp used to 'improve' the common-emitter amplifier: this circuit won't work!

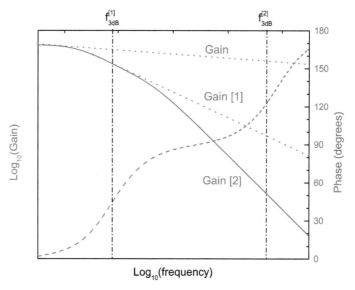

Figure 5.15. The phase shift (red dashed) and the Log of op amp gain (blue solid) versus the Log of the frequency. 'Gain' indicates the open loop gain in the absence of any built-in op amp filtering. 'Gain[1]' indicates the 6 dB per octave roll-off due to some filtering at relatively low frequencies, and 'Gain[2]' indicates the 6 dB per octave roll-off due to some filtering at relatively high frequencies. You can see that the phase shifts nearly 90° for each of the two internal op amp filters. The 3 dB points for each of the filters is indicated.

There are two other points. The first is that phase shifts are additive. In figure 5.14, for example, the phase shift of the common-emitter amplifier adds to the phase shift introduced by the inverting input of the op amp. The other point is that the op amp itself introduces a frequency-dependent phase shift, simply by virtue of its built-in RC filters.

Figure 5.15 shows the phase shift and the log of the open-loop gain of an op amp versus log of frequency. Compare these plots with those of the low-pass filter as shown in figure 2.2. In that graph we had one 3 dB point and the phase ran from

$-\pi/2$ to $+\pi/2$ or, equivalently, from 0 to 180°. In figure 5.15 we can see evidence for two low-pass filters, along with the corresponding 3 dB points. The idea was to compensate the op amp in order to improve its performance. But look again at the phase: the phase shift from the first low-pass was nearly 90°, and the phase shift from the second low-pass brought the cumulative phase shift nearly to 180°. I repeat, phase shifts are additive. Thus, with only a little additional phase shift, as from a reactive load, you could cross the 180° mark and turn your buffer into an oscillator, at least at higher frequencies.

Going back to figure 5.13, you can think of the output on the capacitor as being fed back into the non-inverting input, via the ground, but with the phase having been shifted by a combination of the output capacitor and the op amp's frequency-dependant phase shifts.

There are all sorts of ways that the signal can be coupled back into the op amp. For example, via the op amp power supplies, etc. The point is, if you do experience this parasitic oscillation, you may need to either reduce the circuit gain, or add phase to the feedback via your own reactive elements. You may even want to feed back to the non-inverting input.

IOP Publishing

Practical Analog, Digital, and Embedded Electronics for Scientists

Brett D DePaola

Chapter 6

Digital gates: combinational and sequential logic

6.1 Counting in different bases

There's an old joke that goes something like

There are 10 types of people in this world: those who understand binary and those who don't.

There's also an old riddle that goes

Why is Halloween the same as Christmas? That is, why is the following true:

$$OCT\,31 = DEC\,25$$

The answer is that $31_8 = 25_{10}$, where the subscripts refer to the number bases. Get it? OCT means base-8 and DEC means base-10.

But why do we need other bases anyhow? Isn't base-10 good enough? Base-10 is fine, but logic, which consists of two possible states, TRUE and FALSE, is more naturally represented in base-2, where TRUE $\rightarrow$ 1, and FALSE $\rightarrow$ 0. Furthermore, digital electronics consists of *gates*, the inputs and outputs of which are TRUE or FALSE. We'll get to this soon, but for now, back to bases in general.

When we express the multi-digit number 472 in base-10, what we mean is

10^2	10^1	10^0
4	7	2

or $4 \times 10^2 + 7 \times 10^1 + 2 \times 10^0$.

doi:10.1088/978-0-7503-3491-4ch6

We use the same convention in all bases except that instead of 10^n we have X^n, where n is the column number (starting with $n = 0$ in the right-most column) and X is the base. So, for example, the number 346_8 is

8^2	8^1	8^0
3	4	6

or $3 \times 8^2 + 4 \times 8^1 + 6 \times 8^0 = 230_{10}$.

Base-8, also known as octal, used to be popular for computer work but has now largely been replaced by base-16, also known as hexadecimal or hex for short. Base-8 and base-16 are particularly useful when working with computers because base-2, while natural for TRUE–FALSE logic, can become cumbersome due to the large number of digits it takes to express even a small number. But 8 and 16 are powers of 2, making it very easy to convert between base-2 and base-16, as we will see.

A digit of a number expressed in base-X must be less than or equal to X. Thus the number 392_8 makes no sense because 9 does not exist in base-8. But what do we do about bases in which $X > 10$? For example, in base-16 we cannot use '10' for the number after 9 because $10_{16} = 1 \times 16^1 + 0 \times 16^0 = 16$. In these larger-than-10 bases we have to make up symbols for digits that have values greater than 10_{10}. In the hexadecimal system we use the digits 0, 1, ...8, 9, A, B, C, D, E, F. Thus $F_{16} = 15_{10}$. We will make use of the hexadecimal system when we begin to interface devices with computers, but now let's get back to binary, or base-2.

Consider the binary number 1011,0101. (The comma is optional, but is often convenient as we shall see.) As above, we can convert this number to base-10:

2^7	2^6	2^5	2^4	2^3	2^2	2^1	2^0
1	0	1	1	0	1	0	1

or $2^7 + 2^5 + 2^4 + 2^2 + 2^0 = 181_{10}$.

This conversion was not difficult but it was awkward. In contrast, the conversion to hex can be done by inspection: the left-most four digits are $1011_2 = 11_{10} = B_{16}$ and the right-most four digits are $0101_2 = 5_{10} = 5_{16}$ so $1011, 0101_2 = B5_{16} \equiv$ 0xB5. The point is that because $16 = 2^4$, every four digits of binary can be lumped together and converted directly to hex. This is precisely the reason why we use hexadecimal rather than base-10 when dealing with computers.

TTL or 'transistor–transistor logic' is traditionally thought of as 0 V = FALSE and 5 V = TRUE, but this would give no margin of error: 5 V $\pm$ what? Furthermore, 'mobile' devices now use a different set of voltage levels, nominally 0 V and 3.3 V to represent FALSE and TRUE—and these are also called TTL levels! To avoid confusion, we refer to the 0–5 V TTL as 'high-voltage' and the 0–3.3 TTL system as 'low-voltage'. To further complicate things, for both high-voltage and low-voltage systems, the 'guaranteed' ranges differ, depending on whether you are talking about inputs or outputs.

Table 6.1. Maximum and minimum input and output values for 'traditional' or 'high-voltage' TTL, based on $V_{cc} = 5$ V.

| | 'High-voltage' TTL | | | |
| | FALSE | | TRUE | |
	Min	Max	Min	Max
Input	0	0.8	2.2	5.3 V
Output[a]	0	0.4	2.6	5 V

[a] Output levels may vary with chip manufacturer.

Table 6.2. Maximum and minimum input and output values for CMOS or 'low-voltage' TTL.

| | 'Low-voltage' TTL | | | |
| | FALSE | | TRUE | |
	Min	Max	Min	Max
Input	0	0.8	2.4	3.3 V
Output[a]	0	0.8	2.0	3.3 V

[a] Output levels may vary with chip manufacturer.

Tables 6.1 and 6.2 summarize the acceptable voltage levels for inputs and outputs of 'high-voltage' and 'low-voltage' TTL, respectively. We can by-pass the complications of actual voltage levels by referring to LOW as a logical 0 and HIGH as a logical 1, remembering that when we implement actual logic devices in a circuit, we must be careful to use the correct voltage levels. Level-shifter chips exist that facilitate communication between chips of different TTL conventions—though we note that no conversion is necessary to go *from* low-voltage TTL *to* high-voltage TTL. Going the other way without converters is guaranteed to fry something!

6.2 Binary arithmetic

We all know how to add two multi-digit numbers in base-10:

$$
\begin{array}{r}
7\ 5\ 9 \\
+\ \ 4\ 4\ 5 \\
\hline
1\ 2\ 0\ 4
\end{array}
$$

As any second grader could tell you, we add the 9 to the 5 and, given the result of 14, we write down the 4 and 'carry the 1'. That 1 is added to the 4 and 5 of the next column to the left and the process continues. How about adding two binary numbers? Let's try:

$$
\begin{array}{r}
1\ 1\ 0\ 1 \\
+\ \ 1\ 1\ 0\ 1 \\
\hline
1\ 1\ 0\ 1\ 0
\end{array}
$$

We added the 1 to the 1 and got 10_2. So we write down the 0 and carry the 1. We add that 1 to the $0 + 0$ and get 1. Moving to the next column, we add 1 to the one, write down the 0 and carry the one. We add that 1 to the two ones in the next column and get 11 (base-2, of course). We write this down and congratulate ourselves. But is this correct? To re-assure ourselves, let's convert everything to decimal and try again:

$$
\begin{array}{r}
1\ 3 \\
+\ 1\ 3 \\
\hline
2\ 6
\end{array}
$$

which is the same as 11010_2. Success. The point is that addition in binary is done just as in any other base. But there is one caveat when we want to apply this to digital electronics: we have to agree ahead of time how many digits we have. After all, if I have a digital circuit that only has enough elements in it to represent 20 bits, what do I do if my addition gives me a number with 21 bits? In the above example, let's suppose that we agree we only have 4 bits. Then the sum $1101 + 1101 = 1010$, not 11010! That extra 1 on the left just rolled off the table.

The practical finite number of binary digits, or bits, that a digital circuit has, also impacts the way we express negative numbers. There are three major conventions. The first is signed magnitude. Using this convention, you reserve one extra bit just to indicate the sign of the number. For example, if you want to be able to represent positive and negative four-digit numbers, you need five bits, the first for the sign and the remaining four for the magnitude of the number. Thus, the number $01101_2 = +13_{10}$ while $11101_2 = -13_{10}$ under the signed magnitude convention.

The second convention is the one's complement. The one's complement of x is defined to be the number that when added to x gives all ones. For example, if we stipulate we are using four-digit numbers, then the one's complement of 1010 is 0101 because when added together, these give 1111. This is convenient—and very commonly used on computers—but seems not to make sense: in the above example, when we convert to decimal we are saying that $-10 = 5$. Note that we must agree in advance on the number of digits. For example, if 1010 were really 01010, then the one's complement would be 10101 which is clearly not the same as 0101.

The third convention is two's complement. To find the 2's complement negative of a number we first complement the number (invert it, bit by bit) and then add 1. For example, the 2's complement of 1010 is $0101 + 1 = 0110$. This also seems to make no sense when converted to decimal: $-10 = 6$. But in a weird way it does. If I want to subtract two numbers, say $12_{10} - 10_{10}$ this is simply adding 12 to -10. In 2's complement binary this would be:

$$
\begin{array}{r}
1\ 1\ 0\ 0 \\
+\ 0\ 1\ 1\ 0 \\
\hline
1\ 0\ 0\ 1\ 0
\end{array}
$$

If we had agreed to limit ourselves to four digits, then the result would be $0010_2 = 2_{10}$, the correct answer for $12 - 10$. Two's complement is typically not used on computers (i.e. in software), but is generally the convention of choice in hardware because it is the easiest to implement.

Since we are talking about conventionally agreeing on numbers of bits, we should also mention some standards, or pseudo-standards. The first is the *byte*. Formerly byte always meant 8 bits. While there are some exceptions, you can almost always assume that when someone says or writes 1 byte, what is meant is 8 bits. Here we adopt the convention of 1 byte $\equiv$ 8 bits. Half a byte is a *nybble*, or 4 bits. A *word* is completely context dependent. I've seen word mean anything from 1 byte to 4 bytes, but there really is no limit.

6.3 Gates and truth tables

There are three basic logic operations, and from these several others can be created. The three basics are NOT, AND, and OR. The schematic symbol for the NOT gate and the corresponding 'truth table' are shown in figure 6.1 and table 6.3, respectively. The NOT gate performs the trivial operation of converting a TRUE to a FALSE and vice versa. For this reason, the NOT gate is commonly referred to as an *inverter*. Note, however, that it does *not* invert voltages as the inverting amplifier does, but rather, inverts *logic*.

The schematic and truth table for an AND gate are shown in figure 6.2 and table 6.4, respectively. You can see from the truth table that *both* inputs must be TRUE for the output TRUE, else the output is FALSE.

The schematic and truth table for an OR gate are shown in figure 6.3 and table 6.5, respectively. You can see from the truth table that if *either* of the inputs are TRUE or if *both* inputs are TRUE, then the output will be TRUE, else the output is FALSE. This is somewhat different from common language use of 'or' because in common usage, the case of both inputs being true could imply the output is FALSE. For example, if you said 'For dinner if I had steak OR seafood I would be very happy', it would not be clear whether or not you would be happy with both. But in formal logic there is a big difference. For the *inclusive* OR of figure 6.3 and table 6.5, you mean one or the other or both. There is another, less used, version of OR, the *exclusive OR* or XOR, that means one or the other, but not both. We'll get to that one soon.

Figure 6.1. Schematic symbol for the NOT gate.

Table 6.3. Truth table for the NOT operation. A is the input and Q is the output.

NOT	
A	Q
0	1
1	0

Figure 6.2. Schematic symbol for the AND gate. A and B are the inputs and Q is the output.

Table 6.4. Truth table for the AND operation. A and B are the inputs and Q is the output.

AND		
A	B	Q
0	0	0
0	1	0
1	0	0
1	1	1

Figure 6.3. Schematic symbol for the OR gate. A and B are the inputs and Q is the output.

Table 6.5. Truth table for the OR operation. A and B are the inputs and Q is the output.

OR		
A	B	Q
0	0	0
0	1	1
1	0	1
1	1	1

Figure 6.4. Schematic symbol for the NAND gate. A and B are the inputs and Q is the output.

Combining the NOT with the AND gives us the NAND operation. The schematic symbol and truth table for the NAND are shown in figure 6.4 and table 6.6, respectively. Notice that in the schematic for the NAND we did not reproduce the entire NOT gate, but only the circle. (We've seen this before: recall our discussion of the 7555.)

Combining the NOT with the OR gives us the NOR operation. The schematic symbol and truth table for the OR are shown in figure 6.5 and table 6.7, respectively.

As already mentioned, there is another type of 'or', the exclusive OR or XOR. The schematic symbol and truth table for the XOR are shown in figure 6.6 and table 6.8, respectively.

Table 6.6. Truth table for the NAND operation. A and B are the inputs and Q is the output.

NAND		
A	B	Q
0	0	1
0	1	1
1	0	1
1	1	0

Figure 6.5. Schematic symbol for the NOR gate. A and B are the inputs and Q is the output.

Table 6.7. Truth table for the NOR operation. A and B are the inputs and Q is the output.

NOR		
A	B	Q
0	0	1
0	1	0
1	0	0
1	1	0

Figure 6.6. Schematic symbol for the XOR gate. A and B are the inputs and Q is the output.

Table 6.8. Truth table for the XOR operation. A and B are the inputs and Q is the output.

XOR		
A	B	Q
0	0	0
0	1	1
1	0	1
1	1	0

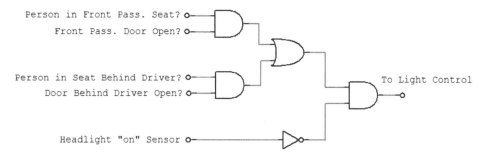

Figure 6.7. Possible logic solution to the 'car problem' example.

Example 1

Suppose you want to wire up a sensor system in your car such that a light turns on when a person is sitting in the front passenger seat AND the front passenger seat door is open OR someone is sitting in the seat behind the driver AND that person's door is open, AND the headlights are NOT on. How could you wire this up? One possibility is shown in figure 6.7.

Homework 6.1

Using a combination of any sorts of gates except XOR and NXOR, create a circuit that has the same truth table as an XOR.

6.3.1 DeMorgan's theorem

A very useful logic analysis construct is known as DeMorgan's theorem which states that if you invert all inputs and all outputs of a logic gate, then if the gate is an AND it becomes an OR and vice versa. For example, if you were to place an inverter on the two inputs to a NOR gate, and an inverter to the output of that gate, this should be logically equivalent to a NAND gate (table 6.9).

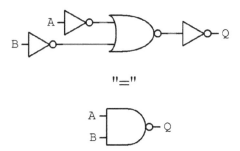

Figure 6.8. Applying DeMorgan's theorem to a NOR gate.

Table 6.9. Truth table for the circuit of figure 6.8. A and B are the inputs and Q is the output.

NAND!		
A	B	Q
0	0	1
0	1	1
1	0	1
1	1	0

Why does this matter to us? There are at least two reasons. First, gates usually come several to a chip.

For example, the 74LS04 is a hex-inverter, which means there are six NOT gates on a single chip.

The 74LS00 is a quad-NAND, which means there are 4 NAND gates on a single chip. So when you design a circuit, it is not unlikely that you will have unused gates available. If you can 'manufacture' a desired gate from 'leftover' gates on other chips, you may have saved yourself space on your pc board as well as lower power consumption.

The second reason gets back to the idea of 'negative-true logic'. Sometimes the world that we interface to will, effectively, give us a 0 V signal for a situation that is logically TRUE and a (nominally) 5 V signal for a situation that is logically FALSE. In this situation, we often draw logic symbols that are more useful to decipher the system logic but are really, through DeMorgan's theorem, switched between OR and AND. For example, the two circuits in figure 6.9 use the same physical gates and have the same truth tables, but *seem* logically different. In the upper circuit, if we think about the A and B inputs being 'inverse logic', then the gate they go to is best thought of as a negative-true NOR. But in the lower circuit, if the A and B inputs are 'conventional' or 'non-inverse' logic, then the gate they go to is best thought of as a NAND. Either way, applying the same signals to the same inputs will give the same output signal.

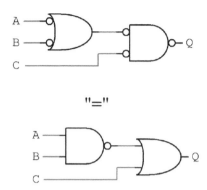

Figure 6.9. These two circuits are logically equivalent.

Homework 6.2
   Verify that the truth tables for the two circuits in figure 6.9 are identical.

6.3.2 Using electronic gates

We've already discussed the voltage levels that must be used with the different TTL logic types. In this section we'd like to discuss using gates to drive analog devices. Consider the circuit in figure 6.7. If we'd like to use that circuit to light an LED, how would be do it? What we would *not* do is directly attach the LED to the output of the gate! Doing so would immediately fry the gate, which typically cannot source or sink more than 20 mA. One possibility would be to current-limit the LED using a resistor, as shown in figure 6.10.

To compute the resistance value, we assume the gate's output is either 0 V or 5.5 V (the maximum possible from table 6.1). If it is 0 V, then no current will flow (and the LED will not light up), so no problem. If the output is 5.5 V, then the voltage drop across the resistor is about 5 V. If we use a 330 Ω resistor the current will be 15 mA, giving us a bit of a safety margin from the presumed 20 mA maximum that the gate can source.

But what if we want the gate to drive other devices as well? Or what if we want to drive a more power-hungry (i.e. uses more current) display? We could use an emitter follower or, even better, we could build a current sink as shown in figure 6.11. The advantage of a sink over a follower is that it is more flexible: you can design it for the specific chip set, LED, power supply, etc that you are using.

To compute the resistance values, you first need to know what you will use for V_{cc} (let's say 5 V for this discussion) and how much current your diode will need (the more current, the brighter it will shine—let's suppose 30 mA). The voltage drop across R_c will be about 4.4 V, and so we will want $R_c \approx 4.4$ V/30 mA ≈ 150 Ω. With $i_c = 30$ mA, we want $i_b \gtrsim i_c/h_{FE}$ to guarantee the transistor will be 'wide open'. If so, $v_b \sim 0.6$ V. For a logic gate output of 5 V, $R_b \approx 15$k ought to work. (Use something

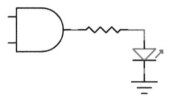

Figure 6.10. Limiting a logic gate's current with a resistor.

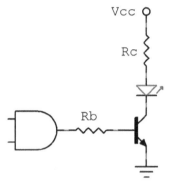

Figure 6.11. A better/safer way to limit an LED's current.

like 10k to ensure the transistor is fully on.) The gate would only have to source 440 µA—easy-peasy.

Just as a logic gate cannot directly drive an LED with as much current as you may wish, a single gate cannot drive an infinite number of other gates. You can check the data sheets to see how many gates (of the type you are using) a single gate (of the type you are using) can drive. The number of gates a single gate can drive is called the *fan-out*.

One more potential issue with logic gates is speed. Different gate classes have different speeds, which are measured in propagation time through the gate as well as rise-time of the TTL output. Check the manufacturer's data sheet if this could be a problem for you.

Finally, there is the issue of capacitor-bypassing the chip power. Though never shown on a schematic, all logic gates require power! Power is usually supplied on two diagonally opposite corners of the chip. Even though logic gates are generally not power hogs, it takes a large spike of current to put out a TTL pulse. The current has to come from somewhere: a chip that has to produce a fast pulse may very well load down the power bus which could adversely affect the performance of the other chips that share that bus.

The solution is to place a capacitor across the power inputs of the chips—not all of them, but enough of them to store power for when it is needed to generate pulses. Once again, the data sheets will offer recommendations on capacitor size and number. Note that when you are bread-boarding circuits, the bypass caps are generally not needed because of the natural capacitance of the breadboard connections.

6.4 Combining outputs

6.4.1 The MUX

Suppose you have two sensors, each giving a TTL output, and you want to send the output of only one of them at a time to the rest of your circuit for processing. And suppose you want to use a TTL signal to control which of these sensor outputs is passed. How would you do it? One way is to use the *multiplexer* circuit (MUX for short) of figure 6.12.

Inputs A and B are from the sensors and input C is used to select between them. (By the way, notice how I've used the NAND gate labeled **1** as a NOT. This enabled me to use a single quad-NAND chip as a MUX, instead of using three NAND gates on one chip and one NOT gate from another.) If C is TRUE, then gate **2** will 'pass' (and invert) signal A: If A is TRUE, then the output of **2** is FALSE; if A is FALSE, the output of **2** will be TRUE. Meanwhile, the output of **3** will always be TRUE, regardless of the status of B. But if C is FALSE, then the roles of **2** and **3** will be reversed. Gate **4** plays a crucial role: we cannot just wire the outputs of **2** and **3** together because if the output of one of them is HIGH and the other is LOW, they will fight and we cannot guarantee who the winner will be. (Certainly not the user!)

You can imagine ganging many two-input MUXs together to make multi-input devices, but fortunately you don't have to because dedicated MUX chips exist. We show one of these, the 74LS151, in figure 6.13.

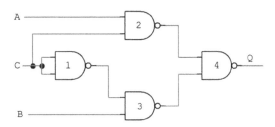

Figure 6.12. A simple MUX circuit. Input C is used to select between inputs A and B.

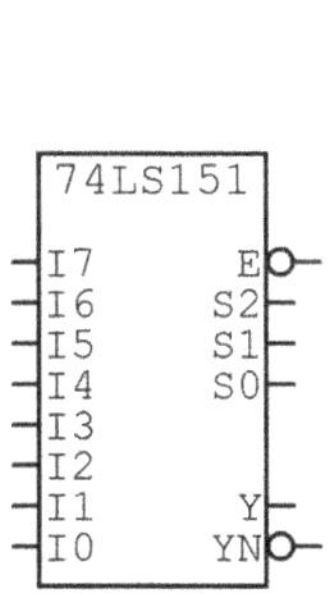

Figure 6.13. An eight-input MUX with tri-state outputs.

The '151 has eight inputs, labeled $I_0 - I_7$. It takes a three-digit binary number to select from among eight inputs. On the '151 this is done using pins $S_0 - S_2$. The '151 outputs the selected input to the pin labeled Y. For the user's convenience, the '151 also outputs the *complement* (inverse) of the passed signal to the pin labeled YN. (Notice that a circle is shown on this pin, indicating an inverse operation.)

Besides power and ground, which are not shown, there is one additional pin. Labeled E; this is the *enable* input. Placing a LOW signal on this pin (notice the circle!) enables the chip's outputs. If the chip is not enabled, both Y and YN will 'float'. That is, they will be neither HIGH nor LOW. This is called a *tri-state* output. Thus, unlike the outputs of a simple logic gate, the outputs of two '151s can be tied together—so long as you guarantee that only one of them will be enabled at a time. This makes it very easy to use two '151s to construct a 16 input MUX: you send the same three-digit binary number to both '151's $S_0 - S_2$ and you send the fourth digit to the enable of one of the '151s and the complement of the digit to the enable of the other '151. Notice that the enable uses 'inverse logic'. That is, you select a chip by putting a FALSE on the enable. *Most chip enables use negative-true or inverse logic.*

Homework 6.3

Show how to use two '151s as a 16 input MUX. Indicate the 4 bit control bus (the four-digit binary number input that you would use to select which output is selected to be passed).

Every so often you need a weird piece of logic—and you can always come up with the required circuit using conventional gates. But it is sometimes more convenient to use a MUX (in a bizarrely non-standard way) to accomplish your 'arbitrary logic' goal. For example, it turns out that you can wire up a '151 to function as a four-input, one-output logic machine. Suppose I have 10 goldfish, simplistically named #1, #2, ... #10. I know that four of them, numbers 2, 5, 8 and 10, need to have their scales cleaned every month—I can remember that I have to clean some of my fish, but I always forget which ones need the cleaning. I could build a logic circuit to tell me. All I need to do is input a number from 1 to 10 (in binary, from 1 to 1010), and if an LED lights up, I know that fish needs its scales scrubbed. The truth table is shown in table 6.10.

The first column in the table is my fish number/name. The next four columns are the fish number/name, expressed as a four-digit binary number. As seen in figure 6.14, A_3, A_2, and A_1 are connected to the chip's S_2, S_1, and S_0, respectively, and therefore select which input is passed.

The selected inputs are shown in the column labeled I_n. The desired output of the circuit is given in the column labeled $Q = Y$. In this column I enter a '0' if I don't want the LED to light and a '1' if I do want it to light. The last column tells me how to wire the inputs so as to obtain the desired outputs. There are only four possibilities: 0, 1, A_0, and $\bar{A}_0$. It's easy to see what to put in this column. If, for a given I, $Q = 0$, then we will hard-wire that I to Ground. If, for a given I, $Q = 1$, then we will hard-wire that I to +5 V. If, for a given I, $Q = A_0$, then we will hard-wire that

Table 6.10. Truth table for the fish scale cleaning example.

fish #	$A_3 = S_2$	$A_2 = S_1$	$A_1 = S_0$	A_0	I_n	$Q = Y$	
0	0	0	0	0	0	0	
1	0	0	0	1	0	0	0
2	0	0	1	0	1	1	
3	0	0	1	1	1	0	$\bar{A}_0$
4	0	1	0	0	2	0	
5	0	1	0	1	2	1	A_0
6	0	1	1	0	3	0	
7	0	1	1	1	3	0	0
8	1	0	0	0	4	1	
9	1	0	0	1	4	0	$\bar{A}_0$
10	1	0	1	0	5	1	
11	1	0	1	1	5	0	$\bar{A}_0$
12	1	1	0	0	6	0	
13	1	1	0	1	6	0	0
14	1	1	1	0	7	0	
15	1	1	1	1	7	0	0

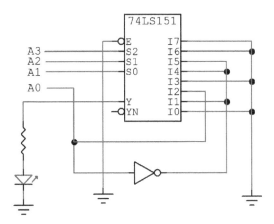

Figure 6.14. Implementation of the truth table of table 6.10 using the '151 MUX.

I to A_0. And if, for a given I, $Q = \bar{A}_0$, then we will hard-wire I to an inverted A_0. Check the schematic in figure 6.14 to see if everything is wired up as you expected.

Homework 6.4

Create a truth table and show the schematic for a circuit that, using a MUX, indicates which animals in the Chinese zodiac are herbivores. (The animals, in order, are Rat, Ox, Tiger, Rabbit, Dragon, Snake, Horse, Goat, Monkey, Rooster, Dog, and Pig. Refer to them as numbers 1–12 in this order.)

6.4.2 The DEMUX

We've seen how to use a MUX to select from among many inputs and send just one of them to a single output. But often you need to do the opposite: you have a single input and you want to send it to one of many outputs. For example, suppose you have many chips, each having an Enable pin, and you want to select only one of those chips to be enabled. The easiest way to do this is with a DEMUX.

Figure 6.15 shows a commonly used DEMUX chip, the 74LS138. There are seven outputs, labeled $Q_0 - Q_7$, three enable pins, $E_1 - E3$, and three 'address' or select pins, $A_0 - A_2$. Notice that the outputs of the '138 are all inverted. This is because the '138, like most DEMUXs is used to enable one of many chips—and enables are usually negative-true logic. Notice also that the '138 has a very flexible enabling arrangement: all three of the enables must be properly set or else the '138's outputs will go tri-state. By 'properly set' we mean $E_1 = E_2 = $ LOW, and $E_3 = $ HIGH. Finally, notice that there is no signal input to the '138. So what gets passed to one of the eight outputs? Actually, nothing is 'passed'. If the chip is enabled, the pin selected by $A_0 - A_2$ outputs a LOW (remember the inverted outputs) and all the rest of the pins output a HIGH. Technically speaking, the '138 is referred to as a *decoder* because it does not actually pass an input through, but generates its own signal. While true DEMUX chips do exist, decoders are far more commonly used.

6.5 Sequential logic

6.5.1 The bistable

Consider the circuit of figure 6.16. Suppose inputs A and B are tied HIGH. What are the values of Q and Q'? If Q is HIGH, then both inputs to gate 2 are high and that makes Q' LOW. And if Q' is LOW, then Q is HIGH, regardless of the value of A. So that's it then: Q is HIGH and Q' is LOW. Just as a check, let's see what happens if we assume Q is LOW. If so, then Q' would be HIGH (regardless of the value of B) and then, indeed, Q would be LOW. What? Both are possible? We can have $Q = 1$, $Q' = 0$ *or* $Q = 0$, $Q' = 1$? Yes! Both are possible and furthermore, both are *stable*. For example, if $Q = 1$ and $Q' = 0$ and we now let $A \rightarrow 0$, nothing will change. But if $Q = 1$ and $Q' = 0$ and, leaving A HIGH, we now let $B \rightarrow 0$, Q and Q' will swap values. Interesting: the values of Q and Q' depend on some *prior* condition. We refer

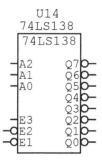

Figure 6.15. An eight-output DEMUX/DECODER with inverting outputs.

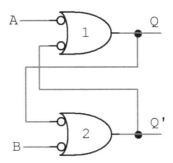

Figure 6.16. The bistable.

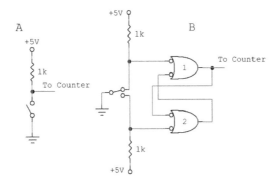

Figure 6.17. (A) A simple switch. (B) A de-bounced switch.

to digital circuits whose outputs depend on previous conditions as *sequential logic*. The circuit of figure 6.16 called a *bistable*.

The bistable is the basis of computer memory, counters, latches, etc. But they are also useful in their own right. Look at the circuits of figure 6.17.

Circuit 6.17(A) is a simple switch. When it is open (as shown) a HIGH value is sent to a counter, by virtue of the 1k pull-up resistor. When the switch is closed, a LOW is sent to the counter. As we will see, counters typically count either a LOW-to-HIGH or a HIGH-to-LOW *transition*, not the LOW or HIGH signal itself.

The problem with this circuit is that mechanical switches 'bounce'. That is, when we close an open switch the contact arm literally bounces, making and breaking contact several times before settling into a stable configuration. Because the counter is counting transitions, each time you toggle the switch, your counter will think you have toggled the switch several times, and will increment accordingly. This is not good.

In contrast, the circuit of figure 6.17(B) is stable against the bouncing of the mechanical switch. For example, in the switch position shown in the figure, gate 1 will output a 1, which is sent to both the counter and to gate 2. Gate 2 will output a 0. When we toggle the switch to the lower contact, the situation is reversed (by symmetry). But after hitting the lower contact (causing gate 1 to have an output of 0 and gate 2 to have an output of 1) suppose the contact bounces, not so high as to contact the upper terminal, but enough to cause the lower contact to be pulled up to a 1. In this case, just as in the circuit of figure 6.16, the outputs of the gates will not change. Because this circuit provides immunity from bouncing switches, it is called a de-bounce and is used in virtually every button that provides input to a computer—including every key on a mechanical keyboard.

The bistable 'holds' a transient value. This can be very useful in many circuits, not just de-bouncing ones. Imagine that your detectors are 'waiting for an event', perhaps a photon, perhaps that elusive particle you are trying to find. The event occurs and you happen to be looking the other way. You've lost the event. But what you could have done is use a bistable to hold the signal from that event until you've had a chance to look at it and then reset the detector again. A bistable that is used in such a manner is referred to as a *latch*.

6.5.2 D flip–flops

Bistables can be combined to give what is called a *flip–flop*. There are two main types of flip–flops, 'D' and 'JK'. Figure 6.18 shows a D flip–flop, wired up to actually flip and flop. The 74LS74 D-type flop–flop has four inputs and two outputs. Two of the inputs, S and R, are for setting the initial state of the flip–flop. Another input is CP. This is a *clock* input and cares only about a LOW–HIGH transition. Upon receiving such a transition, the D-type takes whatever is coming into D at the time of the transition and outputs that to Q. It also inverts D and outputs that to $\bar{Q}$. (There is a slight delay between capturing the D input and outputting it to Q.) Because the flip–flop contains a bistable, Q and $\bar{Q}$ continue to output that new value until CP receives another transition. The way the D-type is wired up in figure 6.18, the inverted D signal is fed back into D on each (LOW–HIGH) transition, also called a clock edge. Thus if D is seeing a HIGH when the first edge comes in, Q will go HIGH and $\bar{Q}$ will go low. Then, when the next edge comes in, Q will go LOW and $\bar{Q}$ will go HIGH, etc. If the input clock signal is a regular square wave, then so will be the output—except that the output will have twice the period or half the frequency. Thus, you can think of a flip–flop as a *frequency divider*.

6.5.3 JK flip–flops

In some sense, the JK-type flip–flop, shown schematically in figure 6.19, is simpler than the D-type because no feedback is required. On the other hand, as is shown in table 6.11, you have quite a bit of flexibility when you operate one. Usually, if one is dividing a frequency by 2, one would use a JK-type, with J and K both hard-wired

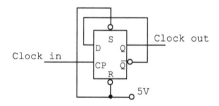

Figure 6.18. A D-type flip–flop.

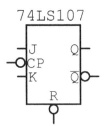

Figure 6.19. 1/2 of a 74LS107 JK-type flip–flop.

Table 6.11. Truth table for a JK-Type flop–flop.

J	K	Q_{n+1}
0	0	Q_n
0	1	0
1	0	1
1	1	$\bar{Q}_n$

HIGH. Then, unlike the D-type, no feedback is required. But the D-type gives flexibility because you have the option of feeding back a signal from farther downstream. The choice of which to use is just depends on what you're doing with it. Notice that this particular JK flip–flop acts on the HIGH–LOW clock transition.

6.6 Counters

An extremely important class of chips is the counter. There are many variations of counters, but they share a common characteristic, they all increment or decrement on the rising or falling edge of a 'clock' input. A typical counter, the 74LS161, is a four-digit binary counter. We show one in figure 6.20, attached to a digital display, the TIL311. Every time the '161 receives a clock edge, the output, pins Q_0 through Q_3, increments by 1. CEP and CET are 'count enable' pins. If either (or both) of these pins is LOW, the output will freeze and will no longer be incremented upon receipt of a clock edge. Internal to the '161, CEP and CET are ANDed with each other and the result is ANDed with the clock input. Once both CET and CEP go high, the '161 resumes counting, picking up where it left off. The '161 has two count enables to allow the user more flexibility in suspending counting.

Often it matters what number you start counting at. The '161 has two ways to start the counting at a known place, one *synchronous* (synchronized to the clock input), the other *asynchronous* (not synchronized to the clock input). Sending a LOW to the MR (master reset) pin immediately sets all the output bits to 0. This is asynchronous because the clearing of the bits does not require a clock edge. You can also initialize the output bits using the *parallel load* option. To do this, you hold the

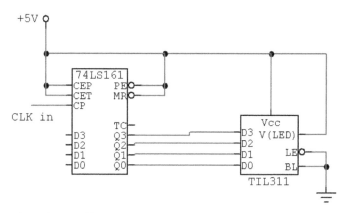

Figure 6.20. A synchronous binary counter, the 74LS161, connected to the TIL311 LED display.

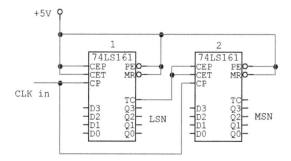

Figure 6.21. How to cascade two synchronous counters. The counter on the left gives the Least Significant Nybble (LSN) while the one on the right gives the MSN.

PE (parallel load enable) pin LOW. Now when a clock edge arrives, whatever values that are present on $D_0 - D_3$ will be 'clocked through' to the Qs. This is a synchronous load because nothing happens until a clock edge comes in.

With 4 bits the counter can only count from 0000 to 1111 (binary), or 0 to 15 (decimal) or F (hexadecimal). This is a very small number. How could a 4 bit counter be useful? The answer is that, like all counters, '161 chips can be cascaded using the carry output. But how the carry output is used depends on whether the chip is a *synchronous counter* or a *ripple counter*. The '161 is a synchronous counter and figure 6.21 shows how to cascade it. First, you tie all the clock inputs together. On a synchronous counter, the pin labeled TC goes HIGH when the counter reaches its maximum value, in the case of the '161 this is 1111; otherwise TC is LOW. Because of this, the '161 on the right does not count except when the '161 on the left has reached 1111. At this point the right '161 is count-enabled and will advance upon receipt of the next clock edge. When that edge arrives, both '161s increment. The left '161 wrapping back to 0000, and clearing TC in the process. This freezes the right '161 until the next time the left '161 reaches 1111. This cascading method can be extended to as many counters as required.

Another useful counter is the 74LS193 shown in figure 6.22. The '193 is also a synchronous counter but it can count up or down, as you desire. As shown in the figure, the cascaded '193s will count up, but flicking the switch to its other position will make it count down. Notice how the '193s are cascaded. Instead of a common clock signal going to both chips, the up- and down-carries from the lower nybble feed the clocks of the next higher nybble. As with the '161 (and most other counters) you can load in a starting point from which to count.

Thus far we have been discussing synchronous counters. A second kind of counter is called a ripple counter. You can think of an N-digit ripple counter as N JK flip–flops cascaded in series. Each succeeding stage is clocked by the previous one. Figure 6.23 shows a 4 bit ripple counter that was made from two 74LS107 packages. (Recall there are two flip–flops on a chip.) Because each succeeding stage of a ripple counter is incremented from the output of the previous stage, a ripple counter is *not* synchronous.

All counters, whether they be ripple or synchronous, can be used as frequency dividers. For example, the output of the nth digit of a counter will have edges that occur at a frequency of $f/2^n$, where f is the driving clock frequency. Dividing by 2^n is straightforward, but how to divide a frequency by some arbitrary number, like 7? figure 6.24 shows how, using a '161 synchronous counter. You bring in a clock signal

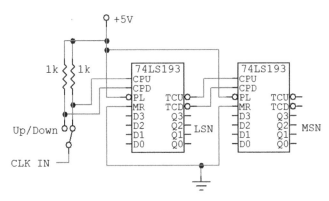

Figure 6.22. How to cascade 2 up/down counters. The direction of the counting is changed by toggling the switch.

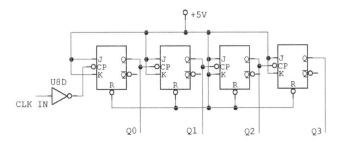

Figure 6.23. A 4 bit ripple counter made from JK flip–flops.

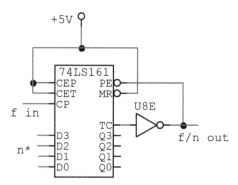

Figure 6.24. Divide by n circuit. The divisor n is input as the 2's complement.

having frequency f. Then you input the number you'd like to divide the frequency by as 'data' in $D_0 - D_3$—but you have to express this as the 2's complement of the number you'd like to divide by. The output at TC (or the inverse of TC) has a frequency of f/n. This works because the 2's complement of n is the negative of n. That is, $n^* + n = 0$. Thus, starting the counter from n^* means that n clock cycles later, you will arrive at 0000 which will set the TC. So the TC will be set one time for each n clock inputs.

6.7 Latches

Let's go back to the TIL311 display chip in figure 6.20. The TIL311 is an LED display chip and it is unnecessarily sophisticated for the application shown in the figure. First of all, it has separate power pins for the chip logic and the LED power. This can be useful, but for the present application was just an annoyance (one more wire to connect). The display also has a blanking feature (BL). If BL is pulled HIGH, the display will be disabled. This is useful if the number being sent to the chip is rapidly changing before settling in on the value that you actually want to read. In that case, you can disable the output during the changes, and enable the output when—and only when—you wish to read it. Not shown in the figure are the inputs for leading and trailing decimal points, clearly not needed in this application, but useful in others. The last feature, in some sense complementary to the blanking, is the *latched* output. The TIL311 has a built-in bistable that allows the user to 'freeze' the inputs and thereby hold the display. The latch is enabled with the LE pin. When LE is tied to ground, as in figure 6.20, the latch is *transparent*, which means that the display will show the number corresponding to the inputs, without any latching.

6.8 Monostable multivibrators

Very often you will want to output a pulse having a specific delay from some input signal. You may also wish to control the temporal length of that pulse. The most precise way to do this is with delays based on an accurate clock, possibly divided down, and one or more counters. However, if the timing need not be terribly precise, you might consider using a monostable multivibrator, commonly known as a one-shot (or 1-shot, and emphasize the 'one' when you say it). Figure 6.25 shows one way to wire up the 74LS123 one-shot. The corresponding signals are shown in figure 6.26. In this application, a pulse comes in from the left of figure 6.25 (red pulse at the bottom of figure 6.26). On the '123 you can choose to trigger on the upward- or downward-going edge; in this example, I chose the downward. When the '123 detects the appropriate edge it outputs a pulse, the temporal width of which is given by

$$\tau = 0.28RC\left(1 + \frac{0.7}{R}\right) \approx 0.28RC. \tag{6.1}$$

The output from the first one-shot is shown in blue in figure 6.26. That pulse is fed to the negative slope input of a second one-shot. That one-shot outputs a pulse that starts with the falling edge of the first pulse and ends at the time given by its R and C, using equation (6.1). This is the most common way to use a one-shot and is no doubt why they typically come as two independent one-shot's per package.

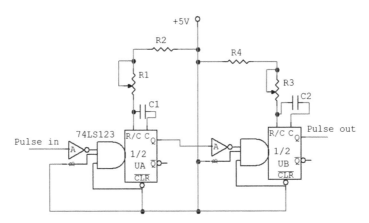

Figure 6.25. Use of a pair of 74LS123 one-shot to generate a pulse of arbitrary delay and width.

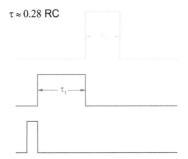

Figure 6.26. Input (in red) and outputs (blue and green) from the circuit of figure 6.25.

IOP Publishing

Practical Analog, Digital, and Embedded Electronics for Scientists

Brett D DePaola

Chapter 7

Digital–analog, analog–digital, and phase-locked loops

The 'real world' is analog; very few things in nature are digital. But more and more, we want to turn the power of digital electronics loose to help us cope with the complexity of our analog world. This often involves converting analog signals into a digital format (analog to digital conversion, or ADC), digitally processing the signal information, and then converting the digital results back into analog (digital to analog conversion, or DAC) for interacting with the world. As an example, think of music. Music is a rhythmic disturbance of air waves that our ears pick up and our brains analyze. But nowadays, signals from the sound waves are electronically detected, digitized, processed, and stored on, say, a dvd or the cloud. But since our human sensors were evolved for processing analog signals, when we play the dvd we have to convert the signal back into analog.

DACs and ADCs are intimately tied to measurement, but so is working with frequencies. Because measuring frequencies is often reduced to just counting, we can often measure quantities in the frequency domain with far greater precision than in the time domain. Therefore, in addition to learning about DACs and ADCs, it is important in an instrumentation course to learn about frequency manipulation.

7.1 Digital–analog conversion

7.1.1 Resolution issues

When selecting a DAC chip, the first question you need to ask yourself is 'how many bits do I need?'. To answer this, think of your desired voltage range being sliced up into N equal sections, each having the resolution you need. For example, suppose I need a 0–10 V signal and I need it with 1 mV resolution. Slicing 10 V into 1 mV pieces gives me $N = 10/10^{-3} = 10^4$ pieces. How many bits does it take to specify 10^4?

Well, $2^{10} = 1024 \approx 1000$, so you only need $10\times$ this, or between $2^3 = 8$ and $2^4 = 16$. To be conservative, we choose 2^4. Together with our 2^{10}, this gives us 2^{14}, or 14 bits. (You may wonder at the klunky method of this calculation, but it is often helpful to use 'key' powers of 2 to help you make quick conversions between decimal and binary, and $2^{10} \approx 10^3$ is one of these.)

We can also work in the other direction: 'Given an 8 bit DAC, what precision can I expect in specifying a 10 V signal?'. This is just $10V/2^8 = 40V/2^{10} \approx 40$ mV. (I once again made use of $2^{10} \approx 10^3$. A more precise answer is 39.06 mV.)

7.1.2 An example: the DAC1408

Consider the circuit shown in figure 7.1.

The MC1408 is an 8 bit DAC It is designed to output a negative *current* that is equal to the product of a reference current and its digital input. Here, the reference current is given by the LM399's 6.95 V output through the 3.3k resistor. (The LM399 is a temperature-compensated precision voltage reference.) It is often more convenient to produce an output current because it can be sent to a remote location without the sag that a voltage would suffer due to the non-zero impedance of the transmission line. The current can then readily be converted to a voltage with a shunt to ground, as shown in figure 7.1.

The '1408 specifies $\pm 1/2$ bit (out of 8 bits) precision and so out of 5 V we should expect ± 10 mV precision.

7.1.3 What's in a DAC?

We've already seen one method of DAC: the summing amplifier of figure 4.6. This is fairly easy to construct, but is not recommended because for an N-channel DAC, you need to have N different-valued, very precise resistors. An improvement over this uses an 'R–2R ladder', in which only one value of resistor is used, though you still need $3N$ of them. (The MC1408 DAC has an R–2R ladder built into it.) An example of using the R–2R ladder is shown in figure 7.2.

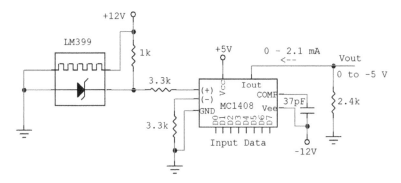

Figure 7.1. The MC1408 DAC, wired up to generate a negative voltage from a digital input.

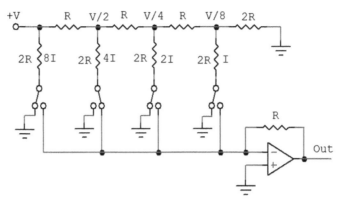

Figure 7.2. A DAC built with an R–2R ladder, plus an op amp.

The way to understand the R–2R ladder is to start from the far right. The point labeled $V/8$ sees two $2R$ resistors in parallel to ground. This is equivalent to one resistor, having a value of R, to ground. Then, the point labeled $V/4$ also sees two $2R$ resistors to ground: one to the right, and the other down. Thus, it also sees a resistance of R to ground. This continues to the left for as many stages as you like. Since each stage is equivalent, the voltage at the nth stage is $V/8$, as labeled in the figure. Then, because the voltages above each vertical resistor is lower by a factor of 2 for each successive stage, the current flowing through that resistor is also lower by a factor of 2. The op amp sums the currents and converts them to a voltage. In this circuit, we are converting the 4 bit number 0100. The switches need not be mechanical; they can be CMOS electronic switches.

Because the $2R$ resistor can be made from two $1R$ resistors, only one resistor type need be used, making this a more capable DAC than the one in figure 4.6. Nevertheless, possible variation in R makes this DAC less precise than some other types, especially when the number of bits is large.

7.2 Analog–digital conversion

7.2.1 The Nyquist criterion

In converting an analog signal into a digital one, there are two main criteria. The first is resolution, and that is determined in the same way as we just discussed for the DAC The second is speed. Speed is important for two reasons. The first, and most obvious one, is that the faster the conversion is done, the sooner we can go on to another conversion. The second one is more subtle and has to do with how many conversions are *required* per unit time in order to accurately digitize a time-varying analog signal—and to some degree *all* analog signals vary with time.

The question is, what is the minimum number of points per period one can sample, and still have enough information to reconstruct a sine wave? The answer according to information theory pioneer Harry Theodor Nyquist, is just a little over 2 samples per period. This is a remarkable result and a bit hard to believe, but it's true! In figure 7.3 I plot points randomly sampled from a sine wave. I sampled, on

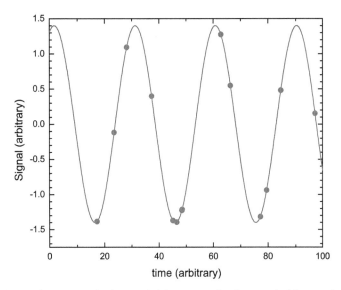

Figure 7.3. The blue points are randomly sampled data, averaging 3 per period from a sine wave. The red curve is the sine wave reconstructed from the points.

average, 3 points per period. Then I fit those points to a sine wave, using as fitting parameters the amplitude, the phase, and the period. The result of the fit is the red curve. It really does work. The penalty for under-sampling is an effect called *aliasing*; it generally looks nothing like the originally sampled signal.

Normally one is not sampling a pure sine wave. So what should the Nyquist criterion be for some arbitrary signal, and how do you avoid aliasing? The usual strategy is to sample at the highest rate that is feasible. Then, just to be safe, you apply a low-pass filter, often called an anti-aliasing filter, to the data to reject all signal frequency components that are high enough to violate the Nyquist criteria.

7.2.2 ADC techniques

The two DACs described above are both very fast since it converts all the bits simultaneously. This method of digital to analog conversion is referred to as a 'parallel' or 'flash' type. Flash DACs have the advantage of speed but are difficult to construct if large numbers of bits need to be converted. Other DAC types may be more precise, but at the cost of speed.

ADCs tend to be slower. An example is shown in figure 7.4. The signal to be digitized, V_{in}, is compared to the output from a DAC, V_{out}. If $V_{in} > V_{out}$, the comparator causes the counter to count UP. If $V_{in} < V_{out}$, the comparator causes the counter to count DOWN. The DAC continuously updates its output as the counter updates.

This *tracking ADC* is slower than some others because it relies on feedback to update the DAC's output voltage. In addition, the last bit is continuously bouncing up and down.

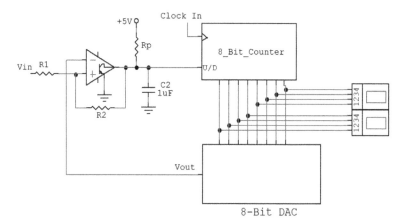

Figure 7.4. A tracking ADC built with an 8 bit DAC.

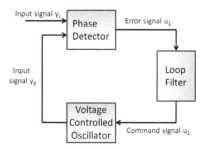

Figure 7.5. A generic phase-locked loop.

7.3 Phase-locked loops

Phase-locked loops, or PLL, are to signal frequencies what op amps are to signal amplitudes. Figure 7.5 illustrates this. The voltage controlled oscillator, or VCO outputs a clock signal at some frequency, centered around ω_0, which is fed to a phase detector. Also going to the phase detector is some input signal. The phase detector detects the difference in phase (or frequency, which is the time derivative of phase) between these two inputs, and outputs a signal related to this difference. That signal is passed through an element we will generically call a loop filter, the output of which goes to back to the VCO. This input to the VCO adjusts its output frequency, bringing it closer to the phase detector's other input signal. The signals pass round the loop until the two inputs to the phase detector are identical in both frequency and phase.

An actual implementation of a PLL as a frequency multiplier is shown in figure 7.6. In this circuit we use the HC4046, a PLL chip that contains a phase detector module and a VCO module. In this PLL implementation, we placed a frequency divider between the VCO output and the phase detector input. Briefly, this is what the circuit does: The VCO outputs a clock signal at some frequency. That clock is used to strobe a ripple counter. The counter acts as a 2^n frequency divider.

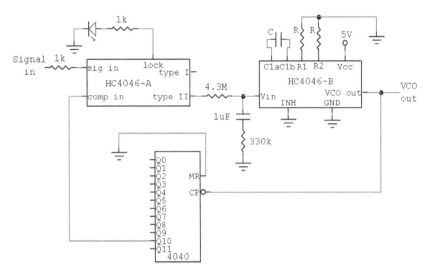

Figure 7.6. A frequency multiplier using a phase-locked loop.

(In this case, $n = 10$ and so we divide the VCO's frequency by 1024.) The divided output goes to the phase detector and is compared to an externally supplied clock signal. The phase detector outputs a voltage that is related to the phase difference between those two signals. After integration, that voltage goes to the VCO, which responds and correspondingly adjusts its output frequency. Once in equilibrium, the VCO frequency will have to be 2^n higher than the clock frequency in order that, when divided by 2^n, it again matches the reference. A piece of the VCO output is then extracted as the circuit output.

Another use of the PLL is as a *demodulator*. Imagine that you have a frequency-modulated signal. This is an ac signal whose frequency is being modulated about some carrier frequency. The modulation is the information content of the signal. If your reference were the carrier frequency, then the output of the phase detector would vary at the modulation frequency. That is, the output of the phase detector *is* the information that is embedded in the modulation. In this case, no loop is required, the phase detector directly giving you the information content you desire. Frequency modulation is important in transmitting information because it has tremendous noise immunity.

We have already discussed the VCO and ripple counters. The major remaining component is the phase detector. The question that we've glossed over is that we say that the HC4046 has a *phase* detector, but then we talk about this *phase* detector outputting a voltage in order to match the two input *frequencies*. So in what sense is a *phase* considered a *frequency*?

7.3.1 Phase detectors

Figure 7.7 shows some typical inputs to a phase detector. Which is signal and which is reference is not important because we are interested in the product of the two, but for the purposes of discussion we will refer to the red curve as the reference. If the

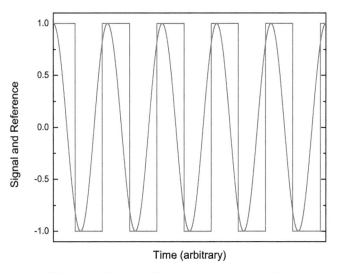

Figure 7.7. A typical signal (blue) and reference (red) input to a phase detector. In this example, the signal has a phase offset of 0.2π with respect to the signal.

phase difference between the sinusoidal curve and the reference were zero, the reference would makes a vertical transition whenever the sinusoid crosses zero. We are calling the blue sinusoidal curve the signal. In this example the signal, a cosine, has a 0.2π phase shift with respect to the reference. It is not necessary that one of these two be a square wave; both can be sinusoids if desired. (We chose one to be square because the analysis is more transparent for that case.) Mathematically, we represent the signal as

$$y_s = A_s \cos(\omega_s t + \phi),$$

where A_s is the signal amplitude, ω_s is the signal (angular) frequency, and ϕ is the signal's phase shift with respect to the reference. The phase detector outputs the product of the signal and reference. This goes to a 'loop filter', as it is designated in figure 7.5. In figure 7.6, we see that the loop filter is just an RC integrator. For the moment we will assume $\omega_s = \omega_r \equiv \omega$. Then, the time-averaged phase detector output is given by

$$\langle S_p \rangle = \frac{1}{T}\left[\int_0^{T/2} A_s \cos(\omega t + \phi)dt - \int_{T/2}^{T} A_s \cos(\omega t + \phi)dt \right], \qquad (7.1)$$

where $T = \frac{2\pi}{\omega}$ is the signal (and reference) period. The minus sign comes from the flipping of the sign of the square wave.

With just a small amount of algebra, equation (7.1) yields

$$\langle S_p \rangle = -\frac{2A_s}{\pi}\sin(\phi). \qquad (7.2)$$

That is, if the reference and signal have the same frequency, the integrated phase detector output is sinusoidal in phase. This is shown in the blue curve of figure 7.8.

But of course the two frequencies will most likely *not* start off at the same frequency. Figure 7.9 shows the integrated output of the phase detector versus fractional frequency difference for $\phi = 0$. Notice the characteristic 'dispersion' shape near $f_r = f_s$. That (roughly) straight line near $f_r = f_s$ is what provides the correction

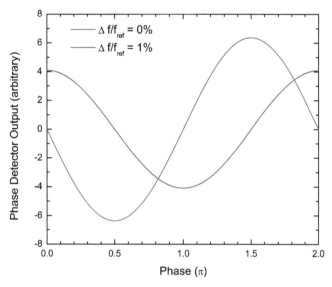

Figure 7.8. Integrated output of a phase detector for the inputs of figure 7.7. The blue curve is for signal frequency equal to reference frequency. The red curve is for a 1% difference in signal and reference frequencies.

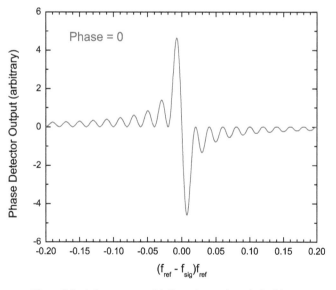

Figure 7.9. A frequency multiplier using a phase-locked loop.

signal to the VCO. Now when $f_r \neq f_s$ it makes no sense to talk about phase difference. But as f_r approaches f_s, it does make sense. The red curve in figure 7.8 shows the integrated phase detector output when f_s differs from f_r by just 1%. The dramatic difference in the phase detector signal for just a small change in frequency is what makes PLLs so powerful: the locks are tight!

But something is fishy here: suppose the phase detector had to supply a correction voltage to the VCO to get its output frequency to match that of the signal. According to figure 7.9, though, once you've got that match, the correction voltage is zero! But if that happens, the VCO will not receive a correction voltage, and its output frequency will go back to ω_0. What gives?! The answer lies with the integration capacitor; it also serves as a sample-and-hold. That is, the VCO input has a high impedance, so when the output of the phase detector goes to zero, the cap just holds the 'correct' potential, keeping the VCO where it needs to be.

You may notice that the phase detector module of figure 7.6 has two outputs, labeled 'type I' and 'type II'. These refer to two kinds of phase detectors. The latter is the one we just discussed; it works with analog signals as illustrated in figures 7.7–7.9. The other, type I, is simply an XOR gate and works just fine with TTL signals.

Homework 7.1
    Derive equation (7.2).

7.4 Phase-sensitive detection (lock-in amplifiers)

Phase-sensitive detectors give us a powerful tool to use in detecting signals in noisy environments. Suppose you have an LED that is flashing a signal at 1 kHz. You want to detect it from across the room, but your photodiode signal is completely dominated by the 120 Hz background from the fluorescent room lights. What can you do? This may seem like a silly example, but communications is actually the first field that benefited from PSD, or phase-sensitive detection.

The essential idea behind PSD is to use a phase detector, discussed in section 7.3.1, to filter out everything that is not at the appropriate signal frequency. Re-examine figure 7.9. Our earlier focus was on the dispersion-like structure near $f_r = f_s$. But in addition, you can see that the overall signal is a strong function of the difference between the signal and reference frequencies. Therefore, all you need do in the LED–photodiode example is feed the output from the photodiode, along with the reference frequency, here 1 kHz, to a phase detector, and then amplify the integrated phase detector output.

One difference between a PLL and a lock-in amplifier is that the feedback loop of the PLL simultaneously locks both the phase and the frequency of the in-loop device. But in a lock-in amplifier there is no feedback. Therefore, to obtain the best signal, you need to be able to adjust the relative phase of the signal and reference. (The reference frequency is presumed to be the same source, both driving the signal and providing the reference to the lock-in.)

7.4.1 PSD: what's under the hood

Commercial lock-in amplifiers come with an amplifier, a phase detector, an integrator whose frequency response can be selected, and a phase shifter. These can be high-dollar units, but we've already discussed most of the individual components, and they are not expensive. The components we have not yet discussed, the hardware of the phase detector and phase shifter, are visited below.

7.4.2 Phase-detectors—again

Figure 7.10 shows a simplified version of the AD630 'modulator–demodulator' chip. It is just an amplifier that has a gain of either +1 (switch in upward position) or −1, switch in downward position. This phase detector will work in a pinch, but an actual AD630 chip has many nice features, like offset nulls etc. Using an FET switch allows fast switching between positive and negative gains. This is equivalent to multiplying a signal by a square wave.

7.4.3 Phase shifter

Figure 7.11 shows a simple but effective phase shifter. The transfer characteristics of the circuit are

$$\left| \frac{V_{\text{out}}}{V_{\text{in}}} \right| = 1, \text{ independent of } \omega \tag{7.3a}$$

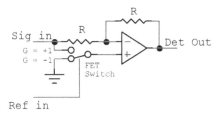

Figure 7.10. An op amp circuit having a gain of ±1, depending on whether the switch is in the upper or lower position. This is a greatly simplified version of the AD630 modulator–demodulator chip.

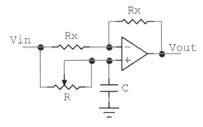

Figure 7.11. A simple phase shifter. The magnitude of the gain is 1, independent of frequency. The output phase lags the input by $-2\tan^{-1}(\omega RC)$. To have an output phase that *leads* the input, swap the R and C.

$$\phi = -2\tan^{-1}(\omega RC). \qquad (7.3b)$$

Thus, by twiddling a pot, you can adjust the relative phases of the signal and references, optimizing the noise rejection, while keeping the output amplitude fixed.

Homework 7.2
    Verify the gain and phase properties of the circuit in figure 7.11.

Chapter 8

Embedded electronics

8.1 Introduction

8.1.1 What are embedded electronics?

An embedded electronics system can be defined as any electronic system that uses a computer chip—but is not a general purpose desktop computer, laptop computer, 'notepad', or even 'smart phone'. Embedded electronics could be based on a microcontroller (like the chip that is at heart of the Arduino), or a microprocessor (like the chip that is at the heart of essentially any computer). An embedded electronics system is usually part of a larger electromechanical device and provides that device with 'intelligent' guidance and/or Internet connectivity. By 'intelligent guidance' we mean a logical procedure that the device itself can follow, based on data from sensors attached to it. Or, that guidance could be supplied by a remote human or another 'intelligent' machine.

8.1.2 Why a computer?

We could have based this lecture on a microcontroller-run device like an Arduino. This family of tools is incredibly powerful and relatively easy to implement. They are also unquestionably the best choice for many applications. Most microcontroller chips have standardized buses, which make it easy to connect external devices to them. But connectivity to the outside world via, for example, the Internet or a GUI (graphical user interface) is not the strong suit of a microcontroller device.

However, this *is* one of the strengths of a computer. But computers have problems of their own. Usually they draw more power than a microcontroller device and they virtually always multi-task. Multitasking can be a great thing—which is why computers have been engineered to do it. But when the computer is working on, say, checking its various peripherals, it is not working on the specific task you programmed it to do. A microcontroller, on the other hand, is usually a single

doi:10.1088/978-0-7503-3491-4ch8

purpose device, slavishly working away on whatever task you tell it to perform until you tell it to stop.

We have chosen a computer for our discussions because it is more general. Most of the material we will cover on buses will also be applicable to microcontroller devices, but we will also have access to the power and flexibility of a computer.

8.1.3 Why the Beagle?

In this chapter we will concentrate on the credit-card sized computer known as the Beaglebone Black (BBB) a photo of which is shown in figure 8.1. The BBB computer is based on the same sort of chip set that is used in mobile electronics and comes ready to use with a Linux operating system, the 'flavor' of which (for the BBBs in this lab) is 'Debian'. (For a quick tutorial on Linux, see appendix B.) One advantage of the BBB over another popular device, the Raspberry Pi, is that the chip set used in the BBB is better documented. But most importantly, the BBB's CPU has built into it what are, effectively, two microcontrollers (called PRUs). This gives us the flexibility of using the BBB as a computer, but with access to the single-mindedness of its dedicated PRUs.

In this chapter we will learn how to attach sensors, motors etc to the BBB. But unlike the earlier circuits we have studied, we must be able to write programs to control our hardware. To write these programs, we will have to master one of the text editors available to us on the Linux operating system. (See appendix D for a brief introduction to the vi and emacs editors.)

As for languages, we could have chosen many. But we have settled on C++. (For a primer on C++, see appendix E.) We chose C++ because it is superior to, say, Python for directly accessing memory—which can be important in working with embedded systems. Furthermore, unlike C, C++ class structures allow us to build

Figure 8.1. A photo of the Beaglebone Black computer. It is shown mounted on an acrylic plate along with a breadboard for auxiliary circuits.

objects for controlling devices seamlessly over the different buses that we have available.

8.2 Inside the Beagle

8.2.1 Hardware

The BBB has a number of connectors and we'll describe them now. First of all, note the black cable coming off the top of the BBB in figure 8.1. This goes to the USB of whatever computer you may want to use to control the Beagle. The BBB can also run in stand-alone mode, with its own monitor, keyboard, mouse, etc. We also have the option of running the BBB via a local area network (LAN) using its Ethernet connector. The final option is to communicate with the BBB via its serial interface (the row of pins on the left side of the board, alongside the 'P9' connector).

On the upper left corner of the BBB, you can see a jack for 5 V. You would use this if not operating the BBB from the USB or if your project requires more power than your host pc can supply though the USB. On the lower left you can see the metal USB jack. You can use this to mount a 'thumb drive', external hard drive, etc, should you wish to move files between the BBB and some other computer. You would also use this to connect a keyboard and mouse if you were operating the Beagle in stand-alone mode. For a brief tutorial on using mass storage such as a, thumb–drive, on the USB, see appendix F.

Just to the right of the USB jack, but not visible in this photo because it is mounted on the board's underside, is a micro-HDMI jack which can be used to connect the BBB to a monitor. The metal can on the upper part of the board (with PMI written on it) is an Ethernet jack. On the underside of the board, just below the Ethernet jack, is a socket for an SD card, in case you need additional memory, or if you 'brick' the computer and need to flash on a new operating system. If you look closely at the photo you will see two banks of sockets running on the left and right edges of the BBB. These are the interface pins. The left bank of sockets is called 'P9' and the right bank is called 'P8'. Each of these banks consists of two rows of sockets. The sockets are numbered starting at the upper left and go across and then down. That is, socket 'P9-1' is the uppermost left hole, socket 'P9-2' is to its right, socket 'P9-3' is just below socket 'P9-1', etc. We specify a socket by giving the connector name followed by the socket number. For example, socket P9-12 is located on the left-hand connector, is 6 rows down from the top, and is on the right side of the connector. It is possible to do considerable damage to the BBB if you connect to the wrong socket. Therefore please double check the socket number before connecting anything to it. All told, there are 2 × 46 pins in these P-connectors, though some of these are redundant. For example, there are multiple ground and power pins. Furthermore, as we will see, pins may have up to eight functions, depending on how they've been designated. Most of the pins are general purpose input/output (GPIO), and/or used in pulse width modulation (PWM) applications. Seven of the pins are dedicated ADCs. A summary of the I/O devices on the Beaglebone's connectors is given in table 8.1. The trick in controlling and communicating with hardware

Table 8.1. I/O devices on the Beaglebone's P8 and P9 connectors. Column 1 is the device name; column 2 indicates how many of each device exists on the BBB; column 3 gives some additional information.

I/O Functions	Number	Comments
SPI	2	Serial peripheral interface
I2C	2	Inter-integrated circuit (I^{2}C or I2C)
UART	4	universal asynch rec/trans
McASP	2	Multichannel audio ser. port
PWM	8	Pulse width modulation
ADC	7	12 bit SAR, 1.8 V
Timer	4	Independent timers
3.3 V	—	up to 250 mA
5 V	—	up to 250 mA
LCD	1	Liquid crystal display
GPIO	65	3.3 V, 4–6 mA

attached to the **BBB** is in figuring out how to work with these pins. This topic will constitute most of the discussion in this lecture.

8.2.2 System variables

Traditional 'tower' computers (e.g. most desktop computers) have physical slots in the back into which you can plug different pieces of hardware. Examples include National Instruments cards, extra ports, hard disk drives, etc. Somehow the computer needs to know what hardware is in what slots, and how each pin in each slot will be used. This information is generally given to the computer during the hardware installation process. Similarly, an embedded system such as the **BBB**, also needs to know about the hardware that you are attaching to it so that it can have its general purpose I/O pins properly configured. In the case of embedded systems, though, the slots are *virtual* rather than physical. In order to configure the pins, you need to write and compile a special piece of code, the device tree overlay (DTO), covered later in this lecture, and load it in. When you've loaded it in, you can see that it loaded properly by looking at the embedded device's virtual slot definitions. The slot information is stored in a special file named `slots`. You can display the contents of slots, and therefore see how the virtual slots have been configured by displaying the `slots` file:

```
cat /sys/devices/bone_capemgr.9/slots
```

(Your directory name could be slightly different from this. Use the auto-complete feature of the Linux command line (a tab) to help you figure out your directory name.)

Similarly, you will wish to see how individual pins have been configured. This information is stored in the file `pins`, which you can also display:

```
sudo cat /sys/kernel/debug/pinctrl/44e10800.pinmux/pins
```

Note that the `pins` file is somewhat protected, requiring you to acquire temporary super user privilege by using the `sudo` command. The contents of the `slots` file may look a bit strange to you at first. We'll discuss slots and pins files a bit more below.

You may often need to interrogate the `slots` and `pins` files and typing all this out every time is inconvenient. To make our lives easier, we can associate *system variables* with those files and their directories:

```
export SLOTS=/sys/devices/bone_capemgr.9/slots
export PINS=/sys/kernel/debug/pinctrl/44e10800.pinmux/pins
```

Now you can display the slots and pins files contents by typing:

```
cat $SLOTS
sudo cat $PINS
```

Well, this is nice but you haven't really saved yourself much work by using those system variables because you need to define them every time you log on. But here's a useful (and very general) trick: edit the `.profile` file in your home directory and add those export commands to the very end of it. The `.profile` file has been hidden from view by pre-pending a '.' to it. It consists of a bash script that is automatically executed every time you log on. After you've edited and saved it, you can execute the `.profile` script by typing:

```
source .profile
```

From now on, however, the script, including the lines that you just entered, will automatically be executed every time you log on. Thus, as soon as you log on you can check the slots and pins files by using the above abbreviated commands.

8.3 The pins

8.3.1 Overview

Tables 8.2–8.5 give a complete list of the pin functions for P8 and P9, respectively. Don't worry yet about all this complexity! I provide these tables now, just so you can see which pins have really simple functions—like 5 V and ground.

What you should notice, however, is that each pin can be referred to in several different ways. For example, in table 8.2 we see that P8-07 is also called '$PINS 36', 'GPIO# 66', 'Name TIMER4', or by its address '0x890'—or even by its 'address offset', which is 090. You should not let this bother you. A computer is complex

Table 8.2. Pin information for the P8 Header. This table shows the different pin designations.

Header #	$PINS	ADDR/OFFSET	GPIO #	Name	Header #	$PINS	ADDR/OFFSET	GPIO #	Name
P8_01				DGND	P8_02				DGND
P8_03	6	0x818/018	38	GPIO1_6	P8_04	7	0x81c/01c	39	GPIO1_7
P8_05	2	0x808/008	34	GPIO1_2	P8_06	3	0x80c/00c	35	GPIO1_3
P8_07	36	0x890/090	66	TIMER4	P8_08	37	0x894/094	67	TIMER7
P8_09	39	0x89c/09c	69	TIMER5	P8_10	38	0x898/098	68	TIMER6
P8_11	13	0x834/034	45	GPIO1_13	P8_12	12	0x830/030	44	GPIO1_12
P8_13	9	0x824/024	23	EHRPWM2B	P8_14	10	0x828/028	26	GPIO0_26
P8_15	15	0x83c/03c	47	GPIO1_15	P8_16	14	0x838/038	46	GPIO1_14
P8_17	11	0x82c/02c	27	GPIO0_27	P8_18	35	0x88c/08c	65	GPIO2_1
P8_19	8	0x820/020	22	EHRPWM2A	P8_20	33	0x884/084	63	GPIO1_31
P8_21	32	0x880/080	62	GPIO1_30	P8_22	5	0x814/014	37	GPIO1_5
P8_23	4	0x810/010	36	GPIO1_4	P8_24	1	0x804/004	33	GPIO1_1
P8_25	0	0x800/000	32	GPIO1_0	P8_26	31	0x87c/07c	61	GPIO1_29
P8_27	56	0x8e0/0e0	86	GPIO2_22	P8_28	58	0x8e8/0e8	88	GPIO2_24
P8_29	57	0x8e4/0e4	87	GPIO2_23	P8_30	59	0x8ec/0ec	89	GPIO2_25
P8_31	54	0x8d8/0d8	10	UART5_CTSN	P8_32	55	0x8dc/0dc	11	UART5_RTSN
P8_33	53	0x8d4/0d4	9	UART4_RTSN	P8_34	51	0x8cc/0cc	81	UART3_RTSN
P8_35	52	0x8d0/0d0	8	UART4_CTSN	P8_36	50	0x8c8/0c8	80	UART3_CTSN
P8_37	48	0x8c0/0c0	78	UART5_TX	P8_38	48	0x8c4/0c4	79	UART5_RXD
P8_39	46	0x8b8/0b8	76	GPIO2_12	P8_40	47	0x8bc/0bc	77	GPIO2_13
P8_41	44	0x8b0/0b0	74	GPIO2_10	P8_42	45	0x8b4/0b4	75	GPIO2_11
P8_43	42	0x8a8/0a8	72	GPIO2_8	P8_44	43	0x8ac/0ac	73	GPIO2_9
P8_45	40	0x8a0/0a0	70	GPIO2_6	P8_46	41	0x8a4/0a4	71	GPIO2_7

Table 8.3. Pin information for the P9 Header. This table shows the different pin designations.

Header #	$PINS	ADDR/OFFSET	GPIO #	Name	Header #	$PINS	ADDR/OFFSET	GPIO #	Name
P9_01				DGND	P9_02				DGND
P9_03				DC 3.3V	P9_04				DC 3.3V
P9_05				VDD 5V	P9_06				VDD 5V
P9_07				SYS 5V	P9_08				SYS 5V
P9_09				PWR BUT	P9_10				SYS RESE
P9_11	28	0x870/070	30	UART4 RXD	P9_12	30	0x878/078	60	GPIO1 28
P9_13	29	0x874/074	31	UART4 TXD	P9_14	18	0x848/048	50	EHRPWM1A
P9_15	16	0x840/040	48	GPIO1 16	P9_16	19	0x84c/04c	51	EHRPWM1B
P9_17	87	0x95c/15c	5	I2C1 SCL	P9_18	86	0x958/158	4	I2C1 SDA
P9_19	95	0x97c/17c	13	I2C2 SCL	P9_20	94	0x978/178	12	I2C2 SDA
P9_21	85	0x954/154	3	UART2 TXD	P9_22	84	0x950/150	2	UART2 RXD
P9_23	17	0x844/044	49	GPIO1 17	P9_24	97	0x984/184	15	UART1 TXD
P9_25	107	0x9ac/1ac	117	GPIO3 21	P9_26	96	0x980/180	14	UART1 RXD
P9_27	105	0x9a4/1a4	115	GPIO3 19	P9_28	103	0x99c/19c	113	SPI1 CS0
P9_29	101	0x994/194	111	SPI1 D0	P9_30	102	0x998/198	112	SPI1 D1
P9_31	100	0x990/190	110	SPI1 SCLK	P9_32				VADC
P9_33				AIN4	P9_34				AGND
P9_35				AIN6	P9_36				AIN5
P9_37				AIN2	P9_38				AIN3
P9_39				AIN0	P9_40				AIN1
P9_41A	109	0x9b4/1b4	20	CLKOUT2	P9_42A	89	0x964/164	7	GPIO0 7
P9_41B		0x9a8/1a8	116	GPIO3 20	P9_42B	45	0x9a0/1a0	114	GPIO3 18
P9_43				GND	P9_44				GND
P9_45				GND	P9_46				GND

Table 8.4. Pin information for the P8 Header. This table shows the different modes for each pin.

Header	mode 7	mode 6	mode 5	mode 4	mode 3	mode 2	mode 1	mode 0
P8_01								
P8_02								
P8_03	gpio1[6]						mmc1_dat6	gpmc_ad6
P8_04	gpio1[7]						mmc1_dat7	gpmc_ad7
P8_05	gpio1[2]						mmc1_dat2	gpmc_ad2
P8_06	gpio1[3]						mmc1_dat3	gpmc_ad3
P8_07	gpio2[2]					timer4		gpmc_advn_ale
P8_08	gpio2[3]					timer7		gpmc_oen_ren
P8_09	gpio2[5]					timer5		gpmc_be0n_cle
P8_10	gpio2[4]					timer6		gpmc_wen
P8_11	gpio1[13]			mcasp0_axr0	mmc2_dat1	mmc1_dat5	lcd_data18	gpmc_ad13
P8_12	gpio1[12]			eqep2a_in	mmc2_dat0	mmc1_dat4	lcd_data19	gpmc_AD12
P8_13	gpio0[23]			ehrpwm2B	mmc2_dat5	mmc1_dat1	lcd_data22	gpmc_ad9
P8_14	gpio0[26]			ehrpwm2_tripzone_in	mmc2_dat6	mmc1_dat2	lcd_data21	gpmc_ad10
P8_15	gpio1[15]			eQEP2_strobe	mmc2_dat3	mmc1_dat7	lcd_data16	gpmc_ad15
P8_16	gpio1[14]			eQEP2_index	mmc2_dat2	mmc1_dat6	lcd_data17	gpmc_ad14
P8_17	gpio0[27]			ehrpwm0_synco	mmc2_dat7	mmc1_dat3	lcd_data20	gpmc_ad11
P8_18	gpio2[1]	mcasp0_fsr			mmc2_clk	gpmc_wait1	lcd_memory_clk	gpmc_clk_mux0
P8_19	gpio0[22]			ehrpwm2A	mmc2_dat4	mmc1_dat0	lcd_data23	gpmc_ad8
P8_20	gpio1[31]					mmc1_cmd	gpmc_be1n	gpmc_csn2
P8_21	gpio1[30]					mmc1_clk	gpmc_clk	gpmc_csn1
P8_22	gpio1[5]						mmc1_dat5	gpmc_ad5
P8_23	gpio1[4]						mmc1_dat4	gpmc_ad4
P8_24	gpio1[1]						mmc1_dat1	gpmc_ad1
P8_25	gpio1[0]						mmc1_dat0	gpmc_ad0
P8_26	gpio2[29]							gpmc_csn0
P8_27	gpio2[22]						gpmc_a8	lcd_vsync
P8_28	gpio2[24]						gpmc_a10	lcd_pclk

Pin	GPIO					gpmc	lcd
P8_29	gpio2[23]					gpmc_a9	lcd_hsync
P8_30	gpio2[25]					gpmc_a11	lcd_ac_bias_en
P8_31	gpio0[10]	mcasp0_fsr	uart5_rxd	mcasp0_axr1	eQEP1_index	gpmc_a18	lcd_data14
P8_32	gpio0[11]	uart5_rtsn	mcasp0_axr3	mcasp0_ahclkx	eQEP1_strobe	gpmc_a19	lcd_data15
P8_33	gpio0[9]	uart4_rtsn	mcasp0_ar3	mcasp0_fsr	eQEP1B_in	gpmc_a17	lcd_data13
P8_34	gpio2[17]	uart3_rtsn	mcasp0_axr2	mcasp0_ahclkr	ehrpwm1B	gpmc_a15	lcd_data11
P8_35	gpio0[8]	uart4_ctsn	mcasp0_axr2	mcasp0_aclkr	eQEP1A_in	gpmc_a16	lcd_data12
P8_36	gpio2[16]	uart3_ctsn		mcasp0_axr0	ehrpwm1A	gpmc_a14	lcd_data10
P8_37	gpio2[14]	uart2_ctsn	uart5_txd	mcasp0_aclkx	ehrpwm1_tripzone_in	gpmc_a12	lcd_data8
P8_38	gpio2[15]	uart2_rtsn	uart5_rxd	mcasp0_fsx	ehrpwm0_synco	gpmc_a13	lcd_data9
P8_39	gpio2[12]			eQEP2_index		gpmc_a6	lcd_data6
P8_40	gpio2[13]		pr1_edio_data_out7	eQEP2_strobe		gpmc_a7	lcd_data7
P8_41	gpio2[10]			eQEP2A_in		gpmc_a4	lcd_data4
P8_42	gpio2[11]			eQEP2B_in		gpmc_a5	lcd_data5
P8_43	gpio2[8]			ehrpwm2_tripzone_in		gpmc_a2	lcd_data2
P8_44	gpio2[9]			ehrpwm0_synco		gpmc_a3	lcd_data3
P8_45	gpio2[6]			ehrpwm2A		gpmc_a0	lcd_data0
P8_46	gpio2[7]			ehrpwm2B		gpmc_a1	lcd_data1

Table 8.5. Pin information for the P9 Header. This table shows the different modes for each pin.

Header	mode 7	mode 6	mode 5	mode 4	mode 3	mode 2	mode 1	mode 0
P9_01								
P9_02								
P9_03								
P9_04								
P9_05								
P9_06								
P9_07								
P9_08								
P9_09								
P9_10								RESET_OUT
P9_11	gpio0[30]	uart4_rxd_mux2		mmc1_sdcd	rmii2_crs_dv	gpmc_csn4	mii2_crs	gpmc_wait0
P9_12	gpio1[28]	mcasp0_aclkr_mux3		gpmc_dir	mmc2_dat3	gpmc_csn6	mii2_col	gpmc_be1n
P9_13	gpio0[31]	uart4_txd_mux2		mmc2_sdcd	rmii2_rxerr	gpmc_csn5	mii2_rxerr	gpmc_wpn
P9_14	gpio1[18]	ehrpwm1A_mux1		gpmc_a18	mmc2_dat1	rgmii2_td3	mii2_txd3	gpmc_a2
P9_15	gpio1[16]	ehrpwm1_tripzone_ input		gpmc_a16	mii2_txen	rmii2_tctl	gmii2_txen	gpmc_a0
P9_16	gpio1[19]	ehrpwm1B_mux1		gpmc_a19	mmc2_dat2	rgmii2_td2	mii2_txd2	gpmc_a3
P9_17	gpio0[5]				ehrpwm0_synci	I2C1_SCL	mmc2_sdwp	spi0_cs0
P9_18	gpio0[4]	mcasp0_fsr			ehrpwm0_tripzone	I2C1_SDA	mmc1_sdwp	spi0_d1
P9_19	gpio0[13]			spi1_cs1	I2C2_SCL	dcan0_rx	timer5	uart1_rtsn
P9_20	gpio0[12]			spi1_cs0	I2C2_SDA	dcan0_tx	timer6	uart1_ctsn
P9_21	gpio0[3]	EMU3_mux1			ehrpwm0B	I2C2_SCL	uart2_txd	spi0_d0
P9_22	gpio0[2]	EMU2_mux1			ehrpwm0A	I2C2_SDA	uart2_rxd	spi0_sclk
P9_23	gpio1[17]	ehrpwm0_synco		gpmc_a17	mmc2_dat0	rgmii2_rxdv	gmii2_rxdv	gpmc_a1
P9_24	gpio0[15]				I2C1_SCL	dcan1_rx	mmc2_sdwp	uart1_txd
P9_25	gpio3[21]			EMU4_mux2	mcasp1_axr1	mcasp0_axr3	eQEP0_strobe	mcasp0_ahclkx
P9_26	gpio0[14]				I2C1_SDA	dcan1_tx	mmc1_sdwp	uart1_rxd
P9_27	gpio3[19]			EMU2_mux2	mcasp1_fsx	mcasp0_axr3	eQEP0B_in	mcasp0_fsr
P9_28	gpio3[17]			eCAP2_in_PWM2_out	spi1_cs0	mcasp0_axr2	ehrpwm0_synci	mcasp0_ahclkr
P9_29	gpio3[15]			mmc1_sdcd_mux1	spi1_d0	mcasp0_axr2	ehrpwm0B	mcasp0_fsx

Pin								gpio
P9_30	mcasp0_axr0	ehrpwm0_tripzone	spi1_d1		mmc2_sdcd_mux1			gpio3[16]
P9_31	mcasp0_aclkx	ehrpwm0A	spi1_sclk		mmc0_sdcd_mux1			gpio3[14]
P9_32								
P9_33								
P9_34								
P9_35								
P9_36								
P9_37								
P9_38								
P9_39								
P9_40								
P9_41A	xdma_event_intr1	eQEP0_index	tclkin	clkout2	timer7_mux1		EMU3_mux0	gpio2[20]
P9_41B	mcasp0_axr1			Mcasp1_axr0	emu3			gpio3[20]
P9_42A	eCAP0_in_PWM0_out	uart3_txd	spi1_cs1	pr1_ecap0_ecap_capin_apwm_0	spi1_sclk	mmc0_sdwp	xdma_event_intr2	gpio0[7]
P9_42B	Mcasp0_aclkr	eQEP0A_in	Mcasp0_axr2	Mcasp1_aclkx				gpio3[18]
P9_43								
P9_44								
P9_45								
P9_46								

device made up of many components, all held together by an operating system. Each part knows a piece of hardware by how it communicates with it. For example, we may know a pin as 'P8-7' because we see it in that location on the connector to which we will physically attach our devices. But the CPU doesn't know anything about physical connectors. Even the operating system, which has to enable all the different parts to communicate with each other doesn't know about physical connectors. The biggest part of our job in interfacing hardware to a computer is telling the operating system where things are so that it can do its job of managing.

8.3.2 The device tree overlay

In order to maintain maximum flexibility, Linux-based embedded systems have a way of modifying the operating system 'on the fly', i.e. without the need to re-build the Linux kernel. This is done through the *device tree overlay* or DTO. The DTO is a special piece of code that you write, compile, and then load. The DTO contains all the information on how you would like your pins to be defined. This includes pin function, as well as direction of data flow. For example, suppose you'd like P9-12 to be able to output a TTL signal. Perhaps you'd like to use this to turn on or off an LED, or even a laser. And in addition, suppose you'd like P9-23 to receive a TTL input. For example, suppose you plan to give the BBB a signal that tells it that it should turn off the laser. Then you'd write an appropriate DTO file, compile it, load it, and you'd be good to go.

Here is a summary of the process for setting up and using the pins on the Beagle:
- Decide what pins you will use for what purpose.
- Write the DTO, commenting it heavily.
- Compile the DTO.
- Load the DTO, checking to see that it loaded correctly.
- 'Export' the pins that you will use.
- Set the direction of data flow for all the pins you will use.
- Use the pins by reading a 'file' (for input) or writing to a 'file' (for output).
- 'Unexport' the pins.

In the penultimate step I refer to reading and writing 'files'. This is because, to Linux, everything is thought of as a file to read from or write to. We'll see examples soon.

You can define all your pin functions in a single DTO if you like, or you can write several DTOs and load them individually. One thing to check for is that your DTO doesn't conflict with a previously loaded DTO, whether that previously loaded DTO was your creation or that of the Beaglebone developers.

Writing a DTO is not difficult, especially if you have a template as a starting point. But it can be a bit intimidating for the beginner, so let's forgo that for the moment. We can do this because the good people who brought you the Beaglebone already supplied it with some useful DTOs, both the source code and the compiled versions, that you can simply load and use. We'll start with a supplied DTO that allows you to use the BBB's ADCs.

8.4 Loading a DTO

8.4.1 The ADC: getting started

Having analog-to-digital converters built right in to your computer is a huge convenience. As we saw in chapter 7, ADCs are not difficult to use, but once you've digitized your analog signal you have to have a way to get all those bits into the computer. Later, we'll see how to do this using one of the computer's buses, but even this is more work than simply attaching your analog signal to a pin on the computer and immediately getting the result.

The Beaglebone actually has a single 12 bit successive approximation register (SAR) ADC built-in to its CPU. It is capable of 200 000 samples per second. The CPU has an eight-fold MUX to select which input is routed to the ADC; seven of these are available to you on the BBB's I/O connectors. The pinouts for these are given in table 8.6.

In addition to separate pins for each of the BBB's seven ADC inputs, you can see that pin P9-34 is used as the ground reference and P9-32 is used for the 'high-voltage' reference of 1.8 V. Exceeding 1.8 V on any of the ADC inputs will most likely result in destroying the BBB.

Before loading the factory-supplied DTO, let's revisit the `slots` file. When you type `cat $SLOTS` the BBB should respond with something like what is shown in table 8.7.

Table 8.6. Pinouts for the ADCs.

Header designation	Function
P9-32	VADC (1.8 V Ref.)
P9-33	AIN4
P9-34	AGND
P9-35	AIN6
P9-36	AIN5
P9-37	AIN2
P9-38	AIN3
P9-39	AIN0
P9-40	AIN1

Table 8.7. Assigned slots, before loading the ADC DTO.

```
0:    54:PF-
1:    55:PF-
2:    56:PF-
3:    57:PF-
4:    ff:P-O-L    Bone-LT-eMMC-2G,00A0,Texas Instrument,BB-BONE-EMMC-2G
5:    ff:P-O-L    BONE-Black-HDMI,00A0,Texas Instrument,BB-BONELT-HDMI
```

The first column of numbers is the (virtual) slot number. Upon booting up, the operating system reserves the first four slots (slots 0–3) for 'EEPROM IDs on the capes'. A 'cape' is what the Beaglebone folks call a piece of add-on electronics that you may wish to attach to the BBB via its P8 and/or P9 connectors. The BBB people are so sure you'll want to do this that they reserve slots for them. A DTO that allows the BBB to access its built-in operating system is loaded into slot 4 at boot. A second DTO that sets up some pins to be used for audio–video output on the HDMI is loaded into slot 5. Note that if you do not intend to use the HDMI, you can edit the appropriate file in the BBB such that this last DTO is not loaded upon booting the system. We've got plenty of pins still available for our use, so we'll leave those DTOs in place.

Now we load in the pre-fab DTO that sets up the ADCs:

```
sudo sh -c 'echo BB-ADC > $SLOTS'
cat $SLOTS
```

Ok, this command is complicated enough that it requires a bit of explanation. The part in quotes just loads the DTO. Remember that `echo` just repeats whatever follows it and '>' redirects output to the file whose name follows it. Thus `echo BB-ADC > $SLOTS` just sends the name 'BB-ADC' to the `slots` file. With that name now in the slots file, the computer can go to the directory where all all the DTOs are kept, and load in the one named `BB-ADC`. But the `slots` file can only be accessed by a 'super-user', so we have to give ourselves temporary `su` privilege using `sudo`. However, the `sudo` command only operates on the entity immediately following it, and that would have been `echo`—which doesn't require `su` privilege. It's the redirection to the `slots` file that requires the privilege, not the `echo` itself. So we jump through a few hoops by using the `sh -c` directives. The first of these temporarily opens a new shell in which you will be a super-user. The second says to take the following string as a single verbatim command in that new shell. This is an important sequence and is generally useful when you want to execute a single command with super-user privilege, but without the hazards of logging on as a super-user.

After loading the DTO, we can see if it 'took' by looking at the `slots` file again, for which the output should look something like that shown in table 8.8.

Table 8.8. Assigned slots, after loading the ADC DTO.

0:	54:PF–	
1:	55:PF–	
2:	56:PF–	
3:	57:PF–	
4:	ff:P-O-L	Bone-LT-eMMC-2G,00A0,Texas Instrument,BB-BONE-EMMC-2G
5:	ff:P-O-L	BONE-Black-HDMI,00A0,Texas Instrument,BB-BONELT-HDMI
7:	ff:P-O-L	Override Board name,00A0,Override Manuf,BB-ADC

We'll learn more about what the details in this output mean when we write our own DTOs.

If the DTO doesn't appear in the `pins` file, we can try to figure out what went wrong by looking at the cryptic messages using `dmesg`. Because `dmesg` usually produces a very long output, you may find it more useful to invoke it this way:

```
dmesg | less
```

which allows you to scroll through the messages. Or, since we want information pertaining to slot 7, we can enter:

```
dmesg | grep '#7'
```

Here we've 'piped' dmesg (using the '|' symbol) to the linux utility 'grep'. This utility searches through dmesg (or whichever text you pipe to grep), looking for the string that follows grep.

Usually, if the DTO doesn't load properly it's because we tried to co-opt pins that have already been defined. If so, the `dmesg` output will help you figure out which ones you've double-reserved.

8.4.2 Testing out the ADC

As already mentioned, you run a very high risk of damaging the BBB if you input a voltage that is greater than 1.8 V into one of the ADC pins. A safe way to avoid doing this is to use the ADC's reference voltage.

For example, suppose we'd like to adjust a voltage between 0 V and 1.8 V and we'd like to monitor that voltage with one of our ADCs, here AIN0 on P9-39. We could just run the output of P9-32 (the 1.8 V reference high) to the top of a pot, put the bottom of the pot at P9-34 (ADC reference ground) and send the pot wiper to AIN0. This *might* work—depending on the value of the pot. If it is too low it will exceed the maximum current specifications of the reference, possibly even damaging the BBB. Furthermore, if you are using that pot output to drive some other electronics, then that could also draw too much current. Instead, we should buffer the ADC reference voltage as shown in figure 8.2. We can power the op amp from the BBB's 'system power' (P9-7, `SYS_5V`) and ground (P9-1, `GND`).

Now look in the directory that contains the ADC 'files':

```
ls /sys/bus/iio/devices/iio:device0
```

You should see the 'files'

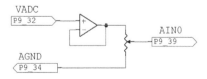

Figure 8.2. Buffering the ADC reference voltage so as not to exceed its current sourcing limits while not exceeding the ADC inputs' maximum voltage limit.

dev	in_voltage2_raw	in_voltage5_raw	name	uevent
in_voltage0_raw	in_voltage3_raw	in_voltage6_raw	power	
in_voltage1_raw	in_voltage4_raw	in_voltage7_raw	subsystem	

Here, in_voltage0_raw corresponds to AIN0, in_voltage1_raw corresponds to AIN1, etc. You can see the contents of, say, in_voltage0_raw by using cat:

```
cat /sys/bus/iio/devices/iio:device0/in_voltage0_raw
```

Because this is a 12 bit ADC, as the input voltage to, say, AIN0 goes from 0 V (its minimum allowed value) to 1.8 V (its maximum allowed value) the content of the 'file' in_voltage0_raw goes from 0 to 4095, that is, $2^{12} - 1$. The resolution should be, in principle,

$$\Delta V = \frac{1.8 \text{ V}}{2^{12}} = 0.4 \text{ mV}.$$

The digitized ADC outputs that are held in the above 'files' are, essentially, uncalibrated. That is, to convert the content of in_voltage0_raw to a voltage, you'd have to divide it by 4096 and multiply it by 1.8 V.

But there's an easier way. The Beaglebone also provides a calibrated output from its ADC To get to these 'files', type the following:

```
ls /sys/devices/ocp.3/helper.15
```

(Some of these directories are created dynamically when the DTO is loaded. Therefore their names may be slightly different. Use the 'auto-complete' (tab) to help find the correct directory.) You should see the 'files'

AIN0	AIN1	AIN2	AIN3	AIN4	AIN5	AIN6	AIN7
driver	modalias	power	subsystem	uevent			

We won't get into the details of the ancillary files and directories, but you can read the *normalized* digitized signal at, for example, AIN0 from the command line by again using cat:

```
cat /sys/devices/ocp.3/helper.15/AIN0
```

Now you should see that the values contained in AIN0 range from 0 to 1800 as the input voltage goes from 0 V to 1.8 V. In other words, the contents of the AINx 'files' are integers whose values correspond to the ADC inputs and expressed in mV.

Clearly, if you want to read either the calibrated or uncalibrated 'files' from inside a program, you'd follow the usual file I/O protocol for reading a file. But there is one caveat to this: Due to the peculiarities of how Linux handles file I/O, you need to `open` and `close` the file between readings. This allows Linux to flush the file I/O buffer and lets you obtain updated ADC results.

8.5 Configuring the general purpose input/output pins

Most of the pins on the Beaglebone Black are for use as general purpose input/output, or GPIO. As we have seen, they may be used for analog–digital conversion; as we shall see, they may be used for pulse-width modulation. But they can also supply clock signals, serve as data buses, or simply send and receive logic signals. In this section we will concentrate on that last function.

Up until now, when we wanted to use a certain pin for a certain function, we simply loaded in a piece of software, a device tree overlay (DTO) that someone else had written. You can get a lot of mileage from this, but you will never really have total control over your embedded device until you can write your own DTOs—and they are not that difficult to write.

The first step in deciding how you will define how your pins will function, is to look at tables 8.4 and 8.5 to see what functions are available to which pins. For example, if we'd like to use pin P8-10 for general purpose I/O, we'd choose mode 7 for that pin. But if we want to use that pin for a timer, we'd choose mode 2 instead. Notice that not all pins can perform all functions.

Once we've determined which pins we'd like to perform which functions, we have to set up those pins. For each pin we have to determine the following characteristics:
1. What is the pin's address?
2. What is the desired mode number?
3. Is the pin going to output or input a signal?
4. Do we want high speed or low speed?
5. Do we want to enable pullup/pulldown or not?
6. If we want pullup/pulldown enabled, which of these do we want?

We can obtain the pin address from tables 8.2 and 8.3 (third and eighth columns), and we've presumably already taken care of item 2. Input/output should be an obvious decision for a given function. We should always choose high speed unless we are trying to drive a long transmission line. The only things left to figure out are the pullup/pulldown questions. What are these anyhow?

Recall in chapter 5 when we used the LF311, a comparator with open collector output. Remember that the '311 could not source a signal; we needed to tie its output high with a pullup resistor. Recall also in chapter 6's figures 6.17 and 6.21 how we used pullup resistors to give a default TRUE value to the inputs. We could also have chosen to give a default FALSE value to the inputs by using a pulldown resistor connected to ground. The size of the pullup/pulldown resistor is, like everything else, a compromise: the smaller the resistor, the smaller the voltage drop across the resistor and the more you can neglect any adverse effects of being resistively coupled to a voltage source. However, the smaller the resistor, the more current is wasted.

In general, you will need to use pullup or pulldown resistors on nearly all your I/O, certainly the GPIO. (The ADCs are a notable exception.) But if choice of the pullup/pulldown resistor values is not critical for your application, you can use the ones that the BBB already has on-board. And if you choose to use those resistors, you must also choose whether you'd like them to be pullup or pulldown.

Let's give some examples. Suppose you'd like to use the pin at P8-10 as a general purpose I/O device. You'd like to use it as an output, and you'd like it to be normally low (FALSE). Then,

Address	=	0x898
Mode number	=	7
Pullup/pulldown	=	yes
choice	=	pulldown
I/O	=	output
speed	=	high

Table 8.9 shows us how to take all of this information, except the address, and store it as a single 1 byte number. In the above example, we have all the desired characteristics (except the pin's address) stored as 0x07, as shown in table 8.10. As a second example, suppose we want to use the pin at P9-24 as GPIO (mode 7), in input mode, and we'd like to use an external pullup/pulldown. The 1 byte descriptor of that pin is 0x2F, as shown in table 8.11.

With this preparation behind us, let's finally get to the DTO code, a sample of which is shown in listing 8.1.

We'll just think of this code as a template and concentrate on what to modify for our own needs. The first of these is in line 6: part-number really means 'what am I going to name this piece of code?'. Line 7's version will always be 00A0. The most important portion of the code, in terms of what you will want to modify, is the chunk called fragment@0. You can see a block of code, lines 15–19, in which pins are defined. The pin definitions are just address offsets (from tables 8.2 and 8.3) followed by a 1 byte number, which we now know how to create. Note that in DTO code, comments are delimited by /* and */. It is a very good idea to comment each of your definitions so that you don't have to scurry over to a table every time you look at your code. As mentioned, the name of the file that contains this code must match the part-number, and it must have the extension .dts

Before you load the code, you must first compile it. To do this on the BBB, type:

```
dtc -O dtb -o DM-GPIO-Test-00A0.dtbo -b 0 -@ DM-GPIO-Test.dts
```

Here, dtc invokes the DTO compiler, -O dtb (dash, followed by an upper case letter 'O') tells the compiler to use the correct format for DTOs, -o DM-GPIO-Test-00A0.dtbo tells the compiler to output the compiled binary file with the given file

Table 8.9. Register Field Descriptions.

Bit	Field	Type	Reset	Description
31-20	Reserved	R	0h	
19-7	Reserved	R	0h	
6	conf <module>_<pin>_slewctrl	R/W	X	Select between faster or slower slew rate: 0: Fast 1: Slow Reset value is pad-dependent.
5	conf_<module>_<pin>_rxactive	R/W	1h	Input enable value for the PAD 0: Receiver disabled 1: Receiver enabled
4	conf_<module>_<pin>_putypesel	R/W	X	PAD pullup/pulldown type selection 0: Pulldown selected 1: Pullup selected Reset value is pad-dependent.
3	conf_<module>_<pin>_puden	R/W	X	PAD pullup/pulldown enable 0: Pullup/pulldown enabled 1: Pullup/pulldown disabled Reset value is PAD-dependent.
2-0	conf_<module>_<pin>_mmode	R/W	X	PAD functional signal mux select. Reset value is PAD-dependent.

Table 8.10. An example of coding a register field description.

slewctrl	rxactive	putypesel	puden	mmode
Fast	Output	Down	Enable	7
0	0	0	0	111
0	7			

Table 8.11. Another example of coding a register field description.

slewctrl	rxactive	putypesel	puden	mmode
Fast	Input	Down	Disable	7
0	1	0	1	111
2	F			

```
1   /dts-v1/;
2   /plugin/;
3
4   /{
5       compatible = 'ti,beaglebone', 'ti,beaglebone-black';
6       part-number = 'DM-GPIO-Test';
7       version = '00A0';
8
9       fragment@0 {
10          target = <&am33xx_pinmux>;
11
12          __overlay__ {
13              pinctrl_test: DM_GPIO_Test_Pins {
14                  pinctrl-single,pins = <
15                      0x078 0x07  /* P9_12 60 OUTPUT MODE7 */
16                      0x184 0x2f  /* P9_24 15 INPUT  MODE7 */
17                      0x034 0x37  /* P8_11 45 INPUT  MODE7 */
18                      0x030 0x27  /* P8_12 44 INPUT  MODE7 */
19                      0x024 0x2f  /* P8_13 23 INPUT  MODE7 */
20                  >;
21              };
22          };
23      };
24
25      fragment@1 {
26          target = <&ocp>;
27          __overlay__ {
28              test_helper: helper {
29                  compatible = 'bone-pinmux-helper';
30                  pinctrl-names = 'default';
31                  pinctrl-0 = <&pinctrl_test>;
32                  status = 'okay';
33              };
34          };
35      };
36  };
```

Listing 8.1: Sample DTO code.

name and extension .dtbo. Note that you need to attach the version number that you had in the code to the output file name. The -b 0 is setting the physical boot CPU (a zero), and the -@ generates a symbols node as part of the dynamic device tree loading of the overlay. (Don't worry if all these terms sound like gobbledygook. The more you see and use them, the more they will make sense.)

Now all you have to do is to copy the compiled code to the usual place where all the other compiled DTOs are located, namely in /lib/firmware, and then load it up in the usual way (as we did with the already-supplied ADC DTO). Note that this is a 'protected' directory and so we have to use sudo with the copy command.

We've just covered a huge amount of information. You may wish to re-read this section before continuing.

8.6 Pulse width modulation (PWM)

Most microcontrollers or embedded systems hardware do not have built-in digital to analog converter (DAC) capabilities, and the Beaglebone is no exception. However most devices, including the Beaglebone, do have pulse width modulation (PWM) capability, which can be used to create an analog signal if appropriately filtered. In PWM, a device pin output oscillates between logical high and low, and the user controls both the repetition rate and the duty cycle, or equivalent parameters. The period is, of course the reciprocal of the frequency and the duty cycle is defined as the ON-time divided by the period. That is,

$$T \equiv \frac{1}{f} \tag{8.1a}$$

$$\text{Duty cycle} \equiv \frac{\text{on--time}}{T}, \tag{8.1b}$$

where T is the period and f is the (linear) frequency. Note that the duty cycle, by definition, must be a number between 0 and 1. Also, because

$$\text{on--time} + \text{off--time} \equiv T,$$
$$\text{Duty cycle} = \frac{T - \text{off--time}}{T},$$

or

$$1 - \text{Duty cycle} = \frac{\text{off--time}}{T}.$$

In the case of the Beaglebone, the user gives the period and either the on-time or off-time (default is off-time). Even though you write that off–time to a file named duty, this is *not* a duty cycle!

You can see from equation (8.1b) that if you low-pass filter or, equivalently, integrate over many periods, you will obtain a quasi-dc signal that is proportional to the duty cycle. It is in this sense that PWM can be used as a DAC.

8.7 Buses

In addition to communicating with the outside world using individual general purpose I/O, the BBB has several instances each of three standardized buses: I2C, SPI, and UART. In this course will work with the first two. A bus is a collection of communication wires, the exact number depending of the type of bus. Buses are designed to have multiple devices on them, a 'master' and one or more 'slaves'. The bus must have some sort of protocol to enable unambiguous communication between the devices on that bus. Buses are designed to transmit information either serially or in parallel. In a serial bus, all the bits in, say, 1 byte, are transmitted one after the other along a single wire. In a parallel bus, all the bits in, say, 1 byte, are transmitted at the same time, using a separate wire for each bit. The address bus on your computer is an example of a parallel bus; the buses we will use in this course are all examples of a serial bus.

8.7.1 I²C

The I²C (inter-integrated circuit, or IIC, or I2C) is a standard serial bus used on many devices, including microcontroller chips and most embedded devices. Here are some of its properties:
- It's a two-wire (plus ground) bus.
  - ○ SDA (Serial DAta) line: Bi-directional transmission of data.
  - ○ SCL (Serial CLock) line: Synchronizes the data transfer.
- Each device on the bus can act as a master or slave.
  - ○ A slave cannot initiate communication.
  - ○ Each slave on the bus is pre-assigned a unique 7 bit (or 10 bit) address. Thus, in principle, one could have up to 128 different slave devices on a single I2C bus.
  - ○ The bus has 'multi-master' facilities, including collision detection and arbitration if two masters activate at once.
- The bus has on-chip noise filtering, built-in as standard.
- Requires pull-up resistors on both SDA and SCL lines. (Usually 1k–10k.)
- User- or device-supplied series resistors ($\sim$250 Ω) help protect against over-current conditions.
- Devices are attached to SDA and SCL lines using Schmitt trigger inputs to help reduce impact of signal noise.
- Transmission line capacitance, for a pair of 22 AWG wire about 15 pF per foot, limits data transfer speed. Hence bus lines must typically be short. (The maximum length is determined by desired transfer speed.)

As shown in table 8.12, the BBB has three I2C buses 'present', though only two are available to the user (figure 8.3).

Table 8.12. I2C buses on the BBB Debian image. (Reproduced from *Exploring BeagleBone: Tools and Techniques for Building with Embedded Linux* by Derek Molloy 2018 with permission. Copyright 2019, John Wiley and Sons, Inc.)

H/W bus	S/W device	SDA pin	SCL pin	Description
I2C0	/dev/i2c-0	N/A	N/A	Internal bus for HDMI control
I2C1	/dev/i2c-2	P9-18	P9-17	General I2C bus. Disabled by default
I2C2	/dev/i2c-1	P9-20	P9-19	General I2C bus. Enabled by default

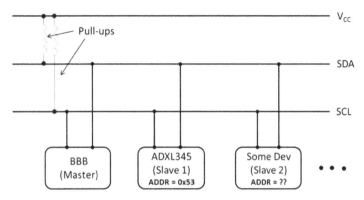

Figure 8.3. A schematic of several devices on an I2C bus.

First notice in table 8.12 that I2C0 is not available from either P8 or P9; it is on an internal bus for HDMI control. That leaves I2C1 and I2C2. Notice in table 8.12 that I2C buses 1 and 2 are reversed between software (S/W) and hardware (H/W). This is most likely a mistake by whoever set these buses up. Regardless, we need to remember that when our software is referring to i2c-1, we need to connect our hardware to I2C-2, and vice versa. In this text, whenever there is ambiguity, we'll use caps to designate the hardware bus and lowercase to designate the software. By default, I2C2 is enabled, but if desired, I2C1 can be enabled as well.

8.7.2 The SPI bus

The I2C is a very common and very convenient bus. It is an example of a so-called two-wire bus. (We don't count the ground wire—even though it is essential!) By contrast, the SPI, or Serial Peripheral Interface bus is either three- or four-wire. For the four-wire, these are:

SCLK: Synchronizing serial clock, provided by the master.
MOSI: Master out, slave in. A data communication line.
MISO: Master in, slave out. A data communication line.
CS: (Slave) chip select.

For the three-wire system, the MOSI and MISO are combined into a single line having bi-directional data flow that is managed by the master. Instead of each slave having a unique address, it must have a chip select (active low). Table 8.13, taken from Molloy's book, summarizes the differences between the SPI and I2C buses.

To this I can add the following: SPI is faster but less convenient for multiple devices; I2C is slower, easier to use, and more easily supports multiple devices. Like the I2C, the SPI is a synchronous bus whose data flow is controlled by a clock signal.

Table 8.13. Comparison of I2C and SPI buses. (Reproduced from *Exploring BeagleBone: Tools and Techniques for Building with Embedded Linux* by Derek Molloy 2018 with permission. Copyright 2019, John Wiley and Sons, Inc.)

Category	I2C	SPI
Connectivity	Two-wires, with which up to 128 addressable devices can be attached.	Typically four-wires, and requires additional logic for more than 1 slave device.
Data rate	I2C fast mode is 400 kHz. Uses 'half-duplex' communication.	Faster performance, typically over 10 MHz. Full duplex (except three-wire variant).
Hardware	Pull-up resistors required.	No pull-up resistors required.
BBB support	Fully supported with two external buses (plus 1 internal).	Fully supported with two buses. Only One slave selection pin on each bus.
Features	Can have multiple masters. Slaves can have addresses, acknowledge transfer, and can control the flow of data.	Simple and fast, but only one master device, no addressing, and no slave control of data flow.
Application	Intermittently accessed devices, e.g. real-time clock, EEPROMS.	For devices that provide data streams, e.g. ADCs.

Table 8.14. SPI modes. (Reproduced from *Exploring BeagleBone: Tools and Techniques for Building with Embedded Linux* by Derek Molloy 2018 with permission. Copyright 2019, John Wiley and Sons, Inc.)

Mode	Clock polarity (CPOL)	Clock phase (CPHA)
0	0 (LOW at idle)	0 (data captured on the rising edge of the clock signal)
1	0 (LOW at idle)	1 (data captured on the falling edge of the clock signal)
2	1 (HIGH at idle)	0 (data captured on the falling edge of the clock signal)
3	1 (HIGH at idle)	1 (data captured on the rising edge of the clock signal)

The clock can be either low or high at idle ('clock polarity') and data can be captured either on the rising or falling edge of the clock signal. This adds up to four different operating modes; which you use depends on the requirements of the slave. These modes are summarized in table 8.14, also from Molloy's book.

Part II

Lab manual

Chapter 9

Getting started

9.1 Use of the lab manual

This lab manual is meant to accompany the preceding text. The manual consists mainly of instructions and questions, not explanations. The intent is for this manual to guide you in your explorations of electronics. The text and the lab manual were designed for a one-semester course.

The student will notice that quite a bit of electronics jargon is used both in the text and in this lab manual. Although at first this may seem to be inconvenient, it is deliberate: one must learn the language of electronics in order to begin to understand the literature, for example component data sheets, equipment manuals, journal articles concerned with electronics apparatus, etc. One of the goals of the text and the lab manual is to develop, over time, a reasonably complete glossary of electronics jargon. Initially, this glossary will be woefully inadequate. It is requested that whenever the student runs across a term which he or she does not understand, the student should report this term as a candidate for inclusion in the glossary.

9.2 Maintaining a lab book

This may be the only course a physics student will take in which he or she will be expected to maintain a 'professional' style lab book. What is meant by a 'professional' style is one which has the following characteristics:
- The lab book must be generated in 'real-time'. That is, it is not some work of art which is put together, after the fact, from notes written on scraps of paper. As observations are made, they are entered directly into the book. As predictions are made, they are entered into the book, etc.
- The book must be bound (stitch binding, not spiral). Pages may not be cut out or removed.

- Pages must be numbered (by the student, if necessary) and a table of contents must be maintained at the front of the book.
- Blank pages are never left in the book (with the optional exception of the last page of a lab section: some professionals prefer that a new day's work always start on a right-hand side page. This option is left to the student, but if used, it must be used consistently throughout the book). A few blank pages should also be left at the very front of the lab book in order to leave room for an expanding table of contents. It is tempting to leave some blank pages in each lab to be filled in later with analysis of the data. *This is a definite no–no!* Even when subsequent data analysis will be done, pages are not left blank. When the analysis is eventually done, one just enters it onto the first available page. One then makes note of what data are being analyzed (for example by page number). One may then turn back to the page containing the analyzed data and make a (dated) marginal note indicating the page number containing the analysis, preferably initialized. While we're on this topic, if you've written something in your lab book and later discovered that it was in error, you'd follow the same procedure of annotating, dating, and initializing. *Note: These are the only cases where one may legitimately go back and add entries to a previous page.*
- Each new day's work should start on a new page. This page should be dated appropriately.
- The book must be written in ink. All entries, with the possible exception of graphs (which can be drawn in pencil) are written in ink. This includes text, schematics, and sketches. It should be noted that clarity may be improved with the use of high-lighters, multiple colors of ink etc. While these are not required, they can make for a better finished product. While real-time entry and the use of ink naturally makes for a somewhat less organized less readable product, the lab book must nevertheless be legible—or it will be useless.
- Mistakes should be struck out with a single line such that the erroneous entry is clearly marked as being incorrect, yet is still legible. Wherever appropriate the reason for mistakes should be explained.
- Units must always be indicated.
- Error must always be indicated. For example, a datum entry might read '11 mV $\pm$ 2 mV' or '67 mV $\pm$ 10%'. For measured data these errors must be entered in real-time; for quantities derived from measured data, the errors may be added later, at the time of the data analysis.

By properly maintaining a professional style lab book the student will first of all learn what a proper lab book is. Secondly, by the end of the semester the student should have a complete, self-contained record of all of their activities in this course —the errors as well as the successes will all be there. If or when the student ever needs to make use of the skills learned in this course, they need only look back through the lab book. When reviewing their lab book for the purposes of, say, building an integrator, the student should be able to avoid the pitfalls encountered while completing the corresponding lab. They should be able to identify the characteristics of a working circuit as well as the symptoms of a faulty device. Thus, the lab book will become a record of what to do and what not to do—and both can be of equal importance in the future.

9.3 Use of general laboratory equipment

9.3.1 The breadboard

A special device, known as a breadboard, will be used for most of the labs in this course. Critical in an educational setting, the breadboard is also very useful for pre-prototyping circuits in the 'professional' world. Breadboards come in a large variety of configurations. They serve as convenient solderless connections between, and holders of, various electrical components, including capacitors, resistors, switches, jumper wires, diodes, transistors, SIP and DIP configuration chips etc. The general configuration of the breadboards we use is as follows. As shown in figure 9.1, there are four pairs of parallel rows of holes running vertically, and one pair running

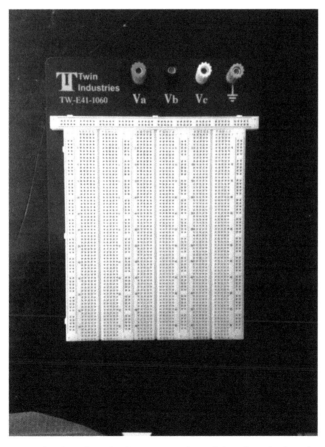

Figure 9.1. Photograph of a breadboard. We use a variety of breadboards, but they are all similarly configured.

horizontally along the top of the breadboard; one row in each pair is designated by a blue bar, the other by a red bar. All of the holes in a single line electrically connected. Although all of the holes in a given column are electrically connected, different columns (even those represented by the same color) are electrically isolated. These columns are very convenient to use as buses, or lines having a common value such as +12 V, ground, etc.

Most of the holes on the breadboard run in groups of five, horizontally across the board. For these holes, only the five holes in a group are electrically connected. Note there is no connection between the two groups of five which are separated by a (sunken) barrier on the board.

If you have any question as to which holes are connected to which, please ask your instructor (or teaching assistant). Because you will start using this board immediately in lab 9, it is imperative that you understand its layout.

9.3.2 Power supplies

We will use a variety of power supplies in this lab. Our workhorse is a single unit, shown in figure 9.2, that has +5 V and ±12 V. The outputs of our power supplies are 'banana connectors', which are color-coded as in table 9.1.

9.3.3 The function generator

Function generators are very useful sources of user-controlled input signals. They are capable of producing sine waves, triangle waves, and square waves with user-controlled amplitude and frequency. In addition, the function generator usually has a 'timing signal' or sync output which can be used to trigger a 'scope, or as a TTL output (for digital electronics applications). We will use 'stand-alone' function generators, as shown in figure 9.3. Their operation is straightforward and you will quickly come up to speed in their use.

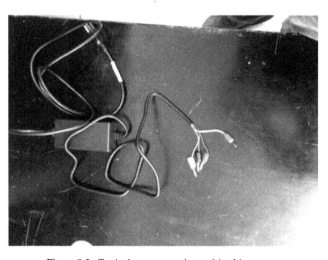

Figure 9.2. Typical power supply used in this course.

Table 9.1. Color coding of the power supply outputs. The voltages are with respect to ground.

Banana plug color	Output voltages
Red	+5 V
Black	+12 V
	−12 V
Green	0 V (Ground)

Figure 9.3. Some function generators.

9.3.4 The multimeter

The digital multimeter (DMM) is an indispensable tool (figure 9.4). With it we can accurately measure voltages, currents, resistances, and capacitances. The most important thing to remember about this device is that one must generally connect the leads differently when it is being used as a digital ammeter than when it is being used as a digital voltmeter or Ohm meter. Failure to connect the leads appropriately could cause damage to the meter! If you have any questions as to how the leads should be connected please ask the instructor or teaching assistant. You can conveniently interface your DMM to your circuit using either the probes that come with the meter, or using banana plugs fitted with alligator connectors.

9.3.5 The oscilloscope

Next to the breadboard, the single most used piece of apparatus used in this lab is the oscilloscope (figure 9.5). Since it is our experience that the typical student has never had to manipulate the controls of a real oscilloscope, a brief review will be presented here. If you are totally unfamiliar with the use of an oscilloscope, don't panic! You

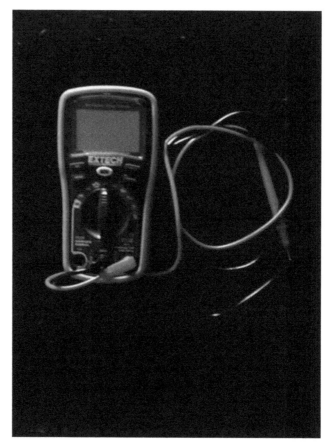

Figure 9.4. Typical digital multimeter.

Figure 9.5. Typical digital oscilloscope.

will find that with a bit of practice (and this course will give you plenty of that!) you will soon be handling your 'scope like a pro. Essentially, a 'scope may be thought of as a real-time voltage versus time plotting device. The vertical (voltage) and horizontal (time) scales are under the control of the user. Under some circumstances, the user may wish to 'plot' one voltage versus another. In this case, the 'scope is put into 'xy-mode'. The 'scopes used in this lab are four-trace devices. This means that four different voltage inputs may be simultaneously displayed on the same time axis. The scales and offsets of the four voltage inputs may be independently controlled. For the 'scopes used in our lab, the relative time between the traces cannot be shifted.

The student should notice that the voltage inputs may be set to be dc-coupled or ac-coupled. The former means that the input goes directly to the amplifier which controls the gain or vertical scale of that input. In the latter case, the input is connected to the amplifier via a series capacitor. Thus, the dc-component of the signal will be blocked. This can be useful when one is looking for a small time-varying component of a signal which carries a large dc-component. The downside of using ac-coupling is that one may be blissfully unaware that one has a signal with a dc-component. Also, depending on the frequency of the ac-component of the signal, the trace which appears on the screen may be severely attenuated or even distorted. Therefore, it is our strong recommendation to keep the scope input in dc-coupled mode, unless ac-coupling is specifically needed.

A final source of confusion with the operation of 'scopes has to do with triggering. As mentioned, a 'scope trace represents a plot of voltage versus time. Triggering determines the time at which the trace starts. More correctly, the trigger setting determines the voltage level for which the trace starts. This trigger level is set using a knob so-labeled. There are several trigger modes available on scopes. One useful mode is referred to as auto. In this mode a 'scope trace will always be present, with or without a voltage input. The trigger level knob still functions to some extent, but it is impossible to disable the triggering completely. This mode is useful when one cannot find the trace and would like to determine if it is merely off-scale, or if it cannot be seen because the 'scope is not triggering. The other commonly used trigger mode is called the normal mode and, as the name implies, is the perhaps the most useful mode after a trace has been found. When the 'scope is in the normal triggering mode the trigger level knob has total control over the trigger level, even to the extent that if the signal is not sufficiently large, the scope will not trigger at all—meaning that you will see no trace. The real advantage of being comfortable with the triggering features of a scope is that they allow the user to control the phase of the displayed trace, and to inhibit triggering on 'noise' in the signal.

The trigger source can be selected to be one of the input channels, line, or external. The line setting means that the 'scope will use the 60 Hz ac power as the trigger reference. This is not used very often, but can be useful when the signal is at line frequencies. The external setting refers to a signal which is supplied to the scope for the purpose of triggering, but cannot be displayed (unless also connected to one of the signal inputs).

You can conveniently connect your oscilloscope to your circuit using the 'scope probes that come with it. Note that these are color-coded to help you keep track of which trace represents the voltage in which part of the circuit. Notice that each of these probes has a switch that allows you to select between attenuations of ×10 or ×1. Keep in mind that the outer connector of a coax is at ground potential.

Therefore, for at least one of the probes you are using, the alligator clip must be connected to a ground of the circuit. Failure to do this could result in a distorted or electrically noise display on your 'scope.

9.4 Play!

This will be the one and only lab in which you will not be required to record your findings in a lab book. If you have not yet purchased a lab book, you'd better have it in hand by the next lab!

Connect your power supply's banana plug outputs to the corresponding jacks on your breadboard and then connect wires between these jacks and the different 'buses' on your breadboard. When you are satisfied that you have things wired up correctly, plug your power supply in at the plug strip.

Now, using more of the wires and your DMM, verify that the voltage differences are what you'd expect. Note that because the DMM is a 'floating' device, you can actually measure the voltage difference between any of the power supply outputs. (You can NOT do this with an oscilloscope because the outer co-ax connector of the 'scope must always be attached to a true ground!)

Plug in your function generator and 'scope. Connect the various function generator outputs to places on your breadboard and use your scope probes to look at the function generator signals. Play with the function generator's settings so that you can see what all the knobs do. Play with your 'scope settings as well. Can you control the point at which the signal is triggered? How about adjusting the amplitude (vertical scale) and time axis? Did you try triggering the scope on the function generator's sync?

IOP Publishing

Practical Analog, Digital, and Embedded Electronics for Scientists

Brett D DePaola

Chapter 10

R and C

10.1 Low-pass filter

Construct the circuit in figure 10.1, connecting the function generator to the input and one 'scope probe to each of the input and output. (We'll use this trick of looking at both the input and output simultaneously to see how our circuits modify the input signals. Heck, we've got lots of channels on our scopes, why not use them?!) Be sure that the function generator ground, the circuit ground, and the 'scope ground are connected to each other. (You may wish to use one of the breadboard buses for this.) Drive the circuit with a 500 Hz sine wave, and look at the output. Be sure to use the 'scope's dc input setting because at this low frequency the blocking capacitor of the scope's ac input could distort your measured waveform.

Input impedance

Here's your first chance to try getting used to quick extreme-case impedance calculations, rather than exact and frequency-dependent calculations.
1. What is the theoretical impedance presented to the signal generator by the circuit (assuming no load is connected at the circuit's output) at $f = 0$?
2. At infinite frequency?

Hint: Think about the capacitor as a frequency-dependent resistor.

Questions like these are important because your function generator is not an 'ideal' source: it has an output impedance of 50 Ω, instead of the 'ideal' value of 0. (This was intentional—and for a very good reason!)

What is the theoretical −3 dB frequency? Drive the circuit with a sine wave for a large range of frequencies. Make a log–log plot of output/input amplitudes and output–input phase shift versus frequency. Does the filter act as advertised?

doi:10.1088/978-0-7503-3491-4ch10

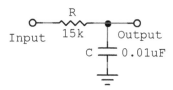

Figure 10.1. The low-pass filter.

In particular, do you see a 6 dB per octave roll off when well above the 3 dB point? Find $f_{-3\,dB}$ experimentally and compare this with your computed value.

±3 dB?

From here on we will follow standard engineering practice (and the text) and refer to 'the 3 dB point' and '$f_{3\,dB}$', not to the *minus* 3 dB point, or $f_{-3\,dB}$.

What is the measured limiting phase shift, both at very low frequencies and at very high frequencies? Does this match what you expected? In particular, measure the output at 10 and 20 times $f_{3\,dB}$. Measure the phase shift vs frequency. In particular, what is the phase shift for

$$f \ll f_{3\,dB} \tag{10.1a}$$

$$f = f_{3\,dB} \tag{10.1b}$$

$$f \gg f_{3\,dB}. \tag{10.1c}$$

Using a square wave, measure the decay time constant by determining the time for the output to drop to $1/e$ of its peak value. Does it equal the product RC? Don't forget to include error analysis. This includes your time measurement error, your resistor error, and your capacitor error.

Measure the time to climb from 0% to 63% (that is, up to $1 - 1/e$) of the peak value. Is it the same as the time to fall to 37%? It had better be! If not, figure out why not. Try varying the frequency of the square wave.

10.2 High-pass filter

Construct a high-pass filter with the components that you used for the low-pass, as in figure 10.2. Using sine waves of various frequencies, experimentally determine circuit's 3 dB point. How does this compare with theory? Remember to do your error analysis. Check out how the circuit treats sine waves: check to see if the output amplitude at low frequencies (well below the 3 dB point) is proportional to frequency. What is the limiting phase shift, both at very low frequencies and at very high frequencies?

There's much more you could learn about filters, but you can get a lot of mileage out of what we've covered here.

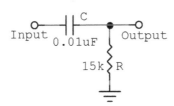

Figure 10.2. The *RC* high-pass filter.

10.3 Differentiator

Now drive the circuit with a square wave at 100 kHz. Is the circuit differentiating? Try a 100 kHz triangle wave. Try a sine.

Can you show that this is only an approximate differentiator? How do you make the circuit fail the condition of equation (2.17)?

'High-pass filter'versus'differentiator'
   The same circuit that we called a high-pass filter seems also to be a differentiator. So which is it?! Try to convince yourself that there is no inconsistency here.

10.4 Integrator

Swap the R and C back again to re-create the low-pass filter of figure 10.1, and described in section 2.3 of the text as an integrator. Drive it with a 100 kHz square wave. Is the circuit's output what you expected?

Now drive the circuit with a triangle wave. Is the result what you expected? Why/why not?

Try dropping the frequency to see if you can show that this is only an approximate integrator. Are we violating the condition of equation (2.21)?

In a differentiator, an *RC* product that is too large tends to violate this restriction. If you are extra curious, you may want to look again at the differentiator of lab 10.3, but this time increase *RC* by a factor of about 1000. The scope trace for the 'derivative' of a square wave should get ugly. Now try the derivative of a triangle wave under these RC conditions.

When we meet operational amplifiers in lecture and lab 4, we will see how to do calculus without the restrictions of these *RC* circuits—but don't forget: these circuits were trivial: just a resistor and a cap!

IOP Publishing

Practical Analog, Digital, and Embedded Electronics for Scientists

Brett D DePaola

Chapter 11

Transistors

11.1 Emitter follower

Wire up an NPN transistor as an emitter follower (figure 11.1), as shown in figure 11.2. Drive the follower with a sine wave that is symmetrical about zero volts. Why is half the signal missing? If you turn up the waveform amplitude you may begin to see bumps below ground. How do you explain these?

Now try connecting the emitter resistor to -12 V instead of to ground, and look at the output. Explain the improvement.

11.2 Input and output impedance of follower

Review the text section 1.4.2 and then measure Z_{in} and Z_{out} for the follower in figure 11.3. Note the changed base resistor.

Measure Z_{in}, which here is the impedance looking into the transistor's base, by looking alternately at both sides of the 10k input resistor. For this measurement the 3.3k emitter resistor is also the 'load'. Note that a much better measurement would be to place a much larger resister in place of the 10k and measure the voltage on either side of it. Why? What's wrong with just using the 10k for this measurement? Use a small signal. Does the result make sense? (See lecture section 3.3.2.) Now try the measurement using a 'sensible' resistor value, instead of the 10k.

Measure Z_{out}, the output impedance of the follower, by connecting a 1k load to the output and observing the drop in output signal amplitude (the voltage at the emitter). For this, use a small input signal, less than a volt. Use a blocking capacitor as shown in the figure. In this case you could get away with omitting the blocking cap, but often you could not. Why? Hint: what does a 'blocking' capacitor block?

Suggestion for measurement of Z_{out}: if you view the emitter follower's output as a signal source in series with $Z_{out,Thevenin}$, then the 1k load forms a divider at signal

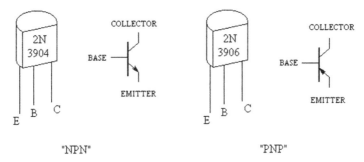

Figure 11.1. Schematics and pinouts for a popular NPN and PNP transistor.

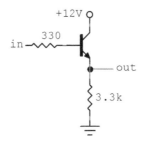

Figure 11.2. A simple emitter follower circuit.

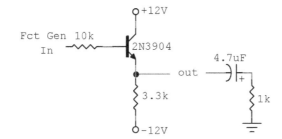

Figure 11.3. Measuring the output impedance of an emitter follower.

frequencies, where the impedance of the blocking capacitor is negligibly small. (But verify that at the frequency you are using, $Z_C \ll 1k$.)

When you have measured Z_{in} and Z_{out}, infer your transistor's β (a.k.a. h_{FE}).

11.3 Single-supply follower

Build the single-supply follower of figure 11.4. This circuit comes from the example in the lecture, section 3.3.2. Check to see if it can generate large output swings before the onset of 'clipping'. Verify that the quiescent voltage is appropriate.

11.4 Push–pull follower

The push–pull circuit is a popular trick to current-boost a bipolar signal, but it does suffer from 'crossover distortion'. (If you've heard this term before, you're probably

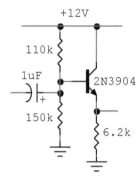

Figure 11.4. A single-supply emitter follower for a bipolar signal.

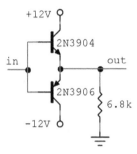

Figure 11.5. A very simple push–pull follower.

an audio buff who owns a tube-based stereo system.) Check it out by building the push–pull output stage shown in figure 11.5. (Note that this circuit is *not* the best push–pull you could build!)

Drive the circuit with sine waves of at least a few volts amplitude in the neighborhood of 1 kHz. Be sure the offset control of the function generator is set to zero. Look closely at the output. Try running the amplitude up and down. Play with the dc offset control. Describe in detail what you observe. See if you can explain it.

11.5 Common emitter amplifier

Wire up the common emitter amplifier shown in figure 11.6. What is the voltage gain? What should it be? Is the quiescent point reasonable? What should the amplifier's low frequency 3 dB point be? Check it. Measure the circuit's input and output impedances, much as you did for the emitter follower. Here you *will* need to use the blocking capacitor. Why?

11.6 Bypassed emitter amplifier

Wire up the circuit in figure 11.7. Is the quiescent voltage appropriate? Drive the circuit with a small triangle wave at 10 kHz. You'll have to turn the amplitude way down to avoid clipping. What is the circuit's gain? Is this reasonable? Why is the

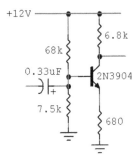

Figure 11.6. A single-supply common emitter amplifier for a bipolar signal.

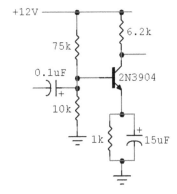

Figure 11.7. A bypassed emitter amplifier.

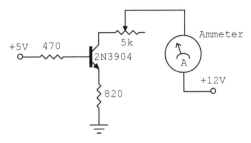

Figure 11.8. A current sink based on an NPN transistor.

output such a poor replica of the input? (This sort of distortion is called 'barn roof'.) What's going on? (Hint: Think about r_e.)

Now remove the 15 μF capacitor and increase the drive amplitude. Now how does the output look? Measure the voltage gain. Again, is it reasonable? Why or why not?

11.7 Current source (sink)

Construct the current source shown in figure 11.8 (or, more precisely, a 'current sink' since the potentiometer is the load). Slowly vary the 5k variable load, and look for changes in current measured by the DMM. What happens at the maximum resistance? Explain your observations in terms of the compliance of the current source. How could you modify the circuit to give constant current for even larger load resistances?

IOP Publishing

Practical Analog, Digital, and Embedded Electronics for Scientists

Brett D DePaola

Chapter 12

Op amps I

12.1 Open-loop test circuit

Before building your first op amp circuit, I remind you of something that should be obvious: the op amp always needs power. It is applied at two pins, the $+V_{cc}$ and the $-V_{ee}$. In the case of the LF411, the op amp used in lab 12, these are pins 7 and 4, respectively. I remind you of this because circuit diagrams nearly always omit the power connections.

Slowly turn the pot for the circuit in figure 12.1 while watching the output voltage on either your 'scope or DMM. Are you able to find a spot where the output has not gone to the rails? ('rail' is jargon for 'the supply voltage'). Is the behavior consistent with an open-loop gain of 2×10^5? That is, how well would you have to control the potentiometer in order *not* to drive the output to the rails? A part in 100? A part in 10^4?

12.2 Inverting amplifier

Construct the inverting amplifier drawn in figure 12.2. Drive the amplifier with a 1 kHz sine wave. What is the gain? How large a signal can you get out before you begin to clip? How about linearity? You can check this by inputting a triangle wave and, putting your 'scope in invert mode, comparing the input to the output signals. Now check the speed of the op amp using sine waves of different frequencies. Note that at some fairly high frequency the amplifier ceases to work well: sine-in does not produce sine-out.

Now drive the circuit with a sine wave at 1 kHz again. Measure the input impedance of this amplifier circuit by adding 1k in series with the input. *In this and other circuits when we say to add something to the input, we mean the input of the entire circuit, not the input to the op amp.* Measure the output impedance (or try to measure it, anyway). Why is no blocking capacitor needed? You should expect to

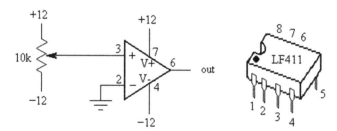

Figure 12.1. Left: Op amp wired for open-loop operation. Right: The LF411 showing the numbering of a DIP (dual inline package) style chip.

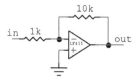

Figure 12.2. The classic inverting amplifier. Pin 3 is still the *non-inverting* input!

fail here: you probably can do no more than confirm that Z_{out} is very low. Do not mistake the effect of the op amp's limited current output for high Z_{out}. You will have to keep the signal quite small here to avoid running into this current limit. Basically, the current is limited to ±25 mA over an output voltage range of ±10 V, and you'll get less current if you push the output to swing close to either rail.

12.3 Non-inverting amplifier

Wire up the non-inverting amplifier shown in figure 12.3. Measure the voltage gain. Is this what you expected? See if you can measure the input and output impedances. How do these compare with those of the non-inverting amplifier you just built?

12.4 Follower

Build the follower shown in figure 12.4. Check out its performance (gain, speed, etc). Don't bother to measure Z_{in} and Z_{out} since this is a special case of the non-inverting amplifier you built earlier. What possible use could this simple circuit have?! (And it *is* useful!)

12.5 Current source

Build the op amp current source shown in figure 12.5. What should the current be? Vary the load pot and watch the current, using a DMM.

Technically, this is a sink not a source because neither side of the load is connected to ground. Furthermore, it is limited by the amount of current that an op amp can source. Finally, being op amp based, this source cannot respond to microsecond changes in the impedance. Nevertheless, this source is far more precise and stable than the transistor source built earlier.

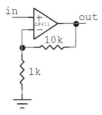

Figure 12.3. Non-inverting amplifier.

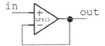

Figure 12.4. The follower or buffer. This is a special case of the non-inverting amplifier in figure 12.3.

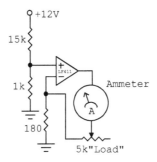

Figure 12.5. Current sink.

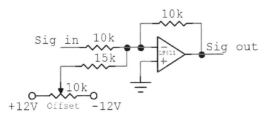

Figure 12.6. Summing amplifier. Here, the signal gain is −1, and the offset range is ±8 V.

12.6 Summing amplifier

The circuit in figure 12.6 sums a DC level with the input signal. Thus, it lets you add a DC offset to a signal. *Make sure your 'scope is not in ac coupling mode.* In practice this is an extremely useful circuit. Check to see that your offset range and gains are as predicted.

12.7 Push–pull follower

Build the circuit shown in figure 12.7. Be very careful to orient your transistors correctly! The 2N3904 and 2N3906 have identical pinouts, but in the schematic they are displayed as if they are mirror imaged. They are not. Failure to orient them correctly could result in two fried transistors! Drive the circuit with a 1 kHz sine wave. Simultaneously look at the input, the output of the op amp and the output of the push–pull stage, making sure you have at least a few volts of output. You should see classic crossover distortion at the emitters. Now remove the 100k feedback resistor from the op amp's output and instead, attach it to the emitters. (It's easiest if you have the resistor going to some 'neutral' hole in the bread board, and then use a wire to attach it to either the op amp output of the push–pull output.) You should see a huge reduction in the crossover distortion. *With the amplitude turned way down* replace the 1k load resistor with a speaker. Slowly turn up the function generator's amplitude until the sound is audible. *Over-driving the speaker will fry those tiny transistors*! Listen to the difference in sound quality as you move the 100k resistor's feedback back and forth from the op amp's output to the emitters.

12.8 Integrator

Construct the active integrator shown in figure 12.8. Try driving it with a 1 kHz square wave. This circuit is sensitive to small dc offsets of the input waveform. (Why? What is its gain at dc?). You will probably have to tweak the function generator's OFFSET control to keep the output from going to the rail. How does the amplitude of the resulting triangle wave compared to what it should be, given the components used in this circuit?

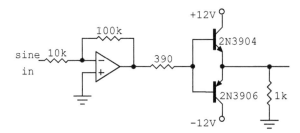

Figure 12.7. Push–pull follower. This is no better than the one in lab 11. It would be better if the feedback came from the transistors' emitters!

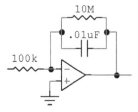

Figure 12.8. The integrator. This is greatly improved over the simple *RC* integrator of lab 10.

Why do we have that 10M resistor in there? Try removing it. Try different waveforms at the input to see if you are really integrating.

12.9 Differentiator

Build the differentiator in figure 12.9. Try driving it with a 1 kHz triangle wave. For reasons of stability, we actually need to integrate at high frequencies—hence the 100 pF cap and the 1k resistor. Near what frequencies would you expect this circuit to act as an integrator?

12.10 Active rectifier

Construct the active half-wave rectifier shown in figure 12.10. Try it with a 10 kHz sine wave. See the glitch on the output? Put a second probe on the output of the op amp. Does this help you figure out the origins of the glitch?

12.11 Improved active rectifier

To fix this problem, build the circuit shown in figure 12.11. The glitch should be much diminished. Look at the op amp output and compare it to the previous circuit's op amp output. Does this help you explain the improved performance?

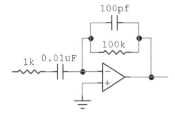

Figure 12.9. The differentiator. This is a big improvement over the *RC* differentiator in lab 10.

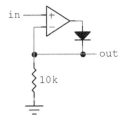

Figure 12.10. The active rectifier. (This one does not work very well.)

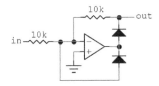

Figure 12.11. A greatly improved rectifier.

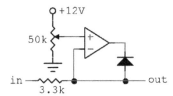

Figure 12.12. The active clamp.

12.12 Active clamp

Build the variable active clamp circuit shown in figure 12.12. Drive the circuit with a 1 kHz sine wave. What do you think the output impedance of this circuit is? (You need not measure it.) What happens when you go to much higher frequencies? What happens if you reverse the diode? Explain.

Chapter 13

Op amps II: positive feedback, good and bad

Until now we have treated positive feedback as something to avoid at all costs. In this lab we'll see that under some circumstances, positive feedback can be useful: it can improve the performance of a comparator and it can be combined with negative feedback to make a relaxation oscillator. We'll also combine positive and negative feedback to produce the most difficult of all waveforms to construct: the sine wave. We'll also explore inadvertent positive feedback. This is the worst kind because it can be difficult to find, and even more difficult to fix.

13.1 Comparators

Comparators work best with positive feedback. But before we show you these good circuits, let's look at two poor comparator circuits: one using an op amp, the other using a special-purpose comparator chip. These circuits will perform poorly; they will help you to see what's good about the improved comparator that does use positive feedback.

13.1.1 Defective comparators: open-loop

Op amp as comparator
You will recognize this 'comparator' circuit as the very first op amp circuit you wired, where the point was just to show you the 'astounding' high gain of the device (figure 13.1). In that first glimpse of the op amp, that excessive gain probably looked useless. Here, when we view the circuit as a comparator, the very high gain and the 'pinned' output are what we want.

Drive the circuit with a sine wave at around 100 kHz, and notice that the output 'square wave' output is not as square as one would hope. Why not?

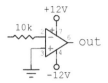

Figure 13.1. Using a 'signal op amp' as a comparator with no feedback.

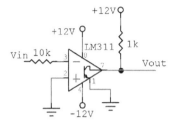

Figure 13.2. The LM311, a special-purpose comparator chip. This one is wired up with no feedback.

Special-purpose comparator IC: the LM311

Now substitute a '311 comparator for the '411. (The pinouts are not the same!) You will notice that the output stage looks funny: it is not like an ordinary op amp's which can source and sink a current. Rather, two pins that are internally connected to the collector and emitter of a built-in transistor, are used to sink a signal. This so-called *open collector* arrangement can do nothing on its own; the user must supply a separate voltage source and a pull-up resistor. When the transistor is 'on', V_{out} is effectively connected to pin 1 (ground in the circuit of figure 13.2); when the transistor is 'off', the connection to pin 1 is no longer open and V_{out} goes to the 'pull-up voltage'. Open collector outputs are not essential for a comparator, but is a nice feature because this arrangement allows the user to decide the upper and lower levels of the output, independent of the comparator's supply voltages. In the circuits below, you will keep the top of the swing at +12 V, but you will take advantage of your control over the bottom of the swing: at first you will set it to ground, later to −12 V. Does the '311 perform better than the '411 as a comparator? If so, in what way?

Oscillations

A side-effect of the '311's fast response is its readiness to oscillate when given a 'close question'—a small voltage difference between its inputs. Try to tease your 311 into oscillation, by feeding it a sine wave with a gentle slope. With some tinkering you can produce some very weird waveforms Give it a try and see what you can come up with. Don't forget to record what you get and how you got it!

13.1.2 Using feedback with a comparator: hysteresis

The positive feedback used in the circuit of figure 13.3 will eliminate those pretty but harmful oscillations by introducing *hysteresis*. Predict the thresholds of the circuit

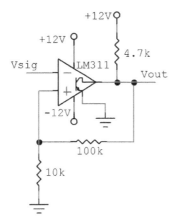

Figure 13.3. A comparator wired with positive feedback that gives it hysteresis.

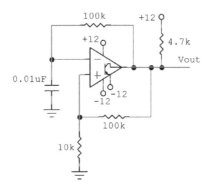

Figure 13.4. Classic *RC* relaxation oscillator.

and then try it out. (See the text, section 5.2.1.) Observe the rapid transitions at the output, independent of the input waveform frequency.

Reconnect the so-called 'Ground' pin of the '311 (poorly named!) to −12 V. This pin is labeled 'Ground' because that is where it is most often connected. But since it is just the emitter of a transistor, you can connect it wherever you like—so long as you do not violate base–emitter voltage maxima. Perhaps you can now see why the chip's designers brought out this pin, as well as why they provided an open collector output.

13.2 The *RC* relaxation oscillator

Now connect an *RC* network from the output to the comparator's inverting input, as shown in figure 13.4. Predict the frequency of oscillation, and then compare your prediction with what you observe. (See lecture section 5.2.2.)

13.3 *RC* relaxation oscillator using the 7555

The 555 and its derivatives have made the design of moderate-frequency oscillators easy. There is seldom any reason to design an oscillator from scratch, using an op amp as we did in the proceeding exercise. The 7555 is an improved 555, made with CMOS technology. It runs up to 500 kHz (versus 100 kHz for the 555), and its very high input impedances and rail-to-rail output swings can simplify designs.

13.3.1 Square waves with the 7555

Figure 13.5 is a textbook use of the 7555. Look at the output. Is the frequency correctly predicted by

$$f = [0.7C(R_A + 2R_B)]^{-1}?\qquad(13.1)$$

Now look at the waveform *on the capacitor*. What voltage levels does it run between? Does this make sense?

Now replace R_B with a short circuit. (Place a wire in parallel with R_B.) What do you expect to see at the capacitor? At the output?

An alternative astable circuit
The 7555 can produce a true 50% duty-cycle square wave if you invent a scheme that lets it charge and discharge the capacitor through a single resistor. See if you can draw such a design, and then try it out. Do *not* allow a short-circuit from V_{cc} to ground via *D*! Here's a hint for one solution: the 7555 has a clean rail-to-rail output. Make use of this!

Derive and then verify your circuit's frequency. If it's the same as mine, it should be

$$f = [1.4RC]^{-1},\qquad(13.2)$$

which is the same as for the 'classic' configuration, except that it eliminates the complication of the different charge and discharge paths. Finally, try $V_{cc} = +5$ V

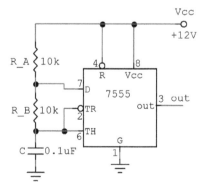

Figure 13.5. The 7555 wired up as a rectangular pulse *RC* relaxation oscillator.

with either of your circuits to verify that the output frequency is independent of the supply voltage.

13.3.2 Sawtooth oscillator

Use the 7555 to produce a sawtooth wave by replacing R_A and R_B of the first circuit with a current source, as in figure 13.6. *Look at the waveform on the capacitor.* What should the frequency be? Measure it. For this circuit, the output is taken from the top of the capacitor—which means in practice you'll probably want to feed it through an op amp buffer. Predict what the 'output' waveform (pin 3) should look like? Were you correct?

13.4 Sine wave oscillator: Wien bridge

Surprisingly, the sine wave is one of the most difficult electronic waveforms to synthesize. We have found that even chips specially designed to produce sine waves are often not good enough. The Wien-bridge oscillator makes a sine by cleverly adjusting its gain so as to prevent clipping (which would occur if gain were too high) while keeping the oscillation from dying away (which would occur if gain were too low) (figure 13.7). The frequency favored by the positive feedback network should be $1/(2\pi RC)$. See whether your oscillator runs at this predicted frequency.

At this frequency, the signal which is fed back should be in phase with the output, and 1/3 the amplitude of V_{out}. The negative feedback adjusts the gain, exploiting the lamp's current-dependent resistance. (The lamp is rated at 14 mA @ 10 V.) Convince yourself that the sense in which the lamp's resistance varies tends to stabilize gain at the necessary value. What gain is necessary to sustain oscillations without clipping?

13.5 Op amp instability: phase shift can make an op amp oscillate

Low-pass filter in the feedback loop

The circuit in figure 13.8 includes a capacitor you are not likely to install (though you might in a sample-and-hold): see section 4.2.6. The truly insidious cases are where the capacitance is part of the load, for example when you try to drive a signal through a long cable.

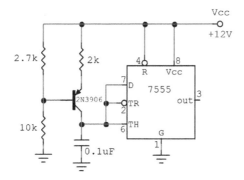

Figure 13.6. The 7555 wired up as a sawtooth oscillator.

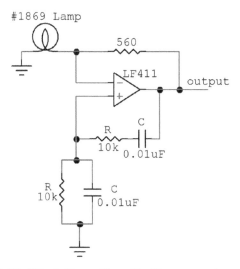

Figure 13.7. The Wien-bridge oscillator. You'll never see a better sine wave!

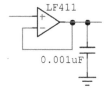

Figure 13.8. A truly evil stealth oscillator!

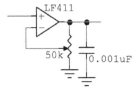

Figure 13.9. Killing the oscillation by reducing the feedback.

This circuit may not oscillate at first. If it does not, drive it with a square wave. That should start it, and once started it is likely to continue even when you turn off the function generator, or change to a sine wave.

Remedy: shrink the disturbance fed back

Modify the follower circuit slightly by inserting a 50k pot in the feedback path (figure 13.9). Begin with the pot turned so as to feed the entire output signal back (gain = 1; this is just the follower again). Again set the circuit oscillating, with a square wave input if necessary.

Now gradually turn the pot so as to shrink the fraction of V_{out} that is fed back. What does do to the gain? When the oscillation stops, feed it a small square wave again, making sure the output does not saturate. If you see what looks like ringing on the edges of the square wave, continue to shrink the fraction of V_{out} that is fed back until that ringing stops.

The point is that the stability of an amplifier circuit depends on the gain (and phase) of the feedback. Understanding this is critical in eliminating unwanted oscillations in circuits you design.

IOP Publishing

Practical Analog, Digital, and Embedded Electronics for Scientists

Brett D DePaola

Chapter 14

Digital gates: combinational and sequential logic

14.1 Gates and truth tables

Using the appropriate gates and LEDs (remembering to use at least a 1k resistor in series with the LED !!) verify the truth tables for the three basic gates, the OR, the AND, and the NOT. You can find the pinouts in lab–appendix I. Don't forget to connect +5 V and Ground to each chip—these things require power to operate!

Verify DeMorgan's theorem for the 'negative true' NOR gate by generating a truth table for it, and showing it to be equivalent to a 'positive true' NAND gate.

Show how to make an inverter from a single NAND gate. Do the same for a single NOR gate. Why might this be a useful trick?

Using a single quad-NAND chip, and a single hex-inverter chip, construct an XOR. Verify its operation by constructing a truth table for it.

14.2 Multiplexer

The 74LS151 is an 'eight-input multiplexer'. Investigate its operation by setting up an address on its A, B, and C inputs, and monitoring the output pin using an LED. Don't forget the resistor !! See which of the inputs are 'passed'. Change the address several times to verify that the '151 is operating as expected. Don't forget to ground the STROBE (ENABLE) pin. HINT: Instead of constantly switching wires, use a four- or eight- package of 'DIP switches'. (Don't forget to use pull–up or pull – down resistors! These are conveniently available in a DIP package.)

The multiplexer may also be used as a four-input 'arbitrary programmable logic' chip. Build the following circuit and verify that it does, indeed, tell which months have 31 days (figure 14.1). Explain how the circuit works. Come up with your own four-input arbitrary logic problem, set up the truth table, and then build and test the circuit. (See the lecture section 6.4.1.) Don't forget to connect power and ground.

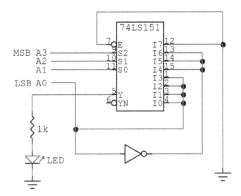

Figure 14.1. Using a multiplexer (MUX) as an arbitrary truth table. This one tells which months have 31 days.

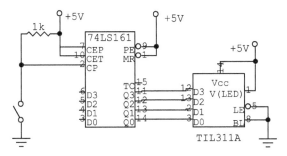

Figure 14.2. A synchronous counter with an LED display. Without a debounce, the counter will skip.

14.3 Sequential logic: *JK* flip–flop

Examine the function of a 74LS107 dual JK flip–flop. (It's described in section 6.5.3 of the text.) Clock the flip–flop with positive pulses from the function generator, set to its lowest frequency. Try all four patterns of J and K, with RESET connected to V_{cc}, and verify the truth table shown in table 6.11 in the text. Now try the RESET input. Notice how the '107 in flip–flop mode ($J = K = 1$) acts as a divide-by-2 device. That is, the frequency of the flip–flop output is half the frequency of the clock input. Also take notice of the duty cycle (on-time divided by period).

Now cascade the two flip–flops in the package: connect the output of the first stage, Q1, to the clock input of the second stage. Connect J and K for toggling ($J = K = 1$). Display the states of the two flip–flops on separate channels of the 'scope. This is a simple divide-by-4 circuit. Clearly you can extend this to divide by 2^n.

14.4 Debouncing

Try clocking a binary counter directly from a switch as in figure 14.2. What does the 1k resistor do? Why doesn't the counter function correctly when driven this way? Fix the problem by adding the debounce circuit shown in figure 14.3. From DeMorgan's theorem (text, section 6.3.1) you can see that the gates in figure 14.3 are actually

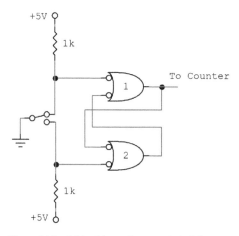

Figure 14.3. A bistable used as a switch debounce.

NANDs. With this addition to the counting circuit, the counter should step one count per cycle of the switch.

14.5 D-type flip–flop

Try a 74LS74 dual D-type flip–flop. Tie both SET and RESET to V_{cc}, then check that the data at the D input is clocked through to the Q output *on the rising edge of the clock*. Now connect the output, Q, to the input, D, to make a toggling flip–flop. Make sure that this works.

The 74LS74 has both SET and RESET inputs. Try to see which is 'the boss' over the other inputs by connecting one, then the other, to ground. Notice that, like most 'control' inputs in the digital world, you *assert* an input by connecting it to 'low' (ground) rather than 'high' (+5 V).

It's easy to use flip–flops or counters to build divide-by-2^n circuits, but how about dividing your frequency by something else? Figure 14.4 shows a divide-by-3 circuit. Wire it up and see if it works as advertised. For the NOR gate you can either use a 74LS02 (quad two-input NOR chip) or a 74LS00 (quad two-input NAND chip). Even if you don't use the 74LS00 chip, how would you wire it up to serve as a NOR? This sort of trick can be invaluable because it allows you the flexibility of more efficiently using all the gates on your board, rather than adding new chips that are not needed.

Sketch the signals seen at Q_1, Q_2 and the input in your lab book and figure out how this divide-by-3 circuit works its magic.

14.6 Programmable divide-by-N counter

The 74LS160-3 series of counters are 4 bit synchronous binary (divide-by-16) and decade (divide-by-10) counters with either synchronous or master (asynchronous) resets. (By 'synchronous' we mean that the change occurs upon receipt of the clock edge.) All of these devices have the feature of direct parallel synchronous loading

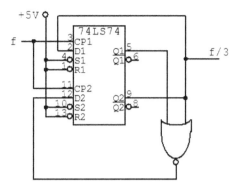

Figure 14.4. A pair of D-type flip–flops used as a divide by three circuit.

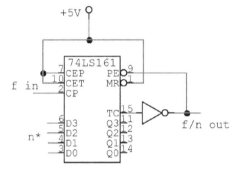

Figure 14.5. Programmable divide-by-N counter.

from inputs D_0 to D_3 enabled by *PE*, 'parallel load enable'. This means that you need not start your counting at 0000, but at any 4 bit binary number you choose.

The uses for a binary counter are pretty obvious. Figure 14.5 shows an unusual way to use a counter: a divide-by-N, where N can be any integer. Try wiring it up, supplying the 2's complement of N at the 'starting inputs'. Try the circuit out for several values of N.

Chapter 15

Digital–analog, analog–digital, and phase-locked loops

15.1 Digital–analog conversion

We're going to demonstrate a DAC (digital to analog converter) by converting the output of a digital counter into an analog signal. Therefore, we'll start by building an up/down counter. Start by hooking up a 74LS191, which is a 4 bit synchronous binary up/down counter. See appendix I for the pin-outs. You should tie the ENABLE input LOW and the 'parallel LOAD' HIGH. (We do *not* want to do a parallel load.) Now connect the outputs to the TIL311 hexadecimal display chip so that we can see what our digital signal value is. Finally, clock the '191 from a debounced push button switch. (Push button switches can be wired such that they are 'normally HIGH' or 'normally LOW'. Use the former.) You use the U/D input to the '191 to control whether the chip is counting up or counting down. Check to see that your counter works in both up and down modes. You should document in your lab book whether a HIGH value to the U/D input makes your counter count UP or DOWN.

Once you are certain that your counter works correctly, use its output to drive a 1408 DAC as in figure 15.1. Connect the counter's four output bits to the most significant input bits (i.e. pins 8,7,6,5) of the DAC Make sure you get the order correct. Now clock the 74LS191 with a 1 kHz TTL signal from the function generator. What waveform do you think you should you see at the DAC output? Did you predict correctly? Now reverse the direction of the counter (the U/D input to the counter) to get the other 'staircase' wave. How about the vertical step sizes: are they reasonable? Make a quantitative calculation of what they should be and compare with what you are measuring.

Add a second 74LS191 as shown in figure 15.2. RCO ('ripple carry output') is used to generate the carry: pin 13 is LOW during the last count of the sequence

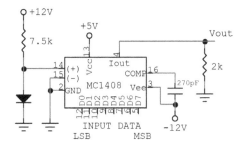

Figure 15.1. The 1408 DAC, wired up to generate a negative voltage from a digital input.

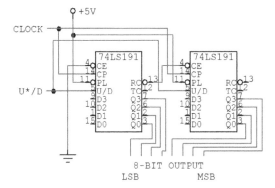

Figure 15.2. Setting up a cascaded ripple counter.

(count 15 in count-up mode, count 0 in count-down mode); this is tied to the count ENABLE of the next stage which then steps synchronously at the next clock pulse. Tie all the bits to the 1408—paying attention to their order! Set the clock to 10 kHz, and look at the new 'staircase' wave, which is now more like a ramp because of the increased resolution (8 bits compared to 4).

15.2 Tracking analog–digital converter

To do analog to digital conversion we could grab an ADC chip and that would be that. But if we add a comparator circuit to our DAC circuit, we can make a *tracking* ADC as shown in figure 15.3. The 2.5k pot simulates an analog input. The '311 compares this with the DAC's output and clocks the counter up or down as needed to make it agree with the analog input. The counter's state is then the digital output of the DAC For this lab, the digital output simply goes to a display. But in a real application, this digital output could go to a computer, or other digital device.

Display the four *most significant* (the bits that matter the most!) bits on a Texas Instruments TIL311 decoded LED display as shown. Run the 2.5k pot slowly up and down through its range. What happens at the ends? Is this reasonable?

Now look at the voltage output of the '1408. This should always be jumping back and forth between two adjacent levels of the staircase. When you turn the pot rapidly you should see larger jumps. But these only occur while you are actually turning the

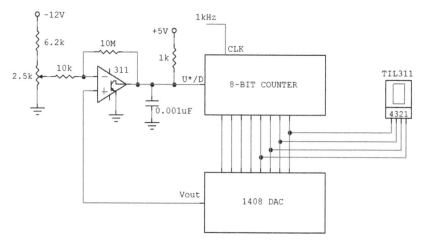

Figure 15.3. Using an ADC with a comparator to create a tracking DAC.

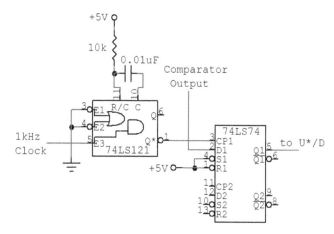

Figure 15.4. Using a one-shot to fix the jumpiness in the tracking ADC of figure 15.3.

pot. This is strange because you might expect that the DAC should always ramp toward a value that represents the current value on the pot's wiper.

The jumps you see occur when the U/D input level changes while the clock is LOW. But the specification of the 74LS191 says that the U/D and ENABLE inputs must be *stable* during the *entire time* that the clock is LOW. However, this rule can be broken if the comparator output changes between clock edges.

If you have trouble seeing this unwanted jumping, disconnect the four least significant bits driving the '1408. Now there will be only 16 (2^4) levels on the 'scope, and the DAC output will always be oscillating between two of them.

A fix for this 'jumping' problem is shown in figure 15.4. The comparator's output is sampled with an edge-triggered flip–flop (the 74LS74) at a time when the clock is *guaranteed* to be HIGH. Monostable multivibrators (or one-shots, see the text, section 6.8) output a pulse of programmable width. In the case of the 74LS121, the pulse width is given by $t_w = 0.7RC$. The resistor and capacitor are attached to the '121 as shown in the figure. Here, the one-shot is used to delay the (rising) clocking edge by 70 μs to allow the DAC output and comparator to settle.

Try the cure. If things don't work at first, check that the one-shot is working. The ADC output should now be free from glitches.

15.3 Phase-locked loop: frequency multiplier

You have already learned how to create a device which divides a frequency. For example, a simple flip–flop can be used as a divide-by-2 device; a counter as a divide-by-2^n device, and in lab 14.6 you built a divide-by-N device. You may find it useful to generate a signal having N *times* an input frequency. This is most conveniently done with a phase-locked loop (PLL). In the circuit you will build here, you will generate a 2^N multiple of 10 Hz.

Construct the circuit shown in figure 15.5. The phase detector and VCO are drawn as separate blocks, but note that they are within one '4046 chip; you do not need two '4046s. The VCO's frequency is determined by the 470 pF capacitor, the 47k resistor, and the vin input; the last takes values from 0 to Vcc, here 5 V. A second resistor could also be connected from pin 12 to ground. In principle, the minimum and maximum output frequencies of the VCO are given by

$$f_{min} = [R_2(C + 32pF)]^{-1} \qquad (15.1a)$$

$$f_{max} = f_{min} + [R_1(C + 32pF)]^{-1}, \qquad (15.1b)$$

where R_1 and R_2 are the resistors from pins 11 and 12 to ground, respectively.

For $R_2 = \infty$, $f_{min} = 0$; for $R_1 = 47$k and $C = 470$ pF, $f_{max} = 42.4$ kHz. Therefore, in principle, the VCO will output a 50% duty cycle TTL wave ranging from 0 Hz to

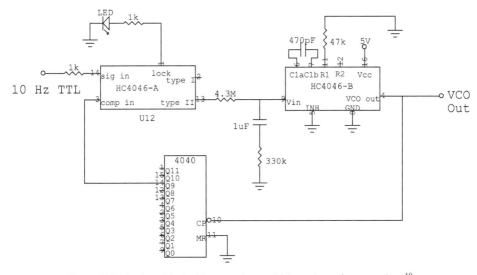

Figure 15.5. A phased-locked loop used to multiply an input frequency by 2^{10}.

42 kHz as vin ranges from 0 V to 5 V (Vcc). However, this particular VCO is famous for not rigidly following the the formulae of equations (15.1). Sometimes trial and error are required.

We're using the '4040 counter as a divide-by-2^N device. Using the Q_n output divides the frequency of the '4040's input by 2^{n+1}. Thus, using the Q_9 output means you are dividing the '4040's input by 1024. Then, the '4046 will try to produce a frequency of 1024×10 Hz so that, when divided down by the '4040, it matches to the input frequency.

As discussed in the text's discussion of PLLs, lecture section 7.3, a critical part of a PLL is the integration stage that lies between the phase detector and the VCO. It must react fast enough to respond to frequency changes at either of the phase detector's inputs, but must integrate on a long enough time scale to provide stability.

Try feeding a 10 Hz TTL signal to the sig in of the HC4046 phase detector and see what the VCO output looks like. Observe the LED: it will be off or flashing while the PLL is trying to lock, but should be solid red once the PLL has managed to lock.

Try connecting the comp in to different outputs of the '4040 to see the impressive locking range (really the impressive frequency range of the VCO). Pick a 'middle Q' and now try to tax the PLL by rapidly jumping the sig in frequency. At large enough function generator frequencies, you'll exceed the VCO's possible output frequency (for those values of R_1 and C) and it will fail to lock.

Replace the 330k resistor with something smaller, like a 33k. Now starting from a 10 Hz signal from the function generator, try jumping the frequency again. How does the choice of resistor 'downstream' of the integration capacitor affect how quickly the PLL can re-lock?

Go back to a 330k resistor and watch the phase detector's output (pin 13) as PLL tries again to lock. Most likely it won't lock because the scope's input impedance is too low. Try putting an op-amp buffer between pin 13 and the scope probe. What does that signal look like? Do you still see the spikes? Are they as bad, or as frequent, as without the buffer?

Those spikes should still exist because of the time difference (phase) between the 'master' signal and the replica. That is, those are correction signals because the poor phase detector is working hard to make the phase difference zero.

Try making the PLL's life easier by using Q_1 in the feedback. How does the phase difference look? How about those spikes?

Gosh, I could play all day with a PLL! Think about what other things you could try.

15.4 Phase sensitive detection: lock-in amplifiers (optional lab)

Build the circuit in figure 15.6, placing the photodiode in near proximity to the LED. Use a function generator to produce a 1 kHz sine wave in order to light up the LED. We are using U1 to combine the sine wave output with a DC offset. This way the diode will be on all the time, but will only have a 'signal' on it when the switch, S1, is closed. Use a second function generator to simulate noise on the detector circuit. (We could just as well have put the 'noise' on the LED.) U2 is doing double duty: it

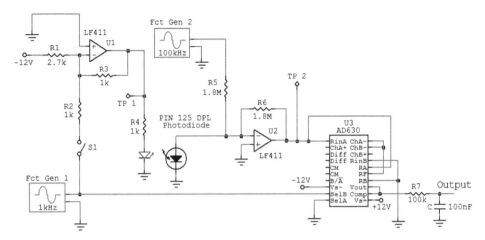

Figure 15.6. Simple application of a lock-in amplifier.

is being used as a *transimpedance amplifier* that converts the photocurrent from the diode into a voltage, while amplifying it; but it is also being used to sum the photocurrent with the simulated noise. TP1 and TP2 are suggested test points (places where you may wish to attach your 'scope probes) to see what you signal you are applying to the LED and what your photodiode is picking up. In addition to the LED signal and the simulated noise, the photodiode should also pick up true noise at about 120 Hz from the room lights. (Why 120 Hz and not 60 Hz?)

Crank up the 1 kHz function generator's amplitude until you can see the LED's signal on the output of U2. You may have to tilt the LED and photodiode toward each other in order to see the signal. The AD630 is used as a phase detector. As simplistically shown in the lecture figure 7.10, the AD630 essentially consists of two amplifiers, one with a gain of $+1$, the other with a gain of -1. The amplified detector signal is fed to both amplifiers, and the reference signal, from the 'signal' function generator, is used to switch back and forth between the two amplifiers. Thus the detector signal is modulated in a manner similar to that shown in figure 7.7 and 7.9. The modulated signal is then integrated using $R7$ and C.

You can look at the output of the integrator with your 'scope, but for sufficient integration, we expect the output to be essentially a DC signal. Thus, it is generally convenient to measure the lock-in's output with a multimeter. Do this and see what the effect is of switching on and off the 'signal' portion of the LED's source. Now play with the 'noise' amplitude. Can you determine your noise rejection ratio from these measurements?

IOP Publishing

Practical Analog, Digital, and Embedded Electronics for Scientists

Brett D DePaola

Chapter 16

Embedded electronics, featuring the Beaglebone Black

First, make sure you have read lecture sections 8.1 and 8.2. It may not all make sense to you as you are reading it but hopefully, as you work your way through the lecture and then this lab, you'll start to get it.

16.1 Getting started

- If you have not used Linux before, especially from the command line, read through appendix E.
- If you plan to use your own computer to control the Beagle, make sure you have read appendix C and installed the appropriate software before coming to lab.

16.1.1 Connect the Beagle

Let's connect up the Beagle.

- Turn on and log onto a laptop computer, using either your own computer, or the one supplied to you in this class. (Regardless of which computer you choose to use, I'll refer to it as 'your computer'.)
- As shown in the lecture figure 8.1, connect the USB cable from the Beaglebone Black (henceforth referred to as the BBB) to the USB port on your computer.
- Within 10 seconds or so, the BBB should come alive: You should see several blue LEDs light up, several of them strobing and blinking. (This is good!) Here's what the blue lights mean:
  - The PWR LED will come on and stay on.
  - USR0 LED is configured at boot to blink in a 'heartbeat pattern'.

- USR1 LED is configured at boot to light during microSD card accesses (which we will *not* need to do in our lab).
- USR2 LED is configured at boot to light during CPU activity.
- USR3 LED is configured at boot to light during eMMC accesses. The eMMC is sort of like a BIOS (basic input/output system). It has the firmware that tells the BBB how to communicate with its environment.

- If you are using your own computer, you'll have to download drivers from the web at `http://beagleboard.org/getting-started`. Drivers are available for Windows (64 bit), Windows (32 bit), Mac OS X, and Linux. If you are using a lab computer, the drivers are already installed. Once the drivers are installed you are ready to communicate with the BBB.

Now do the following:
- double-click on `XMing`.
- double-click on `PuTTY`.
- In the PuTTY window, click on 'Debian',
- click on the 'Load' button.
- click on the 'Open' button.

Regardless of which computer you are using to communicate with the BBB, you will now need to log in. If you are asked for a username, give `debian`. For a password, give `temppwd`.

You should now be logged onto the BBB. If not, ask your instructor for help.

Logging On
Summary of logging:
From a Windows machine:
- Run XMing,
- Run PuTTY,
- Select `Debian` and Load it,
- Hit the Open button,
- username is `debian`,
- password is `temppwd`.

From an Apple or Linux box:
Type `ssh -X debian@192.168.7.2`
While we're at it, here's the safe way to disconnect. Failure to follow this procedure can result in loss of data and corruption of the operating system!

Logging Off
    Type
    sudo shutdown -h now
    If your system is 'hung' and this fails, press and hold the PWR switch on the BBB. The lights will all go out. It is then safe to disconnect the BBB from the laptop computer.

16.1.2 Get familiar with Linux

Work your way through appendix E. From your home directory, create a directory named pmi. You'll do all your work from the pmi directory, or from subdirectories under pmi.

Play with the other Linux commands from appendix E.

16.1.3 Learning how to emacs: it's a lifestyle!

Play with the emacs editor: create a new file named test.txt by typing:

```
emacs test.txt &
```

Note the ampersand. This opens up emacs in a new shell, leaving the original shell available for other tasks. This way, you are not constantly opening and closing your editor—and saving heaps of time.

After typing in some sample text (and saving it), go to the Linux command line and see if you can display the text using the cat command:

```
cat test.txt
```

Go back to the editor and try out as many of the emacs commands from the Appendix D as you can. Try to use the hot keys rather than the pull-down menus—it'll save you loads of time in the long run.

16.1.4 System variables

Get back to your home directory. Then re-re-read the lecture subsection 8.2.2 and follow the instructions there. That is, first find the directories in which the slots and pins files live. These should be similar to what is in lecture subsection 8.2.2, but there could be slight differences. Use the tab key to auto-complete. This will be very helpful in finding the correct directory.

Once you have verified the correct directory locations, use emacs to edit your .profile file, defining the system variables $SLOT and $PINS. Then source your profile and see if you can cat the contents of your slots and pins files.

16.1.5 Clearing the LEDs

By now those LEDs are probably driving you (and your instructor) nuts. Let's turn them off. To do this, all we have to do is to write a '0' to the appropriate file. For example, to turn off the USR0 LED, we type:

```
sudo sh -c 'echo 0 > /sys/class/leds/beaglebone\:green\:usr0/brightness'
```

As we've already learned in the lecture, sudo gives us temporary super user privilege, and echo sends the string that follows it to wherever we direct, in this case the file brightness which is located in the indicated directory. Note the use of the backslash. This is necessary to use because the colons are special (reserved) characters. To tell the computer to treat a colon literally, you must precede it with a backslash.

But we'd like to turn off all four lights. Ok, we can do this using the repeat command and then editing the line to indicate the correct directory, but what if we'd like to do this every time we turn on the BBB? Gosh, that would be too much typing! So let's write a script.

Write a simple script that turns all the LEDs off, and another one that turns them all on. From the /pmi directory, get into emacs and create a file to turn them off:

```
emacs ClearLeds.sh
```

Now enter the following lines and save the file:

```
1 sudo sh -c 'echo 0 > /sys/class/leds/beaglebone\:green\:usr0/brightness'
2 sudo sh -c 'echo 0 > /sys/class/leds/beaglebone\:green\:usr1/brightness'
3 sudo sh -c 'echo 0 > /sys/class/leds/beaglebone\:green\:usr2/brightness'
4 sudo sh -c 'echo 0 > /sys/class/leds/beaglebone\:green\:usr3/brightness'
```

In principle, we execute the script by typing:

```
./ClearLeds.sh
```

Try it. Didn't work, did it? Look at the contents of the directory in list form:

```
ls -l
```

You can see that ClearLeds.sh is not executable. Of course not! How would the computer know that you were creating an executable script? But this is not a problem. We can change the access permissions:

```
chmod +x ClearLeds.sh
```

The chmod command changes the properties of files, including who has the right to edit and execute them. In this case we give 'everyone' the right to execute (+x) the file ClearLeds.sh Implicitly this means that this file must be an 'executable file'.

Check the directory again and you'll see that ClearLeds.sh is now an executable. Execute it. If the lights don't go out, you must have made a typo.

Now write a script called `SetLeds.sh` that turns all the LEDs back on. You do this by sending a '1' to that same address. After making the file an executable, give it a try. Wow, your first Beagle control program! Celebrate with a milk shake. (Ummm, after class.)

16.1.6 Controlling the Beagle from within a program

Review appendix E before continuing.

Writing scripts to control your computer is extremely powerful. Scripts can even have arguments, and simple flow control, like `if` statements. But with the possible exception of the Python scripting language, scripts are nowhere near as powerful as a true programming language. And since Linux treats all its peripherals as files, all you need to do to control your hardware is to read and/or write to these 'files'.

Write a C++ program that turns all the BBB's LEDS off, keeps them off for 10 s, and then turns them back on again. To do this you may want to use the the `usleep(x)` function, where x is the delay time expressed in μs. Note that to use this function, you need to `#include <unistd.h>`. Note also that ':' is *not* a reserved character in C++, so do not precede them with a backslash.

Now that you know how to control the LEDs from within a program, how about doing something really cool: write a C++ program that takes an input number from you (from 0 to 15) and uses the BBB's LEDs to display that number as a 4 bit binary. To do this you may want to review (1) writing to a file, and (2) modulo arithmetic.

16.2 Input/output

In the labs of this section we will use the pins on the Beaglebone to exchange information between the Beagle and the outside world. *Before* you begin the labs in this section, be sure you re-read the lecture sections 8.3 and 8.4.

16.2.1 Analog–digital conversion

As explained in the lecture section 8.4.1, the BBB has 7 ADC channels available to us. (See lecture table 8.6 for the pinouts.)

First we have to load in the appropriate driver software. Following the lecture text, examine what is currently loaded in the slots (`cat $SLOTS`). Now load in the ADC DTO and then check the `slots` file to see if the DTO was successfully loaded:

```
sudo sh -c 'echo BB-ADC > $SLOTS'
cat $SLOTS
```

If there were no problems, you should be ready to test the ADCs. Build the circuit in figure 16.1. Before connecting the wiper of the pot to P − 39, check its voltage on your DMM or 'scope'. If it exceeds 1.8 V, you *will* damage the BBB.

You should now be able to supply one of the ADCs (`AIN0`) with a voltage between 0 and 1.8 V. You can read this voltage from the command line. First, figure out in precisely which directory your ADC 'files' are in by using `ls` together with the auto-complete (tab) feature. The directory should be something like

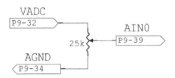

Figure 16.1. Using the ADC reference voltage so as not to exceed the ADC inputs' maximum voltage limit.

/sys/bus/iio/devices/iio:device0. Once you've found the location of AIN0 (associated with the file named in_voltage0_raw), you can read the digitized input voltage by typing:

```
cat /sys/bus/iio/devices/iio:device0/in_voltage0_raw
```

You should get the digitized signal. Because this a 12 bit ADC, the integer contained in the 'file' will have a value between 0 and $2^{12} - 1 = 4095$. With a 12 bit ADC, with what precision should you be able to measure a 0–1.8 V signal?

Take a number of data points and plot DMM reading versus ADC output. Review appendix G to see how to use Gnuplot to plot your data and to fit the points to a straight line. Don't forget error bars. Create a graph in some graphics format like png or jpeg. Then you can move that file to another computer using a 'thumb-drive' (see appendix F) and print it out so you can later tape it into your lab book.

Even with the auto-repeat capability (up-arrow) of the Linux command line, it is painful to constantly update the ADC result. Write a C++ program that constantly reads the ADC and sends the output to the screen. Don't worry about creating a nice exit to the program; just use a cntrl-c to exit.

There are two caveats:

1. In the program you will want to open the in_voltage0_raw 'file' and then read it. But because of the peculiar way that the operating system deals with this pseudo-file, you have to close the file in order to allow the ADC to convert another value. Thus, in your infinite loop, you need to open the file, read the file, then close the file, over and over.

2. You will notice that when you change your potentiometer setting, it takes a bit of time for the ADC to settle in on a value. You can build in a pause between reading and writing a value using the usleep(x) function, where x is the delay time expressed in μs. Again, to use this function, you need to #include <unistd.h>.

Once you've gotten this to work, you can watch the ADC output change in real time as you twiddle the pot. Cool!

16.2.1.1 Measuring distance

You can use your ADC capabilities for many kinds of measurements. We'll use the Sharp 2Y0A21. This is a very cool device that measures distance through triangulation. Basically, an LED emits a collimated beam which is (diffusively) reflected from a surface. The LED spot on that surface is imaged onto a position-sensitive detector. So long as the sensor is far enough from the surface for the entire spot to be imaged onto the detector, your detector output should follow a $1/r$ curve with r being the distance between surface and detector. (Convince yourself that this should be true.)

Figure 16.2 shows a 'typical' curve of detector output versus distance between sensor and surface, taken from the 2Y0A21 data sheet. Note that for distances less than some critical value, typically about 10 cm, the detector output is roughly linear with distance. The sensor data sheet claims a 'useful' distance range of 10–80 cm. Note also that the sensor outputs a signal somewhat in excess of 3 V. But the maximum input voltage for the ADC is only 1.8V! Therefore, we need to reduce the sensor output; the easiest way to do this is with a voltage divider. The 2Y0A21 takes an input of 5 V, which we'll grab from the P-9 connector.

To use the sensor, follow the schematic of figure 16.3: attach the sensor's red wire to +5 V from the BBB's P9-7. Attach the sensor's black wire to a BBB ground, P9-1.

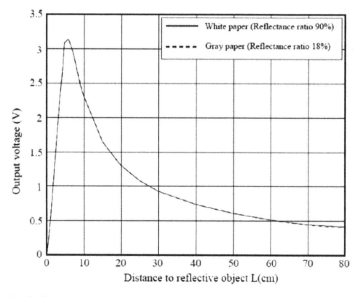

Figure 16.2. A 'typical' voltage versus distance response of the Sharp 2Y0A21. (Reproduced from the Sharp 2Y0A21 data sheet. The diagram is copyright protected by Sharp Corporation.)

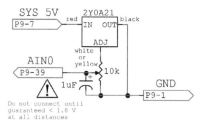

Figure 16.3. Wiring up the Sharp 2Y0A21. Check that the pot output does not exceed 1.8 V for all distances.

Then attach the sensor output (the white or yellow wire, depending on which unit you are using) to one end of a 10k pot. The other end of the pot is connected to ground, and the wiper of the pot is the new output. Do not attach anything to the ADC input on the BBB yet. Now adjust the pot wiper until the maximum voltage you obtain is less than 1.8 V—for any possible sensor−surface distance. The output of the sensor is from 0 to 2.6 V, which is why we need the potentiometer. The capacitor functions as a low-pass filter. Its value was chosen as follows:

- For a 2.6 V (max) detector output to a 1.8 V (max) input to the ADC, and using a 10k potentiometer, we need a voltage divider, we find that the 'upper' resister would be approximately 3k.
- Then for an $f_{3\,db}$ of about 60 Hz, we see we need a capacitor of about 1 μF.

When you've convinced yourself—and your instructor—that it is impossible to obtain an output from the pot that is greater than 1.8 V, you can connect a lead from there to one of the ADC inputs on the BBB, for example, P9-39. Once your sensor is wired up and running, calibrate it: use a flat surface (notebook, lab book, pad of paper, etc) and a ruler. You can then record actual distance versus ADC output over a range of distances. You should then be able to fit the falling part of the curve to a $1/r$ function.

Do the fit, then plot the data with the fit curve on your BBB using Gnuplot. (Don't forget your error bars.) Once again, you will want to save the plot as a nice graphics file that you can download to a thumb-drive so you can print it out and tape it into your lab book.

Leave your distance sensor wired up; we can combine its capabilities with other devices that we hang off the Beaglebone.

16.3 Pulse width modulation (PWM)

Make sure you have read the lecture section 8.6.

16.3.1 Setting up the PWM

In principle, with PWM you specify a frequency and a duty cycle (on-time divided by period). In the case of the Beaglebone, the user gives the period and either the on-time or off-time. (Default is off-time.) The Beaglebone comes with a PWM device tree overlay (DTO) already written, compiled, and ready to load. In this DTO pin P9-14 is used for the PWM. You can run the PWM from the terminal by running the following commands.

```
1 sudo sh -c 'echo am33xx_pwm > $SLOTS'
2 sudo sh -c 'echo bone_pwm_P9_14 > $SLOTS'
3 cat $SLOTS
4 sudo sh -c 'echo 500 > /sys/devices/ocp.3/pwm_test_P9_14.15/period'
5 sudo sh -c 'echo 400 > /sys/devices/ocp.3/pwm_test_P9_14.15/duty'
```

Better yet, write these commands to a file called, say, loadpwm14.sh. Then make that script executable using chmod. Finally, execute the script. The advantage of doing this is the next time you turn on the BBB, the script is sitting there, ready to load. This notion of saving time in the long run by generating simple scripts is a valuable one. In the above script, notice that we were forced to use the sudo command. Note that the statements of line numbers 1–2 need be executed only once, and line 3 is just a diagnostic to make sure the first two commands 'took'. After that you are free to set or reset the period and off-time as often as you wish. This is done using the commands on lines 4 and 5, respectively. (For my own convenience, I wrote two scripts. The first was just lines 1–3 above and the second one was lines 4–5 above. This second script took two parameters, 'period' and 'duty' on the command line and, just for efficiency, first peeked at the $SLOTS file to see if the two DTOs had been loaded—and called the first script if they had not.)

As usual, the exact directories of the period and duty 'files' could change, so it is worthwhile to check. A convenient way to do this is to type:

```
ls /sys/devices/oc<tab>
```

and then continue with:

```
ls /sys/devices/ocp.3/pwm<tab>
```

The command in line 5 is telling the Beaglebone to output a pulse train from pin P9-14, having a period of 500 ns. The command in line 6 requests that the off-time is 400 ns. Note that even though you are writing to a file named duty, this is not actually a duty cycle, but rather an off-time. This is not unreasonable because, by definition, a true duty cycle would have a value between 0 and 1, in other words, a floating point number. But the duty 'file' expects an integer. The duty command must have a time that is less than or equal to the period or it will not implement.

Once set, the computer will continue to output that particular pattern until you change it or until you reset the computer. Type the above commands and look at the output of pin P9-14 on your scope. Make sure you've connected the scope's ground to the Beagle's ground. Now vary the period and duty cycle to see if the BBB's PWM is behaving as advertised.

16.3.2 Driving a load

The I/O pins on the BBB (like those on most computers) cannot source or sink much current, typically only a few mA. Therefore, if you want to use your PWM signal to drive something like an LED or an electric motor, you need to buffer your signal, for example by using a transistor. Here is one way to hook up your LED such that you can use PWM from pin P9-14 to control the brightness of the LED. Connect up the circuit of figure 16.4 and use inputs from your keyboard to control the LED brightness. Experiment with both period and on and off times. Now write a program that changes the duty cycle and off-time. Modify your program to accept frequency and true duty cycle, instead of period and off-time, from the keyboard. Do you see a non-linearity between your set duty cycle and the apparent brightness of the LED? Is your observation reasonable? Try to explain it. Now let's try something fancy:

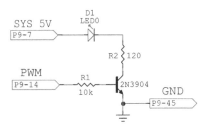

Figure 16.4. Sample circuit showing how to use a PWM to control the brightness of an LED.

combine the capabilities of your proximity sensor and your intensity control. For example, make your LED intensity be some function of the distance between your sensor and a surface. Be imaginative.

Notice that we've essentially been using the PWM as a DAC But we cheated: to really do this properly, we need to integrate the PWM output over a timescale that is long compared to its period. Here, instead of integrating electronically, we just operated at frequencies that were fast enough that our eyes integrated for us. That is, the eye cannot respond quickly enough to see flicker at above about 60 Hz. But if you had a fast detector near the LED, it would 'see' the PWM signal. Try reducing the PWM period to the point where you can just make out the flicker. What frequency is that?

16.3.3 Controlling a servo motor

A servo motor is a special type of motor that rotates to a specified absolute angle. An example of such a motor is the Hitech HS422. (See the data sheet.) The motor is rated to rotate $\pm 45°$ from center. (It can actually rotate ± 90 from center, but beyond $\pm 45°$, its rotation is non-linear.) The servo motor expects a 20 ms period. You control the rotation angle by varying the on-time. To move from $-45°$ to $+45°$, you vary the on-time from 1.100 ms to 1.900 ms. Either from your program or from the command line, set the period to 20 ms and the on-time to something between 1.1 and 1.9 ms. Verify your period and on-time by looking at the PWM output on the scope.

Now connect up the motor. You can power the HS422 from the +5 V and ground of your BBB (P9-7 and P9-1, respectively). Attach the motor's red lead to P9-7 and the black lead to P9-1. Connect the PWM output to the remaining (yellow) motor lead through a 10k resistor. Play around with the servo motor. See if you can program it to do something interesting. For example, see if you can make it rotate through its $\pm 45°$ range, based on how far your hand is from your distance monitor.

16.4 Controlling the GPIO pins

Thus far we've been making very specialized use of the Beaglebone's I/O pins; they've either been used as ADCs or PWMs. In this section we use them to send or receive digital signals.

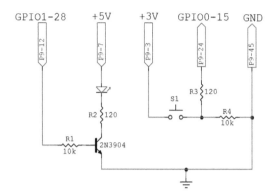

Figure 16.5. GPIO test circuit.

Wire up the circuit in figure 16.5, but do not connect the circuit to the BBB until we have set up the pins. The idea of this project is to set up some pins on the P9 header as GPIO. Specifically, we want pin P9-12 to be an output, and P9-24 to be an input. Pin P9-45 is a dedicated system ground, pin P9-7 is +5 V, and pin P9-3 is +3 V.

When the switch is not pushed, P9-24 sees 0 V, thanks to the pull-down resistor R4. (As we shall see, instead of the off-board pull-down resistor, we could choose to set up P9-24 as an input that uses an on-board pull-down resistor.) When the switch is depressed, P9-24 sees +3 V. It is very important that you use the + 3V supply here and not the + 5 V supply because the GPIO pins cannot handle the higher voltages. R3 is not really necessary but is included as a 'general safety practice'. This helps prevent the pin from seeing too much current. Ok, that's all there is for the hardware, now on to the software.

16.4.1 Defining the pins

As outlined in the lecture section 8.5 we control the GPIO pin characteristics using a device tree overlay, or DTO. I've put the DTO source code for the pin usage of figure 16.5 in the /lib/firmware directory on the BBB. Once you've edited and saved your DTO source code (not necessary here, since I've already created a working version) in whatever directory you choose to archive your DTOs in, you'll need to compile it. This source code was named DM-GPIO-Test.dts. Therefore the commands to compile it to a 'device tree blob object' (no kidding, that's what it's called) and then move it to the firmware directory are:

```
dtc -O dtb -o DM-GPIO-Test-00A0.dtbo -b 0 -@ DM-GPIO-Test.dts
sudo cp DM-GPIO-Test-00A0.dtbo /lib/firmware
```

Before loading the blob, let's save an image of the pins file for later comparison:

```
sudo cat $PINS > pinsBefore.txt
```

Now load your blob the same way we did earlier with the ADC DTO. Notice that the output blob has the same name as the DTO source file, but with the version number appended to it (and, of course, an extension of dtbo instead of dts). But remember that when you load the blob, you leave the version number off. For example, to load this blob, you'd type:

```
sudo sh -c 'echo DM-GPIO-Test > $SLOTS'
cat $SLOTS
```

We recommend always following a DTO load with a cat of the slots file, just to be sure everything worked. In this case, you should see

ff:P-O-L Override Board Name,00A0,Override Manuf,DM-GPIO-Test

added to the list of slots. To further check that everything is as it should be, you could cat the pins file:

```
sudo cat $PINS
```

Unfortunately, you will see information on all the pins—and their designation is *not* in terms of the P8 or P9 connectors. However, because we had the foresight to save an image of the pins file before we loaded the new overlay, we can make an image of the new pins file and compare the new with the old:

```
sudo cat $PINS > pinsAfter.txt
diff pinsBefore.txt pinsAfter.txt
```

When I did this, I got:

11c11						
<	pin	9	(44e10824)	00000027	pinctrl-single
—						
>	pin	9	(44e10824)	0000002f	pinctrl-single
15c15						
<	pin	13	(44e10834)	00000027	pinctrl-single
—						
>	pin	13	(44e10834)	00000037	pinctrl-single
32c32						
<	pin	30	(44e10878)	00000037	pinctrl-single
—						
>	pin	30	(44e10878)	00000007	pinctrl-single
99c99						
<	pin	97	(44e10984)	00000037	pinctrl-single
—						
>	pin	97	(44e10984)	0000002f	pinctrl-single

Let's make sense of this. The `diff` command means 'output the difference between the two files whose names follow'. Looking at the output, we first see '11c11'. This means that line 11 in the first file changed into line 11 of the second file. Next we see that the line in the left file (`pinsBefore.txt`) was changed from the line starting with < into the line starting with > in the right file (`pinsAfter.txt`). With this convenient display we can see at a glance that the only pins that changed their function were numbers 9, 13, 30, and 97. And from the memory locations, or from the $PINS entries in tables 8.2 and 8.3 we can see that these pins were P8-13, P8-11, P9-12, and P9-24, respectively, corresponding to lines 19, 17, 15, and 16 in the DTO listing. Note that the values of the pin configuration all changed to the values in our DTO. Apparently, pin P8-12 didn't change. But we can easily verify that it has the correct value by looking at the `pins` file, making our job easer by using the `grep` filter:

```
sudo cat $PINS | grep '830'
```

Doing this, we find that, indeed, the pin configuration is correctly given as 0x27. (It didn't change because that pin was, by default, already in the desired configuration.)

16.4.1.1 Exporting the pins

Once we've confirmed that the pins have been set up properly, we will need to have the system create the 'files' required to use these pins. First go to /sys/class/gpio and create directories for pins P9-12 (GPIO60) and P9-24 (GPIO15) by typing:

```
sudo sh -c 'echo 60 > export'
sudo sh -c 'echo 15 > export'
```

Now look at your gpio directory again. You should see two new directories, gpio15 and gpio60. These directories contain the 'files' required for setting directions of data flow, as well as for sending data to, and/or receiving data from, the pins.

16.4.1.2 Setting the GPIO directions

We now have to set the directions for the two pins. We want P9-12 (GPIO60) to control the LED and therefore to be an output; we want P9-24 to 'read' the switch setting and therefore to be an input. So we go to directory /sys/class/gpio/gpio60 and 'write' to the direction 'file':

```
sudo sh -c 'echo out > direction'
```

We then go to the directory /sys/class/gpio/gpio15 and type:

```
sudo sh -c 'echo in > direction'
```

16-13

While in those directories we can verify the direction is correct by typing:

```
cat direction
```

Now that the pins are set up, you can go back to the circuit of figure 16.5 and connect it to the BBB.

16.4.1.3 Outputting or inputting a value from the command line
We can now write a value or read a value to/from a pin by going to the appropriate directory and echo-ing or cat-ing the value. For example, we can go to /sys/class/gpio/gpio60 and type:

```
sudo sh -c 'echo 1 > value'
```

This sends a true (3.3 V) to P9-12 and therefore lights up the LED. Typing:

```
sudo sh -c 'echo 0 > value'
```

turns the LED off.

16.4.2 Controlling the pins from within a C++ program

Controlling pins from the command line is very useful for debugging, but is not the ultimate goal: we'd like to control the circuit from within a program. Once the DTO has been loaded, all pin I/O is done via file read/writes. So, at the simplest level, all we need do is to open the file, read or write to it, and then close the file. There is one caveat: when you write to the 'file', nothing happens until you flush the buffer by using endl and then close the file. Give it a try: write a program that
1. Flashes the LED 5 times, at 1 s intervals.
2. Sends a prompt to the screen, telling you to push the button.
3. Sends a confirming statement to the screen when the button has been pressed.

16.5 Get on the bus!

Read lecture section 8.7.

16.5.1 The I^2C bus

We will demonstrate how an I2C bus works by communicating with the ADXL345, a three-axis accelerometer. The device itself is a small surface-mount chip that we've had mounted to a DIP pad. (You probably have one of these in your smart phone.)

(See the data sheet at https://www.sparkfun.com/datasheets/Sensors/Accelerometer/ADXL345.pdf .)

The sensor has a pre-selected device address of 0x53; thus only one of these can be attached to a given I2C bus at a time.

As shown in figure 16.6, it is remarkably easy to connect a device to the BBB's I2C bus. As it turns out, the software is fairly uncomplicated as well. There is a standard I2C package that comes bundled with Debian. Typing:

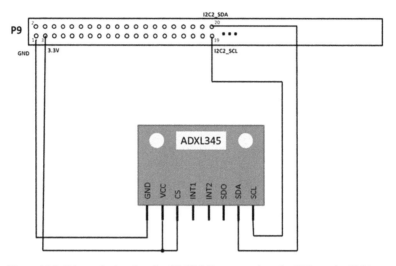

Figure 16.6. Schematic showing the ADXL345 connected to the BBB on the I2C bus.

```
i2cdetect -1
```

from the command line gives an output like

i2c-0	i2c	OMAP I2C adapter	I2C adapter
i2c-1	i2c	OMAP I2C adapter	I2C adapter

We can see that the software 0 and 1 i2c's have been enabled, as claimed in table 8.12 of the lecture. We can enable the remaining I2C bus, I2C1 (which corresponds to software i2c2) by loading in the appropriate DTO:

```
sudo sh -c 'echo BB-I2C1 > $SLOTS'
cat $SLOTS
i2cdetect -1
```

The slots file should show that a device occupies a new 'slot', and we should now see an additional line on the output of the i2cdetect command:

i2c-0	i2c	OMAP I2C adapter	I2C adapter
i2c-1	i2c	OMAP I2C adapter	I2C adapter
i2c-2	i2c	OMAP I2C adapter	I2C adapter

Notice that the driver (DTO file) we sent to the `slots` was associated with the *hardware* device 1; hence we added a *software* `i2c-2`. (Don't worry, this is probably the most confusing aspect of I2C and it is only confusing because the BBB people messed it up.) The `i2cdetect` command has several possible options. They are:

```
i2cdetect [-y] [-a] [-q| [-r] i2cbus
i2cdetect -F i2cbus
i2cdetect -V
i2cdetect -l
```

where the `i2cbus` is the software bus number, and flags are summarized in table 16.1.

Remember, thus far we have been talking about three separate buses, and each of these buses could have many devices on it.

If we were to enter:

```
i2cdetect -y -r 1
```

we should see

	0	1	2	3	4	5	6	7	8	9	a	b	c	d	e	f
00:				–	–		–		–		–	–	–	–	–	–	–
10:	–	–	–	–	–		–		–		–	–	–	–	–	–	–
20:	–	–	–	–	–		–		–		–	–	–	–	–	–	–
30:	–	–	–	–	–		–		–		–	–	–	–	–	–	–
40:	–	–	–	–	–		–		–		–	–	–	–	–	–	–
50:	–	–	–	–	UU	UU	UU	UU	–		–	–	–	–	–	–	–
60:	–	–	–	–	–		–		–		–	–	–	–	–	–	–
70:	–	–	–	–	–		–		–							

Table 16.1. Description of option flags for the i2cbus command. (From `http://www.im-sensors.org/wiki/man/iwcdetect`. GNU Gen Pub License v2.)

Flag	Description
-y	Disable interactive mode. Mainly used for scripts.
-a	Force scanning of non-regular addresses. **Not recommended!**
-q	Use SMBus 'quick write' commands for probing **Not recommended!**
-r	Use SMBus 'read byte' commands for probing.
-F	Display the list of functionalities implemented by the adapter; then exit.
-V	Display the version; then exit.
-l	Output a list of installed buses.

Remember, these are *device* addresses that are being displayed. By default, the displayed range is from 0x03 to 0x77. Using the -a option will extend the range to 0x7f.

But what does this output mean? Well, pretty much it's telling us that nothing is on that bus. (No surprise.) The UU entries mean that those addresses were skipped because they were already in use by a driver. Which driver? You can find out. For example to see the driver that is using address 0x54, we can cd to the appropriate directory, and then cat the modalias 'file':

```
cd /sys/bus/i2c/devices/1-0054
cat modalias
```

which returns i2c:24c256.

I know, not too informative. But if you had known something about the driver, this output would have given you the information you wanted. The point here is that the /sys/bus/i2c/devices directory contains a 'directory' for each address on the i2c bus that is being used. And inside each of those directories are 'files' that can be used. If we connect the ADXL345 as indicated in figure 16.6, and then type:

```
i2cdetect -y -r 1
```

we will see the dump below. (Do this.)

	0	1	2	3	4	5	6	7	8	9	a	b	c	d	e	f
00:				–	–	–	–	–	–	–	–	–	–	–	–	–
10:	–	–	–	–	–	–	–	–	–	–	–	–	–	–	–	–
20:	–	–	–	–	–	–	–	–	–	–	–	–	–	–	–	–
30:	–	–	–	–	–	–	–	–	–	–	–	–	–	–	–	–
40:	–	–	–	–	–	–	–	–	–	–	–	–	–	–	–	–
50:	–	–	–	53	UU	UU	UU	UU	–	–	–	–	–	–	–	–
60:	–	–	–	–	–	–	–	–	–	–	–	–	–	–	–	–
70:	–	–	–	–	–	–	–	–								

That's what we expected! Recall that the ADXL345 has pre-selected the address 0x53, and that's what we see. Perfect. Table 16.2 is a summary of i2c command-line commands along with their functions:

The i2cdump command helps us with device diagnostics. It allows us to get into the guts of the devices that are attached to the I2C bus. But use this command with caution because for some slave devices i2cdump could write to the device, which, depending on the device, could be a problem. You should always consult your

Table 16.2. i2c command-line commands.

Command	Function
i2cdetect [-y] [-a] [-q|-r] i2cbus	Detect active I2C buses or devices on bus.
i2cdump [-y] i2cbus address [mode] [bank [band reg]]	Dump register contents of selected I2C device.
i2cdump -V	
i2cget [-f] [y] i2cbus chip-address [data-address [mode]]	Read the value of a register.
i2cget -V	
i2cset [-y] i2cbus chip-address data-address value [mode] [mask]	Write a value to a register.
i2cset -V	

device's data sheet before attempting a i2cdump. In the case of the ADXL345, we can safely use it. Here's an example:

```
i2cdump -y 1 0x53
```

(Note we used the -y flag followed by the software bus number, followed by the address of the device we wish to investigate.) This should give

```
     0  1  2  3  4  5  6  7  8  9  a  b  c  d  e  f    0123456789abcdef
00: e5 00 00 00 00 00 00 00 00 00 00 00 00 00 00 4a    ?..............J
10: 00 00 10 00 00 00 00 00 00 00 00 00 00 00 00 00    ..?.............
20: 00 00 00 00 00 00 00 00 00 00 00 00 0a 00 00 00    ............?...
30: 02 00 00 00 00 00 00 00 00 00 00 00 00 00 00 00    ?...............
```

(I've displayed just the beginning part of the output.) These are the registers of the device at address 0x53 which is, of course, the ADXL345. Most of the registers are empty because, by default, the device is in the 'power-saving mode'. However, you can see that the register 0x00 (that is, the register at location 0x00 of the device at location 0x53) has the value e5. This is the device ID of the ADXL345. Most devices put their ID number in register 0x00.

Before we can continue, we should take a look at the ADXL345 itself so that we can make sense of what we are seeing when we dump its registers.

Table 16.3 contains a brief description of the content of the registers of the ADXL345. In particular, we can see that the register at 0x2D is where we can find—or place—the command to wake the device up and start taking data. From the data sheet, we can find that the command to do this is 0x08.

Table 16.3. Description of the registers of the ADXL345, a three-axis accelerometer.

ADDR	NAME	R/W?	DESCRIPTION
0x00	DEVID	R	The device ID: This should be E5. Most devices have a fixed ID at the address 0x00.
0x02D	POWER_CTL	R/W	Power-saving features control: Six bits that specify sleep mode, measurement modes, etc
0x31	DATA_FORMAT	R/W	Data format control: Seven bits that set the self-test, SPI mode, interrupt inversion, zero bit, resolution, justify bit, and g range settings (2 bits). See the data sheet.
0x32	DATAX0	R	X-Axis Data 0: One byte containing the LSB of the X-axis accel data.
0x33	DATAX1	R	X-Axis Data 1: One byte containing the MSB of the X-axis accel data.
0x34	DATAY0	R	Y-Axis Data 0: One byte containing the LSB of the Y-axis accel data.
0x35	DATAY1	R	Y-Axis Data 1: One byte containing the MSB of the Y-axis accel data.
0x36	DATAZ0	R	Z-Axis Data 0: One byte containing the LSB of the Z-axis accel data.
0x37	DATAZ1	R	Z-Axis Data 1: One byte containing the MSB of the Z-axis accel data.

Knowing this command and where to place it, let's see what happens when we activate the ADXL345. To do this we use the i2cset command to place the value 0x08 into register 0x2D (in device 0x53, of course):

```
i2cset -y 1 0x53 0x2D 0x08
i2cget -y 1 0x53 0x2D
```

The second command is just to verify that we did, in fact, write a 08 to the register.

Note the syntax is i2cset -y i2c-bus-number device-address device-register *command*. Now when we dump the contents of the device we get the register dump of table 16.4.

Looking back at table 16.3, we see that acceleration data are located in registers 0x32–0x37. The byte storage scheme is interesting: LSB_X, MSB_X, LSB_Y, MSB_Y, LSB_Z, MSB_Z, where negative numbers are expressed as 2's complement. 'LSB' means 'least significant byte' and 'MSB' means 'most significant byte'.

Once you've converted the data in registers 0x32–0x37 into usable numbers, you will probably want to convert them into something having meaningful units. According to the data sheet, the ADXL345 has a resolution of 3.9 mg (that's milli-gees, not milligrams!) per least-significant-bit. That is, to convert from the numbers you obtained from bit-smashing the register data into something with

Table 16.4. Typical dump of the ADXL345 registers.

	0	1	2	3	4	5	6	7	8	9	a	b	c	d	e	f	0123456789abcdef
00:	e5	00	00	00	00	00	00	00	00	00	00	00	00	00	00	4a	?.............J
10:	82	00	30	00	00	01	01	40	00	00	00	f6	00	00	00	00	?.0..??@...?....
20:	00	00	00	00	00	00	00	00	00	00	00	00	0a	08	00	00	............??..
30:	83	00	06	00	06	00	02	01	00	00	00	00	00	00	00	00	?.?.?.??........
40:	e5	00	00	00	00	00	00	00	00	00	00	00	00	00	00	4a	?.............J
50:	82	00	30	00	00	01	01	40	00	00	00	f6	00	00	00	00	?.0..??@...?....
60:	00	00	00	00	00	00	00	00	00	00	00	00	0a	08	00	00	............??..
70:	83	00	06	00	07	00	03	01	00	00	00	00	00	00	00	00	?.?.?.??........
80:	e5	00	00	00	00	00	00	00	00	00	00	00	00	00	00	4a	?.............J
90:	80	00	30	00	00	01	01	40	00	00	00	f6	00	00	00	00	?.0..??@...?....
a0:	00	00	00	00	00	00	00	00	00	00	00	00	0a	08	00	00	............??..
b0:	82	00	07	00	06	00	02	01	00	00	00	00	00	00	00	00	?.?.?.??........
c0:	e5	00	00	00	00	00	00	00	00	00	00	00	00	00	00	4a	?.............J
d0:	80	00	30	00	00	01	01	40	00	00	00	f6	00	00	00	00	?.0..??@...?....
e0:	00	00	00	00	00	00	00	00	00	00	00	00	0a	08	00	00	............??..
f0:	83	00	06	00	06	00	01	01	00	00	00	00	00	00	00	00	?.?.?.??........

Table 16.5. Converting the acceleration data from the register dump, into x, y, and z components of accelerations.

	MSB (Hex)	LSB (Hex)	Base 10	Units of g	MKS units
X-axis:	00	06	6	0.023 4	0.229 5
Y-axis:	00	06	6	0.023 4	0.229 5
Z-axis:	01	02	258	1.006 2	9.867 5

meaningful units, namely gees, you multiply by 3.9×10^{-3} (assuming the device was set to the highest resolution mode of $\pm 2g$. If, for example, you were in the next higher resolution mode of $\pm 4g$, you'd multiply by $2 \times 3.9 \times 10^{-3}$.) You can then further convert this value into mks units by multiplying by 9.80665 ms^{-2}/gee.

In the case of the numbers in the above register dump, we get the number in table 16.5.

Let's get back to the ADXL345 registers summarized in table 16.3. The POWER_CTL register is used to save power by putting the device into sleep mode, or to wake it up. This register is 'encoded' as in table 16.6.

From table 16.6 we can now see that sending a 0x08 to register 0x2D tells the chip that we want to make a measurement.

The other register in table 16.3 that we need to understand is DATA_FORMAT. It is encoded as in table 16.7.

Table 16.6. Bit control of the POWER_CTL register in table 16.3.

D7	D6	D5	D4	D3	D2	D1	D0
0	0	Link	AUTO_SLEEP	Measure	Sleep	Wakeup	

Table 16.7. Bit control of the DATA_FORMAT register in table 16.3.

D7	D6	D5	D4	D3	D2	D1	D0
SELF_TEST	SPI	INT_INVERT	0	FULL_RES	JUSTIFY	RANGE	

Table 16.8. g-Range settings.

Setting		
D1	D0	g-Range
0	0	±2 g
0	1	±4 g
1	0	±8 g
1	1	±16 g

The bit designations in table 16.7 are:
- **SELF-TEST bit:** A setting of 1 in this bit applies a self-test force to the sensor, causing a shift in the output data. A value of 0 disables the self-test force.
- **SPI bit:** A value of 1 sets the device to three-wire SPI mode; a value of 0 sets the device to four-wire SPI mode. (We'll get to the SPI bus shortly.)
- **INT_INVERT bit:** A value of 0 sets the interrupts to active high; a value of 1 sets the interrupts to active low.
- **FULL_RES bit:** A value of 1 puts the device in full resolution mode, where the output resolution increases with the g range set by the range bits to maintain a 4 mg/LSB scale factor; a value of 0 puts the device in 10 bit mode and the range bits determine the maximum g range and scale factor.
- **Justify bit:** A value of 1 selects the left-justified (MSB) mode; a 0 selects right-justified mode with sign extension.
- **Range bits:** These bits set the g range as in table 16.8.

Take another look at the register dump of table 16.4, paying particular attention to the register at address 0x31, the DATA_FORMAT register. It is a 0x00 which, from tables 16.7 and 16.8 mean that we are, indeed, in the ±2 g resolution mode. Of course we can change this using the i2cset command. For example to switch to a range of ±4 g, we would use the command:

```
i2cset -y 1 0x53 0x31 0x01
```

16.5.2 The SPI bus

In principle, we could have many ADXL345 chips hanging off the I2C bus and we could define a separate object for each of them. Unfortunately, in practice we cannot do this because the I2CAddress (0x53) is 'hardwired' into the chip and we cannot change it. However, with the SPI bus this address issue will no longer limit us.

In the case of the BBB, one I2C bus is by default available and an additional one can be made available. But upon boot-up, no SPI buses are available by default. However, one can readily load the first bus (SPI0) by loading in the device tree overlay BB-SPIDEV0, which is located in /lib/firmware with the other DTOs. There is a second SPI bus, (SPI1) that can be made available, but by default those pins are used for HDMI. However, if you are not using the HDMI, you can unload HDMI from the slots and load the SPI1 DTO, BB-SPIDEV1, also located in /lib/firmware. As in the case of I2C, the SPI's actual communication protocol is a bit complicated. But fortunately, the devices that use these protocols have drivers that do all the work. As usual, in the case of a Linux-based embedded system, all it really comes down to is reading and writing files. And as in the case of I2C, there are some tools available to test out the SPI bus. The first of these is a C-program, spidev_test. You can download the source code (which has extension .c) for this program from the course website, or copy and paste it from appendix H. To compile the code, type:

```
gcc spidev_test.c -o spidev_test
```

If you execute the code by typing:

```
./spidev_test
```

You should get the following output:

```
spi mode: 0
bits per word: 8
max speed: 500 000 Hz (500 KHz)
```

FF	FF	FF	FF	FF	FF
FF	FF	FF	FF	FF	FF
FF	FF	FF	FF	FF	FF
FF	FF	FF	FF	FF	FF
FF	FF	FF	FF	FF	FF
FF	FF	FF	FF	FF	FF
FF	FF				

The program has set the mode to 0; the words are each 8 bits; and the maximum speed has been set to 500 kHz (bits per second, or baud). The pins have been set to be in pull-up resistor mode and therefore, with no slave attached to the bus, the outputs are all high—and hence the FF output.

Now put a jumper wire between P9-18 and P9-21 (SPIO_D1 and SPIO_DO, respectively) and run spidev_test again. You should obtain the output:

```
spi mode: 0
bits per word: 8
max speed: 500 000 Hz (500 KHz)

FF        FF        FF        FF        FF        FF
40        00        00        00        00        95
FF        FF        FF        FF        FF        FF
FF        FF        FF        FF        FF        FF
FF        FF        FF        FF        FF        FF
DE        AD        BE        EF        BA        AD
F0        0D
```

which is the exact block of data that was defined in the program (and is, by the way, a classic example of bit-basher humor. Do you get it?)

16.5.2.1 Serial to parallel conversion

Now let's attach a slave to the SPI bus: the 74HC595 chip (data sheet on Canvas (figure 16.7). Also see the site http://www.zembedded.com/shift-registers-explained/). This is an 8 bit shift register, but for our purposes, we can think of it as a serial-to-parallel converter. The pin-outs are explained in table 16.9. This chip is designed to work with the 3.3 V logic employed by the BBB, so connect the Vcc pin to P9-3 (3 DC_3.3V), and the GND to P9-1 (GND). We do not need to set/clear the outputs, so just connect the SRCLR pin to Vcc as well. For this demo we'll only use 4 bits. Connect the lowest 4 bits to the anode side of four different LEDs. (We're going to make a simple binary counter, so it will be most convenient to place the LEDs all in a row with the LSB—connected to QA—to the right.) Make sure the LED cathodes are connected to ground via 1k resistors.

One word about the 'Chip Select' wire (pin 12 on the HC595 or, for example, P9-17 on the BBB): this is not simply a low signal to enable a single device. For some devices, the CS signal has to be properly phased with the clock and/or data exchange. Therefore, you cannot simply use a GPIO pin to select a desired device, but must do something a little more clever. If you wish to select between two devices, you can have the CS go to one input of each of two OR gates. Then have a GPIO pin go to the second input of one gate and the inverted GPIO output go to the second input of the other gate. The output of one gate goes to the CS of the first device, and

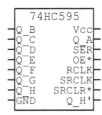

Figure 16.7. Pinouts for the 74HC595.

Table 16.9. 74HC595 inouts and connections to the BBB.

Pin	Function	Connection on BBB
16 (V_{cc})	Power (+3.3 V)	P9-3 (3 DC_3.3V)
15, 1–7 (Q_A—Q_H)	Data out, 8 bits	None
14 (SER)	Serial in (MOSI)	P9-18 (SPI0_D1)
13 (OE*)	Output enable	P9-1 (GND)
12 (RCLK)	Chip select	P9-17 (SPI0_CS0)
11 (SRCLK)	Clock in	P9-22 (SPI0_SCLK)
10 (SRCLR*)	Clear	P9-3 (3 DC_3.3V)
9 (Q_H')	(MISO)	Not used here
8 (GND)	Ground	P9-1

the output of the other gate goes to the CS of the second device. If you wish to select from among eight devices, you could use an HC138 MUX (the 3.3 V version of the MUX we used in lab 14.2) and 3 GPIO pins for the 'address' on the MUX. The idea in this simple one-device example is that we will use the SPI bus to serially pass a single 8 bit number (the upper 4 bits of which we will not monitor) to the HC595. The HC595 will convert those consecutive bits into a parallel 8 bit number, the lowest 4 bits of which will light up the LEDs. In the actual test program, we will sequentially send the numbers 0–15 and watch the LEDs 'count in binary'. But first, let's test the circuit and bus to make sure things are working. We'll do this from the command line using the `spidev1.0` 'file':

```
echo -ne '\xFF' > /dev/spidev1.0 echo -ne '\x00' > /dev/spidev1.0
```

The first command will turn the LEDs on (we're outputting all 1's), and the second one will turn them off. Note, but the way, that because /dev/spidev1.0 is not a 'protected' file, you need not use sudo. The -n suppresses the newline character that echo would otherwise output, and the -e enables escape character interpretation. Here the escape sequence is the '\x' which tells the computer that what follows is a hex number. When you've satisfied yourself that the hardware and bus are working correctly, it is time to control the LEDs from within a program. Download the program spi595.c and build595 from Canvas and place them in the `spi` directory of your **BBB**. You can use `build595` to compile/link the program. (Don't forget to `chmod build595` into executable mode.) Or, you can compile the program with:

```
gcc spi595.c -o spi595
```

When you execute this program, you should see the LEDs 'count' in binary fashion. Now look at this program and how it is put together. It's written in C and so the I/O will look a bit different from what we've been doing, but essentially all it does is set up the files and then write the numbers 0–16 to one of them.

16.5.2.2 Putting the accelerometer on the SPI bus

Now let's return to the `ADXL345` three-axis accelerometer. As mentioned earlier, this device is designed to interface to either the I2C or SPI bus. We've already done the former, so here let's try the latter. First we deal with the wiring, which is summarized in table 16.10.

I give the connections between the `ADXL345` (leftmost column) and *either* the `SPI0` or `SPI1` bus. I recommend using the `SPI0` bus because, as already mentioned, in order to use the `SPI1` bus, one must first unmount the HDMI. Verify that the accelerometer works on the SPI bus as it did on the I2C bus.

This concludes the discussion of buses. We've left out lots of interesting aspects— as well as interesting and useful buses, such as UARTs. But if you understand and can use both SPI and I2C buses, you should have no trouble in picking up what you need to know about any other bus.

Table 16.10. Connections for the ADXL345 on an SPI bus.

ADXL345 pin name	BBB pin (SPI0)	BBB pin (SPI1)
GND	P9-1 (GND)	P9-1 (GND)
V_{cc}	P9-3 (DC_3.3V)	P9-3 (DC_3.3V)
CS	P9-17 (SPI0_CS0)	P9-28 (SPI1_CS0)
INT1	N/C	N/C
INT2	N/C	N/C
SD0 (MISO)	P9-21 (SPI0_D0)	P9-29 (SPI1_D0)
SDA (MOSI)	P9-18 (SPI0_D1)	P9-30 (SPI1_D1)
SCL (CLK)	P9-22 (SPI0_SCLK)	P9-31 (SPI1_SCLK)

Part III

Solutions to homework

IOP Publishing

Practical Analog, Digital, and Embedded Electronics for Scientists

Brett D DePaola

Chapter 17

RC circuits

Solutions to chapter 2

The circuit is reproduced in figure 17.1. Treat this like a voltage divider:

$$\frac{V_{\text{out}}}{V_{\text{in}}} = \frac{R}{R + Z_C}, \tag{17.1}$$

where

$$Z_C = \frac{1}{j\omega c}, \tag{17.2}$$

Then,

$$\frac{V_{\text{out}}}{V_{\text{in}}} = \frac{R}{R + \dfrac{1}{j\omega C}} \tag{17.3a}$$

$$= \frac{j\omega RC}{j\omega RC + 1} \tag{17.3b}$$

$$= \frac{j\omega RC(1 - j\omega RC)}{1 + \omega^2 R^2 C^2} \tag{17.3c}$$

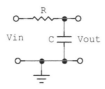

Figure 17.1. A simple RC circuit.

doi:10.1088/978-0-7503-3491-4ch17

$$= \frac{\omega RC(\omega RC + j)}{1 + \omega^2 R^2 C^2}. \tag{17.3d}$$

Recalling that for any complex number z, the phase of z is given by $\tan \phi = \text{Im}(z)/\text{Re}(z)$. Then, from equation (17.3d)

$$\phi = \tan^{-1}\left(\frac{1}{\omega RC}\right). \tag{17.4}$$

Returning to equation (17.3d),

$$\left| \frac{V_{\text{out}}}{V_{\text{in}}} \right| = \frac{\omega RC \sqrt{\omega^2 R^2 C^2 + 1}}{\omega^2 R^2 C^2 + 1} \tag{17.5a}$$

$$= \frac{\omega RC}{\sqrt{\omega^2 R^2 C^2 + 1}}. \tag{17.5b}$$

Finally, for the 3 dB point,

$$\frac{1}{\sqrt{2}} = \frac{\omega_{3\,\text{dB}} RC}{\sqrt{1 + \omega_{3\,\text{dB}}^2 R^2 C^2}} \tag{17.6a}$$

$$1 + \omega_{3\,\text{dB}}^2 R^2 C^2 = 2\omega_{3\,\text{dB}}^2 R^2 C^2 \tag{17.6b}$$

$$\omega_{3\,\text{dB}} = \frac{1}{RC} \tag{17.6c}$$

$$f_{3\,\text{dB}} = \frac{1}{2\pi RC}. \tag{17.6d}$$

IOP Publishing

Practical Analog, Digital, and Embedded Electronics for Scientists

Brett D DePaola

Chapter 18

Diodes and transistors

Solutions to chapter 3

The circuit is reproduced in figure 18.1. For this problem we want

- $+V \equiv V_{cc} = 15$ V,
- $i^{(q)} = 2$ mA,
- frequency in 'audio range': 20 Hz $\leqslant f \leqslant$ 20 kHz.

First set the emitter quiescent voltage: $V^{(q)} = V_{cc}/2 = 7.5$ V. For this to be the case, V_b must be one diode drop above 7.5 V, or $V_b = 8.1$ V. We'll come back to that in a moment.

If $V^{(q)} = 7.5$ V, then for $i^{(q)} = 2$ mA, R_e must be

$$R_e = \frac{7.5 \text{ V}}{2.0 \text{ mA}} = 3.75k \rightarrow 3.9k,$$

where we have substituted a common resistor value for the 'exact' one.

Returning to the base voltage, in order to achieve that value, we set the voltage divider to be

$$8.1 \text{ V} = \frac{R_2}{R_1 + R_2} 15 \text{ V} \tag{18.1a}$$

$$\frac{R_2}{R_1 + R_2} = \frac{8.1}{15}. \tag{18.1b}$$

We obtain a second equation for R_1 and R_2 by requiring that the output impedance of the voltage divider be small compared to the impedance looking into the base:

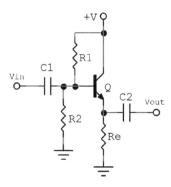

Figure 18.1. Single-supply emitter follower for bipolar input.

$$\frac{R_1 R_2}{R_1 + R_2} \ll h_{FE} R_e \tag{18.2a}$$

$$\frac{R_1 R_2}{R_1 + R_2} = \frac{100}{10} R_e = 39k, \tag{18.2b}$$

where we interpret $\ll$ to mean 'an order of magnitude less', assume a value for $h_{FE} = 100$, and use the above value of $R_e = 3.9k$.

Dividing equation (18.2b) by equation (18.1b) gives us

$$R_1 = \frac{(39k)(15)}{8.1} = 72k \rightarrow 68k, \tag{18.3}$$

where we have again substituted a 'common' resistor value the 'exact' one.

Substituting this value of R_1 back into equation (18.1b) leads to

$$R_2 = \frac{(68k)(8.1)}{6.9} = 79.8k \rightarrow 82k. \tag{18.4}$$

As a check, putting the approximated values of R_1 and R_2 back into equation (18.1a) gives us

$$V_b = \frac{R_2}{R_1 + R_2}(15\text{ V}) = \frac{68k}{82k + 68k}(15\text{ V}) = 8.2\text{ V}, \tag{18.5}$$

which is tolerably close to the optimal value of 8.1 V.

All that is left is to compute the capacitor values. First of all, we want these to serve as high-pass filters, with the low end 3 dB point at 20 Hz. The expression we derived for the 3 dB point is

$$f_{3\,dB} = \frac{1}{2\pi RC}. \tag{18.6}$$

Or,

$$C = \frac{1}{2\pi f_{3\,\text{dB}} R}. \qquad (18.7)$$

All we now have to do is insert the right value of R into equation (18.7) and solve for C. Let's start with determining C_2. In this case, the appropriate value for R is $R_e = 3.9k$. Then,

$$C_2 = \frac{1}{2\pi f_{3\,\text{dB}} R} = \frac{1}{(2\pi)(20\ \text{Hz})(3.9 \times 10^3\ \Omega)} = 2\ \mu\text{F}. \qquad (18.8)$$

The computation for C_1 is a bit more complicated. For R we have the output impedance of the voltage divider in parallel with the impedance looking into the base of the transistor. But we designed the voltage divider such that its output impedance would be a tenth of the base impedance. Therefore we can use the 90% of the divider's output impedance for R. That is,

$$R = 90\% \frac{R_2}{R_1 + R_1} = (0.9)\frac{82k}{68k + 82k} \approx 0.5k. \qquad (18.9)$$

Using this in equation (18.7) gives us

$$C_1 = \frac{1}{(2\pi)(20\ \text{Hz})(500\ \Omega)} \approx 16\ \mu\text{F}, \qquad (18.10)$$

To summarize,

$$R_e = 3.9k \qquad (18.11a)$$

$$R_1 = 68k \qquad (18.11b)$$

$$R_2 = 82k \qquad (18.11c)$$

$$C_1 = 16\ \mu\text{F} \qquad (18.11d)$$

$$C_2 = 2\ \mu\text{F}. \qquad (18.11e)$$

A bare-bones circuit is shown in figure 18.2. The design constraints are $V_{cc} = 20\ V$, and the output current is 2 mA.

I choose V_e to be two diode drops (2×0.6 V) below V_{cc}. Then, $V_e = 20\ V - 1.2\ V = 18.2\ V$. Then, for a current of 2 mA, the combined resistance of R_1 and P_1 (which we'll define to be R) are

$$R = \frac{1.2\ V}{2\ \text{mA}} = 0.6k. \qquad (18.12)$$

I can choose $P_1 = 500\ \Omega$ and $R_1 = 680\ \Omega$, for example.

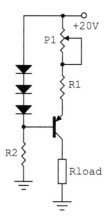

Figure 18.2. Simple adjustable current source.

The three diodes ensure that the base is at the correct potential as long as current can flow through the diodes. The value of R_2 is therefore not critical; $4.7k$ would be fine.

While we're at it, let's determine the compliance of this circuit. The transistor will continue to function as planned so long as $V_c \leqslant V_e$. That is,

$$V_c \leqslant V_e \tag{18.13a}$$

$$i_c R_L \leqslant V_{cc} - i_e R_e \tag{18.13b}$$

$$(2 \text{ mA})R_L \leqslant 20 \text{ V} - (2 \text{ mA})(0.6k) \tag{18.13c}$$

$$R_L \leqslant 10k - 1.2k = 8.8k. \tag{18.13d}$$

Thus, the maximum load resistance is $8.8k$.
The current sink circuit has been reproduced in figure 18.3. The goal is to determine the upper limit on R_L for which the design current of 1 mA will still flow.
First we recognize that

$$V_b = \frac{R_2}{R_1 + R_2}(15 \text{ V}) \tag{18.14a}$$

$$= \frac{(12k)(15 \text{ V})}{112k} \tag{18.14b}$$

$$= 1.6 \text{ V}. \tag{18.14c}$$

This means that $V_e = 1.0$ V. Therefore

$$i_e = \frac{V_e}{R_e} \tag{18.15a}$$

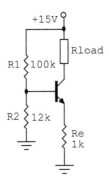

Figure 18.3. Simple current source.

$$= \frac{1.0 \text{ V}}{1k} \tag{18.15b}$$

$$= 1 \text{ mA, and} \tag{18.15c}$$

$$i_c \approx i_e. \tag{18.15d}$$

So the circuit does indeed sink 1 mA.

But a requirement for the transistor to perform as expected is that $V_c \geqslant V_b \implies V_c \geqslant 1.6 \text{ V} \implies V_L \leqslant 15 \text{ V} - 1.6 \text{ V} = 13.4 \text{ V}$. Therefore,

$$R_L \leqslant \frac{13.4 \text{ V}}{1 \text{ mA}} = 13.4k. \tag{18.16}$$

IOP Publishing

Practical Analog, Digital, and Embedded Electronics for Scientists

Brett D DePaola

Chapter 19

Op amps 1

Solutions to chapter 4

If the op-amp is operating correctly, $V_- = V_+$. But V_+ is at ground. Therefore, V_- is at virtual ground. Then the impedance to ground, as seen by V_{in} is R_1 (figure 19.1). Since for this problem we desire the input impedance to be $10k$, this means that $R_1 = 10k$.

The gain of an the simple inverting amplifier is

$$G = -\frac{R_2}{R_1}. \tag{19.1}$$

For the desired $G = -5$ and $R_1 = 10k$, we then have

$$R_2 = -GR_1 = -(-5)(10k) = 50k. \tag{19.2}$$

From the text, and referring to figure 19.2, we have

$$G = \frac{R_2}{R_1} + 1. \tag{19.3}$$

Then, for a gain of $+5$, the ratio of R_2 to R_1 must be 4. No restrictions on the output impedance is given, so we can choose, for example,

$$R_1 = 10k \tag{19.4a}$$

$$R_2 = 4R_1 = (4)(10k) = 40k. \tag{19.4b}$$

doi:10.1088/978-0-7503-3491-4ch19

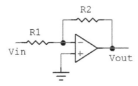

Figure 19.1. Circuit of a simple inverting amplifier.

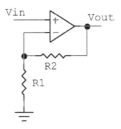

Figure 19.2. Circuit for a simple non-inverting amplifier.

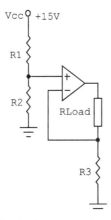

Figure 19.3. Circuit of an op-amp-based current sink.

The schematic in figure 19.3 is based on one shown in the lecture section. All that remains is to come up with component values based on the following criteria:
- Supply voltages are ±15 V.
- The current sinks 3.0 mA.

Suppose we choose $R_3 = 1k$. Then

$$V_- = iR_3 \tag{19.5a}$$

$$= (3 \text{ mA})(3k) \tag{19.5b}$$

$$= 9 \text{ V.} \tag{19.5c}$$

To make $V_- = 9$ V, we need to force V_+ to have this value. Then, treating the R_1 and R_2 combination as a voltage divider,

$$9 \text{ V} = \frac{R_2}{R_1 + R_2}\left(15 \text{ V}\right) \tag{19.6a}$$

$$\frac{15}{9} = 1 + \frac{R_1}{R_2} \tag{19.6b}$$

$$R_2 = \frac{3}{2}R_1. \tag{19.6c}$$

So if we choose $R_1 = 10k$, then

$$R_2 = \frac{3}{2}R_1 \tag{19.7a}$$

$$= \frac{3}{2}\left(10k\right) \tag{19.7b}$$

$$= 15k. \tag{19.7c}$$

Now for compliance. The maximum value for the output of the op-amp is 15 V. Furthermore, the circuit was designed such that the voltage on $R_3 = 9.0$ V. Therefore, the maximum voltage across the load is

$$V_{L\text{max}} = 15 \text{ V} - 9 \text{ V} = 6 \text{ V}. \tag{19.8}$$

Because we desire 3 mA to flow through R_L,

$$R_L \leqslant \frac{6 \text{ V}}{3 \text{ mA}} = 2k. \tag{19.9}$$

Thus, the maximum value of $R_L = 2k$.

IOP Publishing

Practical Analog, Digital, and Embedded Electronics for Scientists

Brett D DePaola

Chapter 20

Op-amps 2

Solutions to chapters 5 and 13

See figure 20.1. In order that the lower threshold can be >0, we've placed a resistor between V_+ and V_{TTL}. Now all we need to do is determine some values for resistors 1–4 such that the circuit has the following characteristics:

- $V_{cc} = +15$ V,
- $V_{ee} = -15$ V,
- $V_{TTL} = +5$ V,
- $V_{threshold} = 3.0$ V,
- $V_{hyst} = 0.1$ V.

Use $V_{threshold}$ as the lower voltage threshold, and V_{hyst} as the hysteresis.

If we choose R_4 to be small compared to the other resistors, then when the output of the comparator is high, $V_{OUT} \approx V_{TTL}$. Then, when $V_{out} = 0$, R_1 is in parallel with R_2 and when $V_{out} = +5$, R_1 is in parallel with R_3. Therefore, for the given desired parameters,

$$\frac{3.0}{5.0} = \frac{R_1 \| R_2}{R_1 \| R_2 + R_3} \tag{20.1a}$$

$$= \frac{R_1 R_2}{R_1 R_2 + R_1 R_3 + R_2 R_3}, \tag{20.1b}$$

$$\frac{3.1}{5.0} = \frac{R_2}{R_2 + R_1 \| R_3} \tag{20.2a}$$

$$= \frac{R_1 R_2 + R_3 R_3}{R_1 R_2 + R_1 R_3 + R_2 R_3}. \tag{20.2b}$$

doi:10.1088/978-0-7503-3491-4ch20

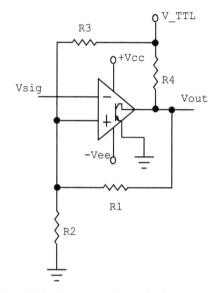

Figure 20.1. Comparator circuit that has hysteresis.

Dividing equation (20.2b) by equation (20.1b) gives

$$\frac{3.1}{3.0} = \frac{R_1 R_2 + R_2 R_3}{R_1 R_2} \tag{20.3a}$$

$$= 1 + \frac{R_3}{R_1}. \tag{20.3b}$$

Or

$$R_1 = 30 R_3. \tag{20.4}$$

Plugging equation (20.4) into equation (20.1b) gives

$$\frac{3.0}{5.0} = \frac{30 R_3 R_2}{30 R_3 (R_2 + R_3) + R_2 R_3} \tag{20.5a}$$

$$= \frac{30 R_2}{31 R_2 + 30 R_3}. \tag{20.5b}$$

Solving for R_2 in terms of R_3 gives

$$R_2 = \frac{18}{11.4} R_3 \tag{20.6a}$$

$$\approx \frac{3}{2} R_3. \tag{20.6b}$$

For $R_4 = 1k$, we can arbitrarily choose $R_3 = 10k$. Then

$$R_1 = 300k \qquad (20.7a)$$

$$R_2 = 15k \qquad (20.7b)$$

$$R_3 = 10k. \qquad (20.7c)$$

Consider the classic RC relaxation oscillator circuit shown in figure 20.2. This circuit was symmetrically designed in order to have a 50% duty cycle. For example, because the capacitor is charging and discharging through the same resistor, R_1, and because potentials are symmetrical about zero, the charge time is equal to the discharge time. Thus, to determine the frequency as a function of R_1, R_1, and R_1, we need compute only one of either the discharge or the charge time, and multiply that by two to get the period. Then we take the reciprocal of the period to obtain the frequency.

Let's just consider the discharging capacitor. The general formula is

$$V(t) = V_0 e^{-t/R_1 C} + k. \qquad (20.8)$$

The strategy, then, is to use boundary conditions to determine V_0 and k, then solve the equation for t.

To help determine the boundary conditions, look at the graph shown in figure 20.3. The oscillator output is shown in red; the voltage on the capacitor is in blue. The vertical scale is labeled by the first column to the right of the graph. We see that when the output of the comparator is low, here $-V_p$, the capacitor will discharge through R_1. If allowed to completely discharge, the capacitor voltage would ultimately reach the comparator output of $-V_p$, as indicated by the dashed portion of the curve.

We also see on the graph that when

$$V_+ = \pm \frac{R_2}{R_2 + R_3} V_p, \qquad (20.9)$$

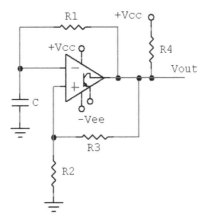

Figure 20.2. The classic RC relaxation oscillator circuit.

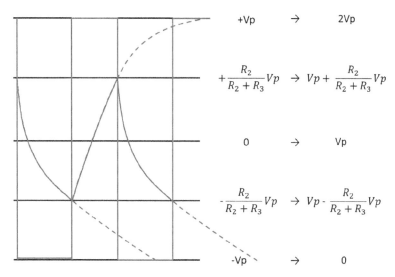

Figure 20.3. Representative output of the classic relaxation circuit of figure 20.2. The red square wave is the oscillator output; the blue curve is the voltage on the capacitor. The horizontal axis is time. The output oscillates between $\pm V_p$. In the analysis, we can choose to shift the vertical scale upwards by V_p, as shown.

the comparator's output flips sign.

We know that $V(t \to \infty) = -V_p$. Then, $k = -V_p$. Now consider $t = 0$. We know that

$$V(t = 0) = \frac{R_2}{R_2 + R_3} V_p. \tag{20.10}$$

Therefore, from equation (20.8),

$$V_0 - V_p = \frac{R_2}{R_2 + R_3} V_p. \tag{20.11}$$

Or

$$V_0 = V_p\left(1 + \frac{R_2}{R_1 + R_2}\right). \tag{20.12}$$

Substituting into equation (20.8), for all times t,

$$V(t) = V_p\left(1 + \frac{R_2}{R_1 + R_2}\right)e^{-t/R_1 C} - V_p. \tag{20.13}$$

We now need to find the time τ required for the capacitor voltage to decay to $-\left(\frac{R_2}{R_2 + R_3} V_p\right)$. Then,

$$V(\tau) \equiv -\left(\frac{R_2}{R_2 + R_3} V_p\right) = V_p\left(1 + \frac{R_2}{R_1 + R_2}\right)e^{-\tau/R_1 C} - V_p. \tag{20.14}$$

Solving for τ, multiplying that expression by two and inverting, gives the frequency:

$$f = \left[2R_1C \ln\left(1 + \frac{2R_2}{R_3}\right) \right]^{-1}. \tag{20.15}$$

Here's an alternative solution. Shifting the vertical axis of the graph in figure 20.3 up by V_p, all the voltages will be as labeled in the right-most column in that figure. It is clear, then, that k from equation (20.8) will be 0. Furthermore, the charging/discharging of the capacitor flips at

$$V_+ = V_p \pm \frac{R_2}{R_2 + R_3} V_p. \tag{20.16}$$

We then see that

$$V_0 = V_p + \frac{R_2}{R_2 + R_3} V_p. \tag{20.17}$$

Equation (20.8) then becomes

$$V(t) = V_p\left(1 + \frac{R_2}{R_1 + R_2}\right) e^{-t/R_1C}. \tag{20.18}$$

Finally,

$$V(\tau) \equiv V_p\left(1 - \frac{R_2}{R_2 + R_3}\right) = V_p\left(1 + \frac{R_2}{R_1 + R_2}\right) e^{-\tau/R_1C}, \tag{20.19}$$

which is equivalent to equation (20.14).

The Wien bridge oscillator circuit is shown in figure 20.4. In this exercise we deduce the magnitude and phase of the positive feedback. We start by defining the parallel RC network's impedance as Z_1 and the series RC network's impedance as Z_2. Then,

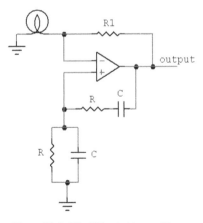

Figure 20.4. The Wien bridge oscillator.

$$\frac{V_+}{V_{\text{out}}} = \frac{Z_1}{Z_1 + Z_2}. \tag{20.20}$$

Now we simply derive expressions for Z_1 and Z_2, plug these into equation (20.20) and do some algebra.

$$Z_1 = \frac{RZ_C}{R + Z_C} \tag{20.21a}$$

$$= \frac{R}{1 + j\omega RC}, \tag{20.21b}$$

$$Z_2 = R + Z_C \tag{20.22a}$$

$$= \frac{-j + \omega RC}{\omega C} \tag{20.22b}$$

$$= \frac{R}{1 + j\omega RC}. \tag{20.22c}$$

Inserting these into equation (20.20) gives

$$\frac{V_+}{V_{\text{out}}} = \frac{\dfrac{R}{1 + j\omega RC}}{\dfrac{R}{1 + j\omega RC} + \dfrac{\omega RC - j}{\omega C}} \tag{20.23a}$$

$$= \frac{\dfrac{\omega RC}{\omega C(1 + j\omega RC)}}{\dfrac{\omega RC + (1 + j\omega RC)(\omega RC - j)}{\omega C(1 + j\omega RC)}} \tag{20.23b}$$

$$= \frac{\omega RC}{\omega RC + \omega RC - j + j\omega^2 R^2 C^2 + \omega RC} = \frac{\omega RC}{3\omega RC - j(1 - \omega^2 R^2 C^2)} \tag{20.23c}$$

$$= \frac{\omega RC[3\omega RC + j(1 - \omega^2 R^2 C^2)]}{[3\omega RC - j(1 - \omega^2 R^2 C^2)][3\omega RC + j(1 - \omega^2 R^2 C^2)]} \tag{20.23d}$$

$$= \frac{\omega RC[3\omega RC + j(1 - \omega^2 R^2 C^2)]}{9\omega^2 R^2 C^2 + (1 - \omega^2 R^2 C^2)^2} = \frac{\omega RC[3\omega RC + j(1 - \omega^2 R^2 C^2)]}{1 + \omega^4 R^4 C^4 + 7\omega^2 R^2 C^2} \tag{20.23e}$$

$$= \frac{\omega RC}{1 + \omega^4 R^4 C^4 + 7\omega^2 R^2 C^2}[3\omega RC + j(1 - \omega^2 R^2 C^2)]. \tag{20.23f}$$

From equation (20.23f), we trivially find the phase:

$$\phi = \tan^{-1}\left(\frac{1 - \omega^2 R^2 C^2}{3\omega RC}\right). \tag{20.24}$$

Also from equation (20.23f), we will find the magnitude. Note that when computing both the phase and the magnitude, we don't have to deal with the purely real term in from of the square brackets of equation (20.23f): for the phase, that term cancels out; for the magnitude we just place that term in front of the magnitude of the term in square brackets.

$$\left.\frac{V_+}{V_{\text{out}}}\right| = \tag{20.25a}$$

$$\frac{\omega RC}{1 + \omega^4 R^4 C^4 + 7\omega^2 R^2 C^2}\sqrt{[3\omega RC + j(1 - \omega^2 R^2 C^2)][3\omega RC - j(1 - \omega^2 R^2 C^2)]}$$

$$= \frac{\omega RC\sqrt{9\omega^2 R^2 C^2 + (1 - \omega^2 R^2 C^2)}}{1 + \omega^4 R^4 C^4 + 7\omega^2 R^2 C^2} \tag{20.25b}$$

$$= \frac{\omega RC}{\sqrt{\omega^4 R^4 C^4 + 7\omega^2 R^2 C^2 + 1}}. \tag{20.25c}$$

We now need to show that at resonance, the phase of the feedback is 0. First though, we need to show what the resonant frequency is. It'll be the frequency for which equation (20.25c) is a maximum. Therefore, setting the derivative of equation (20.25c) with respect to ω equal to zero, and solving for ω gives us

$$\frac{d}{d\omega}\left|\frac{V_+}{V_{\text{out}}}\right| = \frac{RC}{\sqrt{\omega^4 R^4 C^4 + 7\omega^2 R^2 C^2 + 1}}$$
$$- \frac{\frac{1}{2}\omega RC(4\omega^3 R^4 C^4 + 14\omega R^2 C^2)}{(\omega^4 R^4 C^4 + 7\omega^2 R^2 C^2 + 1)^{3/2}}. \tag{20.26}$$

And so,

$$-\omega^4 R^4 C^4 + 1 = 0 \tag{20.27a}$$

$$\omega = \frac{1}{RC}. \tag{20.27b}$$

Plugging this result into equations (20.25c) and (20.23f) gives

$$\text{At resonance:} \left|\frac{V_+}{V_{\text{out}}}\right| = \frac{1}{3}, \text{ and} \tag{20.28a}$$

$$\phi = 0. \tag{20.28b}$$

We'll break up finding the period into first finding the capacitor's discharge time, τ_1, and charge time, τ_2. The period, $\tau = \tau_1 + \tau_2$.

The general equation for the voltage on a discharging capacitor as a function of time, t_1 is

$$V(t_1) = V_{01} \exp\left(\frac{-t_1}{R_2 C}\right) + k_1. \tag{20.29}$$

The boundary conditions for the discharging capacitor in the schematic of figure 20.5 are

$$V(t_1 \to 0) = \frac{2}{3} V_{cc} \tag{20.30a}$$

$$V(t_1 \to \infty) = 0. \tag{20.30b}$$

Applying boundary condition (20.30b) to equation (20.29) gives

$$0 = V_{01} \times 0 + k_1 \text{ or} \tag{20.31a}$$

$$k_1 = 0. \tag{20.31b}$$

Applying boundary condition (20.30a) to equation (20.29) gives

$$\frac{2}{3} V_{cc} = V_{01}. \tag{20.32}$$

Then, equation (20.29) becomes

$$V(t_1) = \frac{2}{3} V_{cc} \exp\left(\frac{-t_1}{R_2 C}\right). \tag{20.33}$$

For $t_1 \to \tau_1$, we get

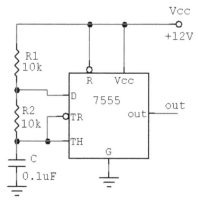

Figure 20.5. The classic 7555 timer chip wired up as a relaxation oscillator.

$$V(\tau_1) = \frac{1}{3}V_{cc} = \frac{2}{3}V_{cc}\exp\left(\frac{-\tau_1}{R_2C}\right). \tag{20.34}$$

Or

$$\tau_1 = R_2C\ln 2. \tag{20.35}$$

For a charging capacitor, the general equation is

$$V(t_2) = k_2 - V_{02}\exp\left(\frac{-t_2}{RC}\right), \tag{20.36}$$

where $R \equiv R_1 + R_2$.

The boundary conditions for the charging capacitor in the schematic of figure 20.5 are

$$V(t_2 \to 0) = \frac{1}{3}V_{cc} \tag{20.37a}$$

$$V(t_2 \to \infty) = V_{cc}. \tag{20.37b}$$

Applying boundary condition (20.37b) to equation (20.36) gives

$$V_{cc} = k_2. \tag{20.38}$$

Applying boundary condition (20.37a) to equation (20.36) gives

$$\frac{1}{3}V_{cc} = V_{cc} - V_{02} \text{ or} \tag{20.39a}$$

$$V_{02} = \frac{2}{3}V_{cc}. \tag{20.39b}$$

Then, equation (20.36) becomes

$$V(t_2) = V_{cc} - \frac{2}{3}V_{cc}\exp\left(\frac{-t_2}{RC}\right). \tag{20.40}$$

And

$$V(\tau_2) = \frac{2}{3}V_{cc} = V_{cc}\left[1 - \frac{2}{3}\exp\left(\frac{-\tau_2}{RC}\right)\right]. \tag{20.41}$$

Or

$$\tau_2 = R_C\ln 2. \tag{20.42}$$

Except for $R_2 \to R$, this is the same result as equation (20.35) for the discharging capacitor—which should not be surprising since it's the same capacitor and the charge/discharge is over the same voltage range. Substituting the appropriate resistance, we get

$$\tau_2 = (R_1 + R_2)C \ln 2. \tag{20.43}$$

Finally, we add the charge and discharge times to give us the period:

$$\tau = \tau_1 + \tau_2 \tag{20.44a}$$

$$= R_2 C \ln 2 + (R_1 + R_2)C \ln 2 \tag{20.44b}$$

$$= (R_1 + 2R_2)C \ln 2. \tag{20.44c}$$

20.5 Square waves from a 7555 (from lab 13.3.1)

The trick here is to find a way to charge and discharge the timing capacitor through the same value of resistance. It seems impossible to do this with a simple modification of the circuit of figure 20.5. But here's the trick: the output of the 7555 goes rail to rail. Thus, when the output is 'high', it is at the supply voltage. So, charge your discharge your capacitor through a resistor R to the **discharge** of the 7555, but charge it from the *output* of the 7555, through a second resistor R, rather than charging from the supply voltage itself. This is shown schematically in figure 20.6. Note the diode in the charging leg of the circuit. This is necessary because otherwise when the output goes low, here 0, the capacitor will discharge to that 'ground' as well as through the *discharge*. Then the discharge will be through two legs in parallel, each having an impedance of R. Then, effectively, the capacitor will be discharging to ground though a resistance of $R/2$, making the discharge leg faster than the charge leg. The diode prevents a discharge to the output.

So now we need only compute the period or frequency of the oscillator. Consider the analysis of the classic 7555 relaxation circuit, starting from equation (20.29).

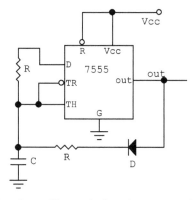

Figure 20.6. A 7555 relaxation oscillator, wired to give an output having a 50% duty cycle.

This resulted in a discharge time shown in equation (20.35). But here, the charging time and discharging time are equal. Therefore,

$$T = RC2\ln 2. \tag{20.45}$$

Or

$$f = [RC2\ln 2]^{-1} \simeq [1.4RC]^{-1}, \tag{20.46}$$

as claimed in the lab text.

Practical Analog, Digital, and Embedded Electronics for Scientists

Brett D DePaola

Chapter 21

Digital gates

Solutions to chapter 6

To solve this problem I first looked at the truth tables for several simple gates, as shown in tables 21.1–21.4. For a two-input, one-output logic circuit, I can then always express Q as a 4 bit number. That is, for possible inputs correspond to the binary numbers 0–3 (00, 01, 10, 11) and Q has a value for each of these. For example, for a NAND gate, I can express $Q = 0111$, where I've chosen to place the value of Q that corresponds to '11' as the left-most digit. Then $Q_{XOR} = 0110$. So now we can re-frame the question as what logic operations can I do to the outputs of the various gates to 'construct' a XOR? I note that if I bit-wise AND the output of a NAND with the output of an OR, I get a XOR. That is, $0111\&1110 = 0110$, where & denotes a bit-wise AND. (This notation is used in many computer languages.) To further elaborate, 0 ANDed with anything is a 0; 1 ANDed with 1 is 1. So moving from left to right I can AND the outputs of a NAND with the output of an OR:

    0111 ANDed with

    1110 gives

    0110.

This is exactly what I did in figure 21.1: A and B are both NANDed and ORed, with the outputs of those gates shown using the above notation. Then those outputs are ANDed to give the desired result.

Consider the two circuits shown in figure 21.2. Show that the truth tables for these two circuits are identical.

Examine table 21.5. In the first column I list all possible combinations of inputs A, B, and C. In the second column I list the output of the first gate in the upper figure; that is, the result of combining inputs A and B with the first gate in the upper part of the figure. In the third column I re-state the value of argument C. In the fourth

Table 21.1. Truth table for the NAND operation. A and B are the inputs and Q is the output.

NAND		
A	B	Q
0	0	1
0	1	1
1	0	1
1	1	0

Table 21.2. Truth table for the OR operation.

OR		
A	B	Q
0	0	0
0	1	1
1	0	1
1	1	1

Table 21.3. Truth table for the AND operation.

AND		
A	B	Q
0	0	0
0	1	0
1	0	0
1	1	1

Table 21.4. Truth table for the NOR operation.

XOR		
A	B	Q
0	0	0
0	1	1
1	0	1
1	1	0

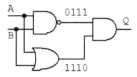

Figure 21.1. One way to make a XOR from other gates.

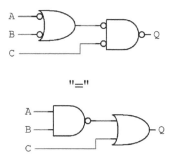

Figure 21.2. These two circuits are logically equivalent.

Table 21.5. Truth table for both logic circuits.

Inputs A B C	1st Upper gate out AB	C C	Upper out Q	1st Lower gate out AB	C C	Lower out Q
000	1	0	1	1	1	1
001	1	1	1	1	1	1
010	1	0	1	1	1	1
011	1	1	1	1	1	1
100	1	0	1	1	1	1
101	1	1	1	1	1	1
110	0	0	0	0	0	0
111	0	1	1	1	0	1

column I list the final output of the right-most gate in the upper figure. That is, this is the result of combining the contents of the previous two columns, using the right-most gate in the upper part of the figure.

The final three columns follow the same pattern as the previous columns, except using the gates in the lower schematic in figure 21.2. Clearly, the two columns labeled Q are identical.

See figure 21.3. The 16 inputs are on the left, with lowest 'bit' on the bottom. The 4 bit binary number used to select which input gets passed is labeled $A0–A3$ on the right.

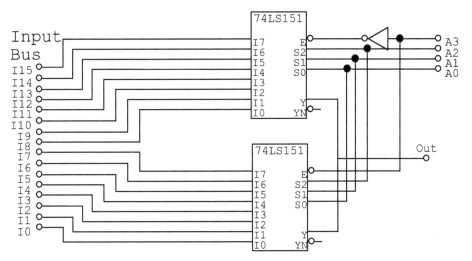

Figure 21.3. Wiring two '151s to act as a 16-input MUX.

Table 21.6. Truth table for herbivores among the animals in the Chinese Zodiac.

Animal #	$A_3 = S_2$	$A_2 = S_1$	$A_1 = S_0$	A_0	I_n	$Q = Y$	
0	0	0	0	0	0	0	
1	0	0	0	1	0	0	0
2	0	0	1	0	1	1	
3	0	0	1	1	1	0	$\overline{A_0}$
4	0	1	0	0	2	1	
5	0	1	0	1	2	0	$\overline{A_0}$
6	0	1	1	0	3	0	
7	0	1	1	1	3	1	A_0
8	1	0	0	0	4	1	
9	1	0	0	1	4	1	1
10	1	0	1	0	5	1	
11	1	0	1	1	5	0	$\overline{A_0}$
12	1	1	0	0	6	0	
13	1	1	0	1	6	0	0
14	1	1	1	0	7	0	
15	1	1	1	1	7	0	0

The order of the animals is: Rat, Ox, Tiger, Rabbit, Dragon, Snake, Horse, Goat, Monkey, Rooster, Dog, and Pig. However, I have no idea what the eating preferences for some of these animals are. But based on my best guesses, the truth table should look like that in table 21.6. (See text for an explanation of the table.) The corresponding circuit is shown in figure 21.4.

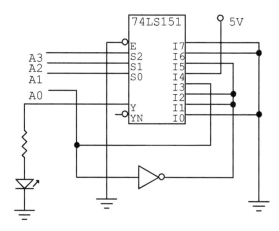

Figure 21.4. Implementation of the truth table of table 21.6 using the '151 MUX.

Practical Analog, Digital, and Embedded Electronics for Scientists

Brett D DePaola

Chapter 22

Digital–analog, analog–digital and phase-locked loops

Solutions to chapter 7

We start with

$$\langle S_p \rangle = \frac{1}{T} \left[\int_0^{T/2} A_s \cos(\omega t + \phi)dt - \int_{T/2}^T A_s \cos(\omega t + \phi)dt \right], \qquad (22.1)$$

with $T = \frac{2\pi}{\omega}$. Then,

$$\langle S_p \rangle = \frac{\omega A_s}{2\pi\omega} \left[\int_\phi^{\pi+\phi} \cos(u)du - \int_{\pi+\phi}^{2\pi+\phi} \cos(u)du \right] \qquad (22.2a)$$

$$= \frac{A_s}{2\pi} \left[\sin(u)\big|_\phi^{\pi+\phi} - \sin(u)\big|_{\pi+\phi}^{2\pi+\phi} \right] \qquad (22.2b)$$

$$= \frac{A_s}{2\pi} [\sin(\pi + \phi) - \sin(\phi) - \sin(2\pi + \phi) + \sin(\pi + \phi)] \qquad (22.2c)$$

$$= -\frac{2A_s}{\pi} \sin(\phi). \qquad (22.2d)$$

In figure 22.1, show that the magnitude of the gain is 1, independent of frequency. Then show that the output phase lags the input by $-2\tan^{-1}(\omega RC)$.

Treating the circuitry near the non-inverting input as a voltage divider:

$$V_+ = \frac{Z_C}{Z_C + R} V_{\text{in}} \qquad (22.3a)$$

doi:10.1088/978-0-7503-3491-4ch22

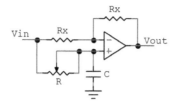

Figure 22.1. A simple phase shifter.

$$= \frac{\dfrac{1}{j\omega C}}{\dfrac{1}{j\omega C} + R} V_{\text{in}} \quad (22.3b)$$

$$= \frac{V_{\text{in}}}{1 + j\omega RC}. \quad (22.3c)$$

Now looking at the current flowing through the two R_x resisters:

$$\frac{V_{\text{in}} - V_-}{R_x} = \frac{V_- - V_{\text{out}}}{R_x} \quad (22.4a)$$

$$V_{\text{out}} = 2V_- - V_{\text{in}} \quad (22.4b)$$

$$= \frac{2V_{\text{in}}}{1 j\omega RC} - V_{\text{in}} \quad (22.4c)$$

$$= \frac{1 - j\omega RC}{1 + j\omega RC} V_{\text{in}}. \quad (22.4d)$$

Then,

$$\frac{V_{\text{out}}}{V_{\text{in}}} = \frac{1 - j\omega RC}{1 + j\omega RC} \quad (22.5a)$$

$$= \frac{(1 - j\omega RC)^2}{1 + \omega^2 R^2 C^2} \quad (22.5b)$$

$$= \frac{(1 - \omega^2 R^2 C^2) - j2\omega RC}{1 + \omega^2 R^2 C^2}. \quad (22.5c)$$

Now find the magnitude:

$$\left| \frac{V_{\text{out}}}{V_{\text{in}}} \right| = \frac{\sqrt{(1 - \omega^2 R^2 C^2)^2 + 4\omega^2 R^2 C^2}}{1 + j\omega RC} \quad (22.6a)$$

$$= 1. \quad (22.6b)$$

Thus, the magnitude of the gain is 1, independent of the frequency or any of the components. Now the phase:

$$\tan(\phi) = \frac{-2\omega RC}{1 - \omega^2 R^2 C^2}. \tag{22.7}$$

Then defining

$$u \equiv \omega RC, \tag{22.8}$$

we get

$$\tan(\phi) = \frac{-2u}{1 - u^2}. \tag{22.9}$$

Solving for u,

$$u^2 \tan(\phi) - 2u - \tan(\phi) = 0 \tag{22.10a}$$

$$u = \frac{2 \pm \sqrt{4 + 4\tan^2(\phi)}}{2\tan(\phi)} \tag{22.10b}$$

$$= \frac{1 \pm \sqrt{1 + \dfrac{\sin^2(\phi)}{\cos^2(\phi)}}}{\dfrac{\sin(\phi)}{\cos(\phi)}} \tag{22.10c}$$

$$= \frac{1 \pm \sqrt{\dfrac{1}{\cos^2(\phi)}}}{\dfrac{\sin(\phi)}{\cos(\phi)}} \tag{22.10d}$$

$$= \frac{\cos(\phi) \pm 1}{\sin(phi)}. \tag{22.10e}$$

Now using the negative root and making use of a trig identity,

$$u = -\frac{1 - \cos(\phi)}{\sin(\phi)} \tag{22.11a}$$

$$= -\tan\left(\frac{\phi}{2}\right). \tag{22.11b}$$

Or,

$$\phi = -2\tan^{-1}(\omega RC). \tag{22.12}$$

Part IV

Appendices

Appendix A

Glossary of terms

This is a work in progress. Page numbers refer to the location in the book *The Art of Electronics*, Second Edition, by P Horowitz and W Hill.

3 dB point	Frequency at which $V_{out} = 0.707 V_{in}$. Though technically should be referred to as a '−3 dB point', the minus sign is rarely, if ever, used. See dB [p 16].
6 dB point	Frequency at which $V_{out} = V_{in}/2$. Though technically should be referred to as a '−6 dB point', the minus sign is rarely, if ever, used. See dB [p 16].
β	The ratio of collector current to base current in a bipolar transistor, it is essentially the current gain of a transistor. Also known as h_{FE} [p 62].
ac	Alternating current. Generally refers to a voltage or current which sinusoidally varies between positive and negative values. See dc [p 9].
Active high/low	Defines voltage level (high or low) in which signal is 'TRUE', or 'ON'.
A/D	Analog to digital converter. Same as ADC [p 612].
ADC	Analog to digital converter. Same as A/D [p 612].
Aliasing	Production, by a sampled-data circuit or system, of a spurious output caused by sampling at an insufficient rate [p 775].
Assert	Pertaining to the properties of a logic signal. Means something like 'make FALSE' or 'make FALSE'. In other words, do something.
Asynchronous	(loading or interrupt). A characteristic of a digital device or circuit, in which the loading or interrupt occurs independent of receipt of a clock signal. See synchronous.
BCD	Binary-coded decimal. A scheme for representing base-2 numbers in base-10 [p 476].

Bias current	The difference in input current flowing into the two inputs of an op amp, when the input voltages are equal; due to the unequal input impedances of the op amp [p 136].
Biasing	Applying a voltage for the purpose of shifting a circuit into a working configuration. For example, a diode may be biased into conduction; a transistor circuit may be biased in order to properly set its quiescent conditions [p 69].
Bipolar	When referring to a signal, a signal which may be, at different times, positive or negative; when referring to transistors, either a pnp or npn transistor.
Bistable	A flip–flop [p 504].
Bus	A set of lines having a common purpose such as connecting all of the addresses of a memory to a microprocessor [p 487].
Bootstrap	a trick in which repetitive circuit elements are used to incrementally optimize the overall circuit performance, such as high gain [p 96].
Capture range	For a phase-locked loop, the range if input frequencies over which the circuit can 'lock' to an input [p 651].
Cascode	Circuit that uses one transistor to buffer or isolate another from voltage variation, so as to improve performance of the protected transistor [p 103].
Clamp	A circuit, or part of a circuit, which prevents the voltage from rising above a fixed value. The voltage is then said to be 'clamped' at that value [p 49].
Clear	Force the output of sequential digital devices to zero. Same as reset [p 509].
Clipping	When the extreme part of a signal is cut off. Like clamping, but usually not a planned or desired effect. See clamp [p 70].
CMOS	A class of low power-consumption digital device [p 484].
Combinational	Logic gates whose output is only a function of present inputs, not previous inputs. See sequential [p 490].
Complement	In Boolean algebra, changing a '1' or 'TRUE' into a '0' or 'FALSE', and vice versa. In TTL logic, change a 5 V signal with a 0 V signal, or vice versa [p 477].
Compliance	The output voltage range over which a current source delivers a constant current [p 73].
Crowbar	Over-voltage protection circuit which functions by shorting the supply output to ground when excessive voltage is detected [p 311].
Current sink	A circuit or device which draws (or sinks) a desired and fixed current from a second circuit, regardless of that circuit's output voltage. Closely related to a current source.
Current source	A circuit or device which supplies a desired and fixed current to a second circuit, regardless of that circuit's input impedance [p 9].
DAC	Digital to analog converter [p 614].
dB	decibels. Defined as $20 \log 101$ $(A_{\mathrm{out}}/A_{\mathrm{in}})$ for A_{out} and A_{in} output and input amplitudes, such as voltage. Note that for expressing ratios of powers, replace the '20' in the above relation by '10'. Also note that '6 dB' implies a factor of 2 [p 16].

dc	Direct current. Refers to a voltage or current which does not vary in time. See ac.
Decoder	A combinational circuit that takes in a binary number and asserts one of its outputs defined by that input number [p 496].
DeMorgan's theorem	A theorem in Boolean logic which states that when all inputs and outputs of an and or or gate are complemented, the result is equivalent to an uncomplemented case, but with the and replaced by an or, or the or replaced by an and [p 491].
Depletion mode	Class of FETs that are fully ON until a voltage at gate begins to turn the transistor OFF. Includes all JFETs and occasional MOSFETs. See enhancement mode [p 118].
DIP	Dual in-line package. Refers to the typical packaging for many ICs, in which a parallel set of 'legs' runs down each side of the 'chip' [p 836].
DIP switch	Set of switches mounted in a dual in-line package [p 687].
DPDT	Double pole, double throw. A switch configuration in which there are two switch positions (double throw) with two independent sets of connections for each throw [p 54].
DPST	Double pole, single throw. A switch configuration in which there is 1 switch position (single throw) with two independent sets of connections.
Droop rate	Rate at which the voltage stored on a capacitor departs from the original stored value ($\Delta V/\Delta t$) [p 220].
Dropout voltage	Minimum required voltage difference between input and output of voltage regulator. Circuit will dropout of regulation if this difference is not maintained [p 311].
Duty cycle	On-time divided by total time $\times 100\%$.
Early effect	Variation of IC with V_{CE}. Thus, it describes a transistor's departure from true current source behavior [p 74].
Edge-triggered	Describes a flip–flop, counter, or clock behavior in which the device responds to a transition (HIGH to LOW or LOW to HIGH), as opposed to a level [p 508].
EPROM	Erasable programmable read-only memory [p 816].
EEPROM	Electrically erasable programmable read-only memory [p 818].
Emitter follower	A circuit which has a high input impedance and low output impedance. This circuit's output replicates input, except with the above-mentioned impedance characteristics. See follower [p 65].
Enable	An input on a chip which essentially turns that device on. When not enabled, such a chip is, essentially, out of the circuit. Refers to digital, D/A, or ADC devices only [p 488].
Enhancement mode	Class of FETs that are OFF until V_{GS} begins to turn the transistor ON. Includes most MOSFETs, no JFETs. See depletion mode [p 118].
Feedback	Circuitry in which some of the output of an amplifier is routed back to one of the inputs. This arrangement generally allows one greater control of the amplifier, at the expense of reduced gain [p 175].
FET	Field effect transistor. Subspecies include JFET and MOSFET [p 113].
Flip–flop	Slang for bistable multivibrator [p 478].

Float	In digital, driven neither high nor low; in analog, not driven at all. Just 'hanging' in a virtually disconnected manner.
Follower	A circuit which has a high input impedance and low output impedance. This circuit's output replicates input, except with the above-mentioned impedance characteristics. See emitter follower [p 65].
Frequency compensation	Deliberate rolling off of op amp gain with increasing frequency. This is done to provide stability (against unwanted oscillations) to op amps due to large potentially large phase shifts which may occur at high frequencies [p 242].
Hold time	In digital, the time after the clock edge (or other timing signal) during which the data inputs must be held stable in order to be valid [p 510].
Gain	V_{out}/V_{in}. May also be expressed in dB [p 76].
h_{FE}	The ratio of collector current to base current in a bipolar transistor, it is essentially the current gain of a transistor. Also known as [p 62].
Hysteresis	In Schmitt trigger comparator circuits, the voltage difference between upper and lower thresholds [p 231].
Hz	Hertz. s^{-1}.
IDSS	Drain current which flows when gate is shorted to source: maximum current for a JFET [p 120].
I/O	Input–output.
Jam clear/load	Asynchronous clear/load [p 525].
JFET	Junction FET [p 117].
Latch	A device which can take a signal which has been clocked into it, and output that signal for an indefinite length of time [p 523].
Latchup	Pathological condition in which excessive current at input of a FET causes the device to pass a large current from supply to ground. Destructive [p 150].
LCD	Liquid crystal display. A type of display based on liquid crystal technology [p 591].
LED	Light emitting diode. A diode which emits light when current flows through it [p 591].
Load	impedance through which the output of a circuit must pass on its way to ground [p 12].
Lock	In a phase-locked loop, the condition in which the replica signal is held in a fixed phase relationship with the input signal [p 641].
Lock range	In a phase-locked loop, the range of input frequencies over which the circuit can retain lock, once locked [p 651].
Miller effect	Exaggeration of actual capacitance between output and input of an inverting amplifier, tending to make a small capacitance behave like a much larger capacitance to ground: 1 + Gain times as large as actual C [p 103].
Monostable multivibrator	A device which, upon receipt of a momentary input pulse, outputs a pulse whose width is determined by a user-supplied RC combination. Also known as a one-shot or 1-shot [p 517].
MOSFET	Metallic oxide semiconductor FET [p 117].

Multiplexer	Also known as a 'MUX'. Combinational circuit that passes one out of n inputs to a single output. A binary code input determines which input is passed [p 495].
Nyquist theorem	Observation that at least two samples must be taken within each period of an input sine wave in order to gather enough information to characterize the waveform fully [p 775].
Octave	A factor of 2 in frequency [p 39].
Offset current	The difference between the input currents on the two inputs of an op amp [p 190].
Offset voltage	The deviation in an op amp's output from 0 V when 0 V is applied to both of its inputs [p 192].
One-shot	A monostable multivibrator [p 517].
Open collector output	A device output which is internally connected to the collector of a npn transistor. Thus, the device cannot source a signal, but provides control by selectively sinking a signal [p 230].
Open loop gain	The gain in an amplifier which has no feedback connection [p 193].
PLL	Phase-locked loop [p 641].
Pot	See potentiometer.
Potentiometer	Three-terminal variable resistor.
Propagation delay	The amount of time for a signal to pass through a device.
PROM	Programmable read-only memory.
Push–pull	an arrangement of a pnp and npn transistors, wired as emitter followers such that a bipolar signal may be current-boosted without the use of biasing [p 91].
Quiescent current/voltage	Conditions in an amplifier existing when no input signal has been applied [p 70].
Rail	Supply voltage. RAM—Random access memory.
Reset	Force the output of sequential digital devices to zero. Same as clear and set.
Ripple counter	A type of asynchronous counter in which the output of one flip–flop drives the clock of the next [p 524].
rms	Root-mean-square. Means to first square a quantity, then take its average, then take the square root. For a sine wave, this makes the rms $= \sqrt{2} \times$ amplitude [p 16].
ROM	Read-only memory [p 816].
Saturation	Condition in which additional change input signal produces no more change in the output [p 63].
Sawtooth wave	A waveform consisting of a rising (or falling) slope, followed by a (theoretically infinite) drop (or rise). Thus, the sawtooth may be thought of as an asymmetric triangle wave [p 17].
Schmitt trigger	A comparator circuit that includes positive feedback to allow one to have hysteresis [p 231].
SCR	Silicon controlled rectifier. A semiconductor device which acts as a switch [p 312].
Sequential	Logic gates whose output is only a function of present inputs, as well as previous inputs. See combinational [p 490].
Set	Force the output of sequential digital devices to zero. Same as clear and set [p 509].
Setup time	Time before clock during which inputs must be held stable.

Single supply	A power supply having only one polarity at a time available. See split supply.
SIP	Single in-line package. Refers to the pin-out arrangement of some ICs in which a single row of pins runs down one side of the IC.
Slew rate	Rate of change of a voltage. $\Delta V/\Delta t$ [p 192].
Slow-blow fuse	Fuse with a long thermal time constant so that is can be over-currented for a brief amount of time. Allows for transients at startup.
SPDT	Single pole, double throw. A switch configuration in which there are two switch positions (double throw) with only one independent set of connections for each throw [p 53].
SPST	Single pole, single throw. A switch configuration in which there is one switch position (single throw) having only one independent set of connections [p 54].
Split supply	Power supply having both positive and negative polarities. See single supply.
Square wave	A waveform consisting of a train of positive square pulses, separated by equal width and amplitude negative (or zero amplitude) square pulses [p 18].
State	Condition of a sequential circuit defined by the levels on its flip–flop outputs.
Summing junction	Inverting terminal of op amp, when op amp is wired in inverting configuration: inverting terminal then sums the feedback and input currents.
Synchronous	(loading or interrupt). A characteristic of a digital device or circuit, in which the loading or interrupt occurs upon receipt of a clock signal. See asynchronous [p 512].
Thevenin	Thevenin's theorem states that any circuit made up only of voltage sources and resistances may be replaced by an equivalent circuit made up of a single voltage source (Thevenin voltage) and a single resistance (Thevenin resistance) [p 11].
Three-state	Describes a gate output, capable of turning off, in addition to LOW or HIGH logic levels [p 487].
Transconductance	Defined to be $\Delta I_{out}/\Delta V_{in}$ [p 80].
Transresistance amplifier	Current to voltage converter [p 184].
Triangle wave	A waveform consisting of a rising (or falling) slope, followed by an equal, but opposite (in sign) falling (or rising) slope [p 17].
Tri-state	National Semiconductor trade name for three-state [p 487].
TTL	Transistor–transistor logic. A convention in digital electronics in which a logical FALSE is represented by a voltage < 0.8 V, and a logical TRUE is represented by a voltage > 2.0 V [p 473].
VCO	Voltage controlled oscillator. An oscillator whose frequency is controlled by an externally supplied voltage [p 301].
Virtual ground	The terminal of one of the inputs of an op amp when the other input is at a true ground. (Assuming the op amp is not in saturation.) [p 178]
Voltage source	A circuit or device which supplies a desired and fixed voltage to a second circuit, regardless of that circuit's input impedance [p 9].

Wilson mirror   Improved form of a current mirror in which a third transistor protects the sensitive output transistor against effects of variation in voltage across the load. (See cascode.) [p 89]

Appendix B

The Linux operating system

As mentioned, the default operating system for the Beaglebone Black is some flavor of Linux, here assumed to be Debian. If your BBB has some other flavor of Linux, most of what we say here will still be correct; the main differences will concern enabling 'super user' powers.

The first thing you'll want to do is connect to some Linux computer. Perhaps this is your own laptop, but most likely it will be a computer that you will connect to 'online'. For a brief tutorial on how to connect to an online Linux (or Unix) computer from a desktop or laptop computer, see lecture −Appendix C. This will briefly walk you through the steps required to connect to an online Linux system from a Windows, Apple − OS, or other Linux box.

When you first log in, you should see the Linux prompt

```
debian@beaglebone:~$
```

A Linux prompt consists of your user name, here, 'debian', followed by the computer's name, here 'beaglebone', followed by a colon, then your directory name, and then either a dollar sign or a hash (#). When you first log on to a Linux machine you are placed in your 'home' directory, the shorthand for which is a '~'. The 'root' or lowest level directory is *not* the one Linux places you in when you log on. The root directory is indicated by the symbol '/'. You can find out exactly where you are by typing:

```
pwd
```

On the BBB, typing this from your home directory would return:

```
/home/debian
```

which means that there is a subdirectory in root called 'home', and that *your* home directory, named 'debian' is in that 'home' directory. Because it is a space and time

doi:10.1088/978-0-7503-3491-4ch24

waster to write out '/home/debian' every time you wish to refer to your home directory, Linux uses the shorthand ~. Hence the reason for that symbol in your prompt.

While on the topic of shorthand, ~ always means 'home directory', / always means the root directory, and ./ always means 'current directory'.

The '$' in the prompt tells you that you are an 'ordinary' user—that is, you do not have 'root privilege'. Root privilege, which would be indicated by a '#' in place of the '$', is essentially the same as 'administrative privilege', which means you would have the power to totally screw up the operating system. Thus, if you find the need to temporarily give yourself root privilege, be extremely careful with what you type as you could very easily 'brick' the computer. Someone with root privilege is sometimes referred to as a 'super user'.

You can create a new directory with the mkdir command. For example, if I want to create a directory, sitting under my home directory, named 'pmi', I would type:

```
mkdir pmi
```

(It is presumed that when you've typed a specified command, you hit the enter or return key.)

You can move to the pmi directory by typing:

```
cd pmi
```

In general, you can create a directory anywhere by specifying the complete directory tree. For example, if I were in some random directory, but I wanted to create the directory pmi in my home directory, I could type:

```
mkdir /home/debian/pmi
```

It is important to be able to move around from directory to directory. In Linux, you can go *down* one level in your tree (farther from the root) by typing cd followed by the name of the directory we want to go to (as just demonstrated). We can go *up* one level (closer to the root by typing):

```
cd ..
```

of course you can get to any directory, anywhere, by typing cd followed by the complete directory location. For example, from anywhere in the directory tree, I can move to the pmi directory by typing:

```
cd /home/debian/pmi
```

Getting to a directory is nice, but it is also very useful to see what's in the directory. To do so, we use the ls command. Because the pmi directory was just created, it will be empty, but if I had placed some files in it, and then typed ls I'd see the following:

```
test1.dat test2.cpp
```

where 'test1.dat' and 'test2.cpp' are the names of the files residing in pmi. You can find out more information about these files by adding a 'flag' to the command. For example, going back to the home directory, I can display 'hidden' files using the '-a' or 'all' flag:

```
ls —a
```

which will display all the files, even the hidden ones. In this case I get:

.	.bash_ history	.config	.gvfs	.wicd	Desktop
..	.bash_ logout	.dbus	.npmrc	.xsession-errors	bin
.BBIO Server	.bashrc	.dmrc	.pastebinit.xml	.xsession-errors.old	pmi
.Xauthority	.cache	.fontconfig	.profile	.xsessionrc	

Notice, by the way, that you can hide a file by starting its name with a period.

There are other flags associated with the ls command as well. The most popular is -l for 'long' (or 'list', depending on whom you ask). For example, the output of typing ls -l in my home directory gives:

total 12								
drwxr-xr-x	2	debian	debian	4096	Mar	1	20:08	Desktop
drwxr-xr-x	2	debian	debian	4096	Mar	1	20:27	bin
drwxr-xr-x	2	debian	debian	4096	Mar	1	20:44	pmi

The first line gives the total number of *blocks* (a unit of storage) that the listed files occupy. The rest of the lines give details about the files themselves. The first field lists the type of file and the *permissions* associated with it. If that letter is a 'd' (as in all of the cases above) the file is actually a *directory*. If the letter is a '-', it is an ordinary file. If the letter is b, c, or p, it is some sort of special file. Note that in the above, all the files are of type 'directory'. They were the only non-hidden files in that directory. But I could have combined flags. I could have typed:

```
ls —al
```

In which case I'd have received a complete listing of all the files in the directory, along with all the information about those files.

The next part of the first field gives *permissions*. That is, who can *read, write* and/ or *execute* the file. These three actions are abbreviated as r, w, x. There are three entities that receive permission: *user, group*, and *other*. Thus, the permissions field for Desktop says that the user can read, write, and execute the file. (In the case of a directory, you must have both read and execute permission to open a directory.) The group can read and execute, but not write to that directory. (A '-' means 'no permission' for that action.) 'Other' has the same permissions as group. We'll learn later how to change these permissions.

The next several fields include number of blocks, user and group names, size of blocks, date and time of file creation, and filename. But by far the most important fields are the ones that tell you what kind of file and who has permission to use it, and how.

Table B.1 gives a summery of common Linux commands. This list is *not* even close to being complete. But these basic commands, which we will use over and over here, will at least get you started.

By now you must be getting disgusted with all the typing you have to do, rather than just drag and drop as you would with most modern operating systems. I should point out that Linux is also GUI (graphical user interface) oriented. But there is so much more power at the command line and so that's where we will stay.

But it's worth noting that in Linux you can often avoid a great deal of typing by using the 'repeat command' and 'auto-finish' features. To repeat an earlier command, and optionally edit it, simply press the up-arrow key (or cntrl-p). If you went to an earlier command than you intended, you can press the down-arrow key (or cntrl-n). The 'hot-keys', cntrl-p and cntrl-n, are actually from a popular editor, emacs, and when used in emacs move the cursor to the 'previous' and 'next' lines, respectively. You'll find that many of the editing hot-keys in emacs can be used

Table B.1. Some useful Linux commands.

Command	Function
cp <name1> <name2>	Copies file (name1) to new file (name2).
mv <name1> <name2>	Moves (or renames) file (name1) to (name2).
ls, ls -a, ls -l	Lists directory. Flag -a includes hidden files; flag -l shows file details.
ps -a	'process show': Displays all processes & process numbers; required to kill processes.
echo <command> > <file>	'display' a 'command' somewhere. Ex: **echo 'abc' >file.txt** inserts text 'abc' into file.txt. The default 'file' is the console.
kill -9 <process number>	Kills process 'with extreme prejudice'.
df -H	Check memory usage.
chmod +x <filename>	Changes mode of a file to be executable.
uname -a	Gives information about distribution version number.
git clone <URL>	Downloads stuff from github.
system('<linux command>');	Execute linux command from within C program. Requires #include<stdlib.h>.
cat <filename>	Lists file having name 'filename'. Can be used with more: cat ex.txt | more.
grep <pattern> <files>	Search file(s) for <pattern>. Ex: **cat example.txt | grep abc**.
evince <file.pdf>	View a pdf file.
ifconfig -a	Lists the connection information like MAC address and IP Address (may need to supply directory: /sbin/ifconfig -a).

to edit the command line in Linux—just the first great reason to make emacs your editor of choice!

In Linux if you want to execute a file named, for example, 'doit', you simply type:

```
./doit
```

That is, you need tell the operating system where the executable file is, even if it is in your current directory.

IOP Publishing

Practical Analog, Digital, and Embedded Electronics for Scientists

Brett D DePaola

Appendix C

Connecting to a remote computer on the Internet

C.1 Connecting from a Linux box

This is just too simple:

```
ssh -X user_name@url.of.host.computer
```

For example, for the K-State Unix system, use `unix.ksu.edu`; for the Beaglebone, use `192.168.7.2`. When prompted, enter the password for your account on that system. For the Beaglebone running Debian, the default username is `debian`, and the default password is `temppwd`.

C.2 Connecting from an Apple-OS box

This is almost as easy as for a Linux system—because Apple-OS is built on top of Linux. First you need to install and execute Xquartz. Then get to your Apple `terminal` and follow the instructions for Linux.

C.3 Connecting from a Windows box

The first thing to do is to go out on the web and find, download, and install Xming and PuTTY. They are free. Watch out for sites that try to inflict bloat-ware on you!

C.3.1 Xming

If you want to get full graphics capability from your Windows machine when it is remotely connected to a Linux/UNIX system, you need to configure and launch Xming before you run PuTTY. Here I give step by step instruction on how to configure Xming. This should be a one-time operation, and it is very simple.

C.3.2 Configuring and using PuTTY

Once you've installed PuTTY, you will probably have to configure it to get the most out of it. This is not difficult, but could be a bit confusing if you've never configured a program before. Here are step by step instructions (figures C1–C10).

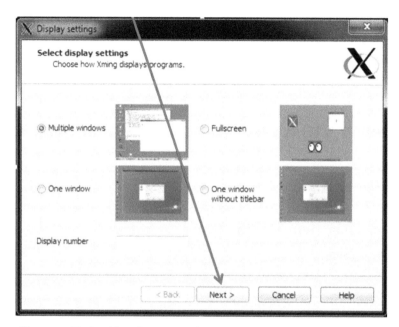

Figure C1. Step 1: Find and launch XLaunch (not Xming!). Step 2: Hit the 'Next' button twice.

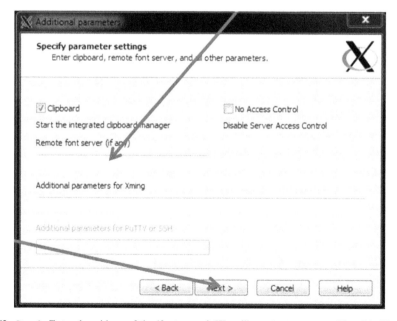

Figure C2. Step 3: Enter the address of the 'font server'. We will use fs.ksu.edu. Then hit 'Next' again.

Figure C3. Step 4: Save the configuration. Then press the 'Finish' button. Step 5: You've done it! Go celebrate with a cold one. (Pepsi products, of course!) Now when you run Xming, you'll get full functionality. You should never need to run XLaunch again!

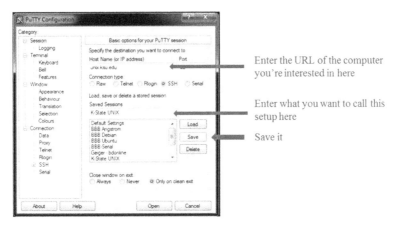

Figure C4. Step 1: Start PuTTY and enter your terminal session information. (For the Beaglebone it's 192.168.7.2.)

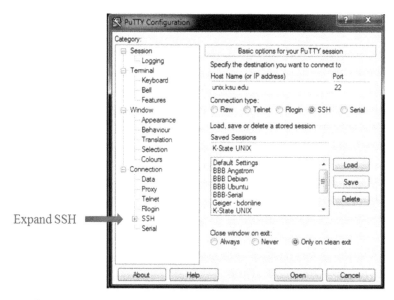

Figure C5. Step 2: Allow X11 commands to get through (very important!).

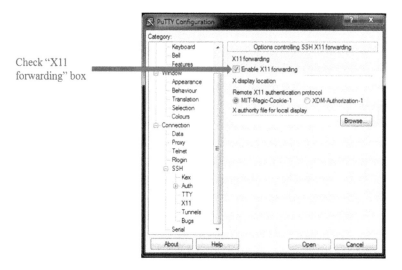

Figure C6. Step 2 (cont.).

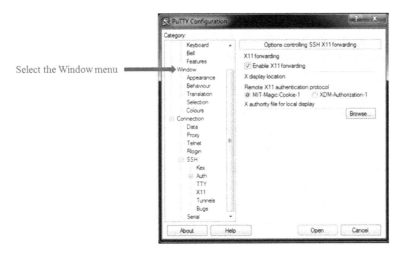

Select the Window menu

Figure C7. Step 3: Configure the terminal window.

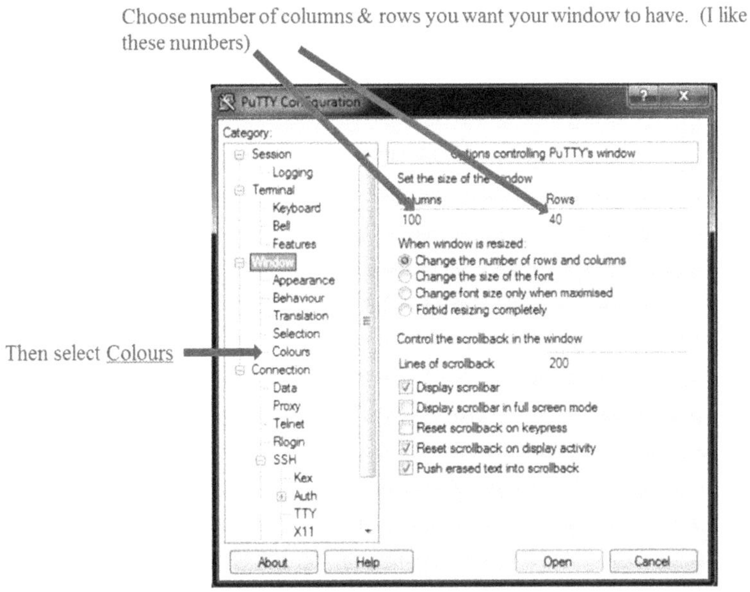

Choose number of columns & rows you want your window to have. (I like these numbers)

Then select Colours

Figure C8. Step 5: Choose number of columns and rows you want your window to have. (I like these numbers.) Then select 'Colours'.

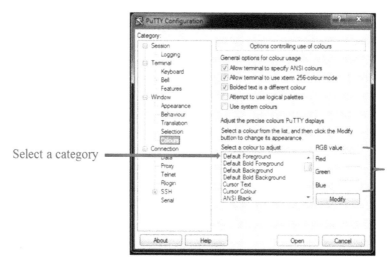

Select a category

Figure C9. Step 6: Select a category and enter RGB values according to table C1.

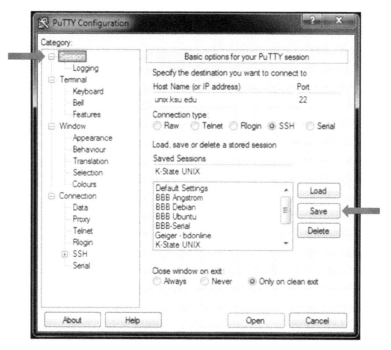

Figure C10. Step 7: Save your session!! Step 8: Celebrate!! You've just configured PuTTY!

Table C1. Recommended RGB settings for PuTTY.

Color to adjust	Red	Green	Blue
Default foreground	0	0	0
Default bold foreground	255	255	255
Default background	255	255	255
Default bold background	085	085	085
Cursor text	0	0	0
Cursor colour	0	0	255
ANSI 'stuff'	**Leave unchanged**		

IOP Publishing

Practical Analog, Digital, and Embedded Electronics for Scientists

Brett D DePaola

Appendix D

Editors

So now you're on Linux/Unix. Now what? You could surf the web or play a game, but presumably you've learned about Linux and moved away from Windows and/or Apple OS for a better reason than that. It's time to start writing scripts and programs! But to do this you need to know how to use one of the editors on your new system. Here are the most common options:

- vi—the granddaddy of all Unix (the original from which Linux was knocked off) text editors. vi is virtually guaranteed to exist on all Linux implementations. That's the good news. The bad news is that it's pretty primitive. But I recommend knowing the basics of vi just because you may find yourself on a 'foreign' Linux system and that is the one text editor you can count on being there. vi is a really basic bare-bones line editor. It is, of course present by default on the Beaglebone.

- vim—vim stands for vi-improved. It is based on vi. (I can't really see a huge difference between vi and vim.) It is present by default on most Linux/Unix machines.

- nano—this editor emulated the pico text editor which is part of the pine email client. So if you use/used pine a lot, you'll feel comfortable with nano. It is present by default on the Beaglebone.

- gedit—gedit is an editor that works inside of a GUI (graphical user interface). Many people move up to gedit when they're tired of the basic line editing capability offered by the above editors. It is present by default on the Beaglebone.

- emacs—It is often said that emacs is not an editor; it is a lifestyle. Easily the most powerful text editor in existence, emacs gives you the ability to easily create macros, read or compose email, manage your files and directories, run programs from within it, and even play games. Emacs does not come bundled with the Beaglebone, but I have installed it on all the Beagles in our class.

There are many more editors out there, but these are the most common. Note that these are not word processors: they don't embed funny control characters in the text to aid with formatting. (The control characters would confuse your compilers etc.) Below I give the most common commands for vi and emacs, the first because it is everywhere, and the second because, well, because that is the editor I use—and I love it.

D.1 vi

This primitive editor has two modes: **command mode** and **insert mode**. On many Linux systems, when you type vi to enter the editor, you are actually directed to vim (figure D1). No matter; the two are very similar.

D.1.1 Command mode

This is the default mode that you are in when you enter vi. (You enter vi by typing 'vi' or 'vi filename'.) From the command mode you can (as taken from *LINUX in a Nutshell*)

- Invoke insert mode (in a number of ways).
- Issue editing commands.
- Move the cursor to a different position in the file.
- Invoke the ex commands.
- Invoke a Linux shell.
- Save or exit the current version of the file.

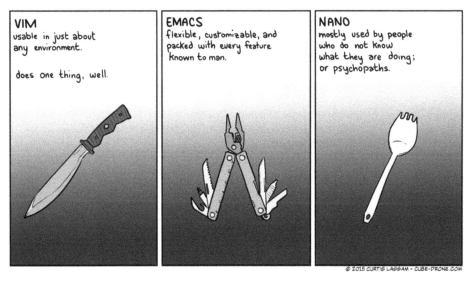

Figure D1. Summary of the functional differences between some editors. Reproduced with permission of Curtis Lassam at cube-drone.com.

D.1.2 Insert mode

You use insert mode to enter new text or edit existing text in a file. Just type what you want. You enter insert mode by typing one of the appropriate commands in table D.1 (the last several lines from the table, starting from 'a'). You exit insert mode (i.e. go back to command mode) by hitting the Esc button. It's that simple. Now for the true `vi` geek, there are a huge number of commands that you can type when invoking `vi`—but we won't get into that here. You can explore the greater set of `vi` commands by checking out the web.

Table D.1. Some common vi commands

Some common vi commands	
Binding	Action
dd	Delete current line
D	Delete up to the end of current line
h or ←	Move char to left
j or ↓	Move down one line
k or ↑	Move up one line
l or →	Move char to right
yy	Yank (copy) current line to buffer
nyy	Yank n lines to buffer
P	Put (paste) yanked line above current line
p	Put (paste) yanked line below current line
x	Delete char under cursor
/	Finds a word going forward
:q	Quit editor
:q!	Quit without save
:r file	Read file and insert after current line
:w file	Write buffer to file
:wq	Save changes and exit
Esc	End input mode; enter command mode
a	Insert text after cursor
A	Insert text at end of current line
c	Begin change operation (must be followed by movement command)
C	Change to end of line
I	Enter insert mode at beginning of current line
i	Enter insert mode before cursor
o	Open a line below current line
O	Open a line above current line
r	Replace character under cursor
R	Begin overwriting text
s	Substitute a char
S	Substitute an entire line

D.2 emacs

You invoke emacs by typing:

```
emacs
```

or

```
emacs filename
```

from the Linux command-line. As with most other programs in Linux, you can force emacs to start in a new shell, leaving your Linux command-line available for entering other commands, by appending a '&' at the end of the command:

```
emacs &
```

or

```
emacs filename &
```

By default, emacs recognizes certain file extensions and automatically enters into what is called a 'minor mode' that makes your life easier for editing that file type. For example, if you type 'emacs test.cpp &' (I almost always use the & option, but it is not necessary) emacs will open up the file test.cpp in the C-language mode. In C-mode, emacs will automatically indent statements and colorize keywords in order to make your code more readable. Many such minor-modes are supported by emacs.

In order to personalize emacs with the defaults that you like, you can create a .emacs file. (Recall that filenames that start with a '.' are not visible when you list files, unless you command them to be by using the '-a' flag.) You can put all sorts of defaults inside the .emacs file. I've created a basic .emacs file on all the Beaglebones that my class uses but you may wish to create your own .emacs files on your physics or university accounts. Sample .emacs files can easily be found on the web.

With the X-version of emacs, you can access most or all commands from drop-down menus. However, 'old school' users prefer the hot-key approach. Table D.2 is a list of commonly used commands for moving the cursor around in a file. The first column shows the hot-keys; the second column shows the full command (if you wanted to type it out) and the third column shows the result of issuing the command.

Here, the 'C-' means hold the control key down while hitting the accompanying key. 'M-' means 'meta-key'. This doesn't exist on most modern keyboards so this have been mapped to mean 'hit the Esc key (don't hold it down!) and then press the accompanying key'.

Besides the commands listed in tables D.2–D.7 there are many, many more. But don't be intimidated: you only need to learn a few basic commands to load, navigate in, and save a buffer (file). You can actually open up a new Linux process from within emacs. Once you've invoked emacs, you can type:

Table D.2. Some common emacs cursor movement commands.

Emacs cursor movement commands		
Binding	Command	Action
C-f or →	forward-char	Move cursor one char to right
C-b or ←	backward-char	Move cursor one char to left
C-p or ↑	previous-char	Move cursor up a line
C-n or ↓	next-line	Move cursor down a line
M-f	forward-word	Move one word forward
M-b	backward-word	Move one word backward
C-a	beginning-of-line	Move to beginning of line
C-e	end-of-line	Move to end of line
M-a	backward-sentence	Move backward one sentence
M-e	forward-sentence	Move forward one sentence
M-{	backward-paragraph	Move backward one paragraph
M-}	forward-paragraph	Move forward one paragraph
C-v	scroll-up	Move forward one screen
M-v	scroll-down	Move backward one screen
C-x[	backward-page	Move backward one page
C-x]	forward-page	Move forward one page
M->	end-of-buffer	Move to end of file
M-<	beginning-of-buffer	Move to beginning of file
(none)	goto-line	Go to line n of file
(none)	goto-char	Go to character n of file
C-l	recenter	Redraw screen with current line in the center
M-n	digit-argument	Repeat next command n times
C-un	universal-argument	Repeat the next command n times

Table D.3. Some common emacs file-handling commands.

Emacs file-handling commands		
Binding	Command	Action
C-x C-f	find-file	Find file and read it
Cx C-v	find-alternate-file	Read another file; replace the one currently in the buffer
C-xi	insert-file	Insert file at cursor position
C-x C-s	save-buffer	Save file without exiting
C-x C-w	write-file	Write the buffer to file (like a 'save as' command)
C-x C-c	save-buffers-kill-emacs	Exit emacs
C-z	suspend-emacs	Suspend emacs (use exit of fg to restart)

Table D.4. Some common emacs deletion commands.

Emacs deletion commands		
Binding	Command	Action
Del	backward-delete-char	Delete previous character
C-d	delete-char	Delete character under cursor
M-Del	backward-kill-word	Delete previous word
M-d	kill-word	Delete the word the cursor is on
C-k	kill-line	Delete from cursor to end of line
M-k	kill-sentence	Delete sentence the cursor is on
C-x Del	backward-kill-sentence	Delete previous sentence
C-y	yank	Restore what you've deleted
C-w	kill-region	Delete a marked region
(none)	backward-kill-paragraph	Delete previous paragraph
(none)	kill-paragraph	Delete from cursor to end of the paragraph

Table D.5. Some common emacs deletion commands.

Emacs incremental search commands		
Binding	Command	Action
C-s	isearch-forward	Start or repeat incremental search forward
C-r	isearch-backward	Start or repeat incremental search backward
Return	(none)	Exit a successful search
C-g	keyboard-quit	Cancel incremental search; return to starting point
Del	(none)	Delete incorrect character of search string
M-C-r	isearch-backward-regexp	Incremental search backward for regular expressions
M-C-s	isearch-forward-regexp	Incremental search forward for regular expressions

```
M-x shell
```

You will see a new buffer open up and inside of it you will see the usual Linux prompt. You can now type any Linux command-line command just as if you were on the normal Linux command-line. The advantage of this is that (1) you are automatically logging what you've done (because this is, after all, taking place inside your editor) and (2) any program output that would normally go to the screen is being 'captured' by your editor. You can then edit the output as you wish.

Once inside of emacs you can also edit your directories—and directly edit files in those directories. From within emacs just type M-x dired. You will see a new

Table D.6. Some common emacs deletion commands.

Emacs buffer manipulation commands		
Binding	Command	Action
C-x b	switch-to-buffer	Move to specified buffer
C-x C-b	list-buffers	Display buffer list
C-x k	kill-buffer	Delete specified buffer
(none)	kill-some-buffers	Ask about deleting each buffer
(none)	rename-buffer	Change buffer name to specified name
C-x s	save-some-buffers	Ask whether to save each modified buffer

Table D.7. Some common emacs deletion commands.

Emacs macro commands		
Binding	Command	Action
C-x(	start-kbd-macro	Start macro definition
C-x)	end-kbd-macro	End macro definition
C-x e	call-last-kbd-macro	Execute last macro defined
(none)	name-last-kbd-macro	Name last macro you created (before saving it)
(none)	insert-last-keyboard-macro	Insert the macro you named into a file
(none)	load-file	Load macro files you've saved
(none)	*macroname*	Execute a keyboard macro you've saved
C-x q	kbd-macro-query	Insert a query in a macro definition
c-u C-x q	(none)	Insert a recursive edit in a macro definition
M-C-c	exit-recursive-edit	Exit a recursive edit

window open up and inside that window you will see the current directory displayed, as if you had typed ls -la from the Linux command-line. You can edit a file (or open a directory) in that list by positioning your cursor over the entry and hitting 'f'. There are many other emacs directory manipulation commands that you can find on the web.

IOP Publishing

Practical Analog, Digital, and Embedded Electronics for Scientists

Brett D DePaola

Appendix E

Brief primer on C++

In these few pages I will attempt to give a very brief overview on programming in the C++ language. I will just present the very basics of defining types, flow control, and writing and calling procedures.

E.1 The Hello World program

What would an introduction to a computer language be without some version of the 'Hello World' program? Well, here is a way to do this in C++: see listing E.1:

Comments in C++ can take two forms: they can be delimited by /* and */, or they can follow a pair of slashes, //. In the first case, exemplified above in the first five lines, everything following '/*' is a comment, until a '*/' is encountered. In this form, comments can extend over multiple lines. In the second case, shown in lines 6 and 7, everything to the right of '//' is a comment. But in this form, the comment ends at the end of the line.

It is customary to start a program with a few lines that tell some useful details about the program, such as what the program is called, when it was written, who wrote it, when was it last modified and by whom, and, usually, what the purpose of the program is. (I omitted the last of these.) Note that in subsequent listings shown in this document, I will omit these comments in order to save space. But it is *strongly* recommended that you start any program with a few lines of comments that serve as an explanation of what the program's purpose is.

Next, it is customary to include all the libraries that the program will require in order to compile and be run. In this case, I use the built-in C++ library named iostream.

While not required, it is usually useful to specify a namespace. In C++ all the standard library functions and classes are contained in the standard namespace. If you didn't include the line 'using namespace std;' then the compiler wouldn't know what you meant by, for example, cout. That is, cout is a built-in procedure that is defined in the iostream library. Unless told, the compiler has no idea where

doi:10.1088/978-0-7503-3491-4ch27

```
 1  /****************************************
 2  *   Program name: HelloWorld01.cpp      *
 3  *   Written 03/05/2015 by B. DePaola    *
 4  *   Last edit: 03/05/2015 by B. DePaola *
 5  ****************************************/
 6  #include<iostream> // This contains the library for the I/O
 7                     // functions that I am using
 8  using namespace std;
 9
10  int main() {
11      cout << "Hello World" << endl;
12      return 0;
13  }
```

Listing E.1: HelloWorld01.cpp, version 1

cout's definition is. But the location of cout's definition is contained in the built-in namespace called std. So I can either choose to use the construct 'std::cout' every time I want to print something, or I can identify the namespace I use to the compiler using the statement 'using namespace std;', in which case I can simply write 'cout' when I want to print something out. Unless you start creating your own namespaces, I strongly recommend that you use the standard namespace as in listing 1.

After all the includes and the namespace declaration, it is customary to declare all the user-defined procedures that the main routine uses. In this example there are none of these and so I move on to the next part of the program, the definition of the main procedure, main.

All procedures, including the main one have the form:

```
procedure_type procedure_name(argument list) {
    procedure_definition;
}
```

In listing E.1, the procedure is of type int (or integer). This is the usual (and for many compilers the required) type for the main procedure. The main procedure's name is 'main'. The main procedure can have a list of arguments, the values of which are supplied at runtime. The procedure's definition is contained between curly brackets. Every statement in a definition must end in a ';'. In listing E.1, the main procedure's definition consists of merely two lines. The first is an output stream. The keyword cout represents the standard output device which, unless otherwise stated, is the screen. The special character function '≪' directs the string (the words contained between quotes) to the standard output device represented by cout. After the string has been sent to cout, the program then sends a special construct, endl, to the output device. This effectively consists of a carriage return followed by a line-feed. Sending endl to an output device also flushes the output buffer, ensuring that the data are all sent at the moment that command is executed. Note that the cout line, like all others in a procedure definition, ends in a semicolon. At the end of the procedure, I have a return statement. In the case of a procedure that does not actually return a value, the return is not technically required. But to be consistent with defining main to be of type int, that is, by claiming that main will return a value of type integer, I include the return statement. Ok, there's my program; now how do I run it? First I have to go through a compile and link step. So after saving

```
string str1 = 'Mama Mia!';
string str2 = 'That's a fine pasta!';
string str3;
str3 = str1 + ' ' + str2;
cout << str3.c_str() << endl;
```

Listing E.2: Code snippet showing some string work.

the program in a file named `HelloWorld01.cpp`, I type the following on the Linux command line:

```
g++ HelloWorld01.cpp -o HelloWorld
```

Here, I executed the compiler/linker program, named g++, and give it some arguments. The first argument is the name of the file that contains the source code that must be compiled. The -o flag tells the compiler to store the compiled and linked code in a file named in the string that follows this flag, here HelloWorld. It is not required that the executable filename match the source code filename, but it is a good idea that the two are named in such a way that one can readily determine their connection. Now to execute the compiled and linked program, simply type ./HelloWorld. The './' tells the system to look in the current directory for an executable file. That's all there is to it.

E.2 Strings and things

In C, a 'string' is an array of characters. (See arrays in section E.5.) There are many built-in functions to massage these so-called C-strings, including catenation etc. In C++ there is actually a string class. The built-in operators in this class are much more intuitive than the klunky functions for handling C-strings, but many C++ functions still require C-string arguments. Often the most convenient thing to do is to create and manipulate C++ strings, and then convert them to C-strings at the point where that construct is required. The function to do this is `c_str()`. For example, in the following code snippet, I define the C++ strings, `str1` and `str2`. Then I combine them to create `str3`. Notice that for C++ strings, the concatenation function is just the plus sign. Finally, I convert `str3` into a C-string and output it. Note that in this example the conversion was not necessary; I did it just to show how (listing E.2).

Note, to use the C++ string class, you must include the `string` library.

E.3 Input/output

Input/output (I/O) in C++ is pretty flexible. In addition to the C-type `printf` statement, you can use output streams. Streams are nice because they can be directed to any device; the printf statement is nice because it allows simpler formatting than streams.

E.3.1 Streams

The principle method for I/O is the stream to/from the 'console' (keyboard for input, screen for output). We've already discussed the `cout` command. The input stream

```
1 #include<iostream>
2 using namespace std;
3 int main(){
4    int N;
5    cout << 'Give me a number\n';
6    cin >> N;
7    cout << 'Your number is ' << N << endl;
8 }
```

Listing E.3: Code snippet showing the use of cin and cout

command, cin works in a similar fashion except that it takes input from the keyboard. When a cin is given, the program waits for input from the keyboard, terminated by a 'carriage return' (or 'enter' on most modern keyboards). Both cin and cout libraries are in the iostream library. Here's a simple code snippet to demonstrate cin (listing E.3).

E.3.2 Reading and writing files

First of all, why would you want to? Aren't the screen and keyboard enough? No, they usually are not. Even using redirection (<, ≪, >, ≫) at the command line, while extremely useful, is usually not sufficient to take the place of having your program directly access a file. There are lots of ins and outs here (pun intended) but I'll give the really short version.

Listing E.4 starts out by adding a couple of extra includes. The first of these is the file I/O library. The second contains the definition of the exit statement—which is used to exit the program if there is a problem opening either the input or output file. Next I define the input and output file stream variables, input_file and output_file, respectively. These are used just like cin and cout, and function just like those streams except that the input/output comes from/to files rather than the keyboard and monitor. Next I associate files with the stream variables. Note that following those associations, which involve using the 'open' method, I test that the files opened with no problems, and if there was a problem I send an appropriate message to the monitor and exit the program. This check on whether the file was opened is not mandatory, but can save you much aggravation. In this example, the input file, named 'inputdata.dat', is assumed to consist of two columns of data, arranged in NumLines = 5 rows. After the input and output files are successfully opened I read, line by line, the two values, which I store in the double precision variables x and y. I then write values associated with x and y to the file 'outputdata.dat'.

E.4 Flow control 1

E.4.1 The for-loop

Suppose I would like to print out this useless 'Hello World' message 10 times. How would I do this? I could simply repeat the cout statement 10 times, but this is awkward and would become even more so if I needed to do this millions of times. Instead we use something called a loop.

Listing E.5 is identical to listing E.1 except that I added two lines, 4 and 5, and I enclosed the cout line in curly brackets. In the first of these, I define i and

```
1  #include <iostream>
2  #include <fstream>   // need this for file I/O
3  #include <cstdlib>   // need this for the exit function
4  using namespace std;
5
6  int main() {
7      int j, NumLines = 5;
8      double x, y;
9  // declare input/output stream variables:
10     ifstream input_file;
11     ofstream output_file;
12
13     input_file.open('inputdata.dat');  // open the input file
14     if (input_file.fail())  // Check to see that it did open
15     {
16         cout << 'Input file opening failed.' << endl;
17         exit (1);
18     }
19     output_file.open('outputdata.dat');  // open the output file
20     if (output_file.fail())    // Check to see that it did open
21     {
22         cout << 'Output file failed to open.' << endl;
23         input_file.close();
24         exit(1);
25     }
26
27     for (j = 0; j < NumLines; j++)
28     {
29         input_file >> x >> y;
30         output_file << 2.0*x << '\t' << 3.0*y + j << endl;
31     }
32     input_file.close();
33     output_file.close();
34     return 0;
35 }
```

Listing E.4: `FileIOtst01.cpp`, version 1

```
1  #include <iostream>
2  using namespace std;
3
4  int main() {
5      int i, NumRepeats = 10;
6      for (i = 0; i < NumRepeats; i++)
7      {
8          cout << 'Hello World' << endl;
9      }
10     return 0;
11 }
```

Listing E.5: `HelloWorld02.cpp`

`NumRepeats` to be variables of type integer. I furthermore initialize `NumRepeats` to a value of 10. The second addition is a `for-loop`. What this `for`-line says is that the block that follows (everything enclosed by the pair of curly brackets that follow the for-line) will be repeated as `i` is run through values from 0 through `NumRepeats-1`, in steps of 1. Huh? How did I get that? Well, we start with `i = 0` and we execute the block. Now the program increments `i` by 1, the short-hand for which is `i++`. And so long as `i` does not violate the condition `i < NumRepeats`, the program will execute the block that follows. So how many times does the message get printed out? Well, it will be printed out for `i = 0`, `i = 1` ⋯ `i = 9`. This makes 10 times. Don't make the mistake of writing `i <= NumRepeats`. This will work if you start `i` at 1, but not 0. And why start at 0? It saves you 1 keystroke,

```
 1  #include<iostream>
 2  using namespace std;
 3  int main() {
 4    int i, NumRepeats = 10;
 5    for (i = 0; i < NumRepeats; i++)
 6    {
 7      if (i %2 == 0)
 8      {
 9        cout << i << '\t' << 'Hello World' << endl;
10      }
11    }
12    return 0;
13  }
```

Listing E.6: `HelloWorld03.cpp`

namely you can write < instead of <=. Furthermore, you will find this convenient when we come to arrays. Besides the integer type, there are quite a few options for defining variables. The most common of these are int, float, double, char, and bool. Respectively, these are integer, floating point, double precision floating point, character, and Boolean. By the way, the number of bits in an integer of type int is system-dependent.

E.4.2 Conditionals

You can also control program flow by using conditionals, for example, the if construct.

In listing E.6, we've inserted a few lines into the for-block. The first of these is an if-statement. If the contents of the parenthesis that follow 'if' are TRUE, then the statement in the block that follows will be executed. If the if-statement is not TRUE, then the entire block following that statement is skipped. In this case, we used the modulo operator (%). This divides the first argument (here, i) by the second argument (here, 2) and returns the remainder. So here, if the remainder is 0, that is if i is an even number, we will print out both i and 'Hello World'. You will note that I am also printing out \t between i and 'Hello World'. This is one of several possible 'printer control characters' and means 'print a tab'. Another commonly used printer control character is '\n' which means 'print a carriage return and linefeed'. (This means 'Go to a new line and move to the beginning of that line'. 'Carriage return' and 'linefeed' are the names of the special 'characters' that do this.) An if statement can also be made more complicated than this by using logical AND (&) or logical OR (|). Furthermore if can also be used with else:

```
if (Boolean expression)
  {block 1}
else
  {block 2}
```

The if constructs can be made even more complicated through the use of else-if:

```
if (Boolean expression 1)
   {block 1}
else if (Boolean expression 2)
   {block 2}
              .
              .
              .
else if (Boolean expression N)
   {block N}
else
   {block for all other possibilities}
```

E.4.3 User-defined functions (procedures)

C++ has a number of built-in functions like sin, cos, log, etc, but sometimes you will need to create your own functions (often referred to as *procedures*). These are very easy to create. In listing E.7 we show a simple program that calls two different user-defined procedures. Now there are several things to note here. First is that this is a really silly example! Second is that I somehow had to let the compiler know that the procedures exist before it actually encountered them in the code. There are at least three ways to do this. The first is to define all the procedures before they are used in main. This option has the disadvantage that whoever is looking at the code would have to wade through all the definitions before finally getting to the main

```
1  #include <iostream>
2  using namespace std;
3
4  double tstfct(int x);
5  void header();
6  void footer();
7  void printit(double x, double y);
8
9  int main() {
10     double q;
11
12     header();
13     for (int k = 0; k < 10; k++)
14     {
15        q = tstfct(k);
16        printit(double(k), q);
17     }
18     footer();
19 return 0; }
20
21 void header() {
22     cout << "****************\n";
23     cout << "*   x\ty\t*\n";
24 }
25
26 void printit(double x, double y) {
27     cout << "*   " << x << '\t' << y << '\t*' << endl;
28 }
29
30 void footer() {
31     cout << "****************\n";
32 }
33
34 double tstfct(int i) {
35     return 3.0*i +8.0;
36 }
```

Listing E.7: ProcTst01.cpp

routine. For one or two procedures this is not a big deal; but if you have dozens of complicated procedures, this can be annoying. I discuss the other options below.

The next thing to note is that both in the function *declaration* and in the function *definition* you must tell the compiler the type of each variable in the argument list, and you must tell the compiler what type of value the function will return. Note that if, like `header`, `footer`, and `printit`, the procedure does not return a value, you must still declare something, and so you use `void`.

Finally note that name of a variable in a procedure's argument list in the definition or declaration need not match the name of the variable in the argument list when the procedure is called. For example, the values of k and q, arguments of `printit` when it is called, are passed to `printit`'s definition by *position*, not by name. However, the argument type must still match—hence the need for *type casting* k by putting `double(k)` in the argument list.

There are two ways to pass argument lists in C++ (and C). The first is 'by value', as was done in the above example. The second is 'by reference'.

When you 'call by value', the value of the number or variable in the calling program's argument list is given to the local variable in the function definition's argument list. Thus the function can do whatever it wants to that variable without changing the corresponding value in the calling program. But in 'call by reference', the *memory location* of the variable in the calling program is passed to the function. Thus, if you change the value of that variable in the function, you will also change its value in the calling program. An example of passing by reference is shown in listing E.8. It's a simple program that takes an input temperature expressed in degrees Fahrenheit, and converts it to degrees Celsius.

Note that when you define your function, if you want an argument to be passed by reference, you just stick an '&' to the end of the argument type. Just as in passing by value, the argument name is a dummy. But unlike passing by value, the value of the passed variable, here `Temperature`, can be changed by the called function. Passing by reference can be useful for any number of reasons. Here's just one example: Suppose you want to define a function that is used to initialize two variables. You could define a function that returns an array of values (more on

```cpp
1  #include <iostream>
2  using namespace std;
3
4  void F2C(double& Temp) {
5      Temp = (Temp − 32.0)*5.0/9.0;
6  }
7
8  int main() {
9      double Temperature = 1.0
10
11     while(Temperature < 1000.0)
12         {
13         cout << 'Give a temperature in F. (Give T > 1000 C to quit.)' << endl;
14         cin >> Temperature;
15         F2C(Temperature);
16         cout << 'The temperature in C is ' << Temperature << endl << endl;
17         }
18 }
```

Listing E.8: `ProcTst02.cpp`

arrays later), or, you could put those two variables in the argument list and pass them by reference. Then, when your function gives values to those arguments, it is also putting those values in the memory location of the calling program's argument list. Simple.

You will note that in listing E.8 I've changed something else compared to listing E.7. In listing E.7 I've defined my functions at the end of the main routine. But since the compiler needs to know about these functions before they are defined (as discussed above) I had to declare the functions ahead of main. Listing E.8 shows an alternative. I simply put the definition ahead of the main routine. This way the definition (sort of) also serves as the declaration. The advantage of putting just the declarations ahead of the main routine is that you need not scroll through masses of definitions just to get to the 'meat' of the program because all those definitions are at the end. On the other hand, you have to do double-duty if you want to put the declarations at the front and the definitions at the end. (Though cut-n-paste make that a snap.) It's your choice.

But there is a third option: You could put all your function definitions in a separate file called, for example, myfcts.cpp. Then, before any of those functions are called (but after any included libraries that are used by your functions) just use:

```
#include <'myfcts.cpp'>
```

Note the use of quotes. This assumes that your library of functions are in the same directory that you are compiling from. You could, of course, include the full directory:

```
#include <'/home/home/debian/pmi/mystuff/myfcts.cpp'>
```

E.4.4 Pointers

Suppose variable x is of type int. And suppose x is given some value. Then that value must be stored in some location in memory. But where? This is simple enough to find out:

```
int x = 347;
cout << &x << endl;
```

This last statement will print out the location in memory wherein the value of x is stored. The statement makes use of the de-referencing operator &. When placed on the front end of a variable, the symbol & means 'give me the address of the variable that follows'. (This is not inconsistent with the use of & in passing values by reference.)

But can we store this *address* someplace—just in case we need it later for some reason? The answer is yes. A variable that stores the address at which another variable's value is stored is called a *pointer*. Different variable types required different amounts of memory. For example, a variable of type char requires precisely 8 bits. But a variable of type int requires, depending on the system, 16 bits. Therefore, when we declare a pointer, we need to specify the type of variable to which that pointer points. Consider the following code snippet:

```
1 int x = 347;
2 int *p;
3 p = &x;
4 cout << x << '\t' << &x << '\t' << p << endl;
```

When I ran this snippet I got the results

347	0xbffad828	0xbffad828

It's not surprising that &x and p have the same value—after all, I set them equal to each other. But the key is that it takes a specially declared variable to point. For example this snippet will not work:

```
int x = 347;
int p;
p = &x;
cout << x << '\t' << &x << '\t' << p << endl;
```

This will give an error at compile time because p is not of the correct type to point; it must be of 'type' pointer, and that pointer must be of type int (since I want it to point to an int. If I want it to point to a type double, I'd declare it with a statement like double *p.).

In the above (correct) snippet p points to x. Since p 'knows' where x's value is, is there some way to interrogate p in order to get that value? Yes! We just make the * do double-duty: we used it to say that p is a pointer, and now we use it to extract the value that lies at that memory location. Consider the following:

```
int x = 347;
int *p;
p = &x;
cout << x << '\t' << &x << '\t' << p << '\t' << *p << endl;
```

Now my output will be:

347	0xbffad828	0xbffad828	347

Thus, *p is the same as x, and p is the same as &x. You can even assign values:

```
int x = 347;
int *p;
p = &x;
*p = 122;
cout << x << '\t' << \&x << '\t' << p << endl;
```

which gives:

122	0xbffad828	0xbffad828	122

Notice that not only has the value of *p become 122, but so has the value of x. This is because in the statement *p = 122, we actually placed the value 122 into the memory location reserved for x.

Does p have a memory location of its own? Sure. It has to store that memory address somewhere! Can we find out what that address is? Sure! Guess how?

```
cout << &p;
```

All this is pretty simple, but it pays to follow the old Zen maxim:

Do not mistake the pointing finger for the moon

To avoid the programming equivalent of this philosophical conundrum, it is often the practice to start a pointer variable's name with a 'p', and to avoid having p as the first letter of a non-pointing variable. This is not a requirement, but it can be a useful practice. A second trick is to define a pointer type. This can save you many headaches. For example, in the statement:

```
int *p1, p2;
```

the variable p1 will be a pointer to an int but p2 will just be an int. In order for them both to be pointers to ints we would need to write:

```
int *p1, *p2;
```

An alternative would be to define a type called, for example, IntPtr and use this newly defined type to declare your pointers to ints:

```
typedef int* IntPtr;
```

Now we can write:

```
IntPtr p1, p2;
```

and these variables will have been typed as pointers to ints. Obviously you can also define pointers to floats, doubles, chars, etc. in a similar fashion.

E.5 Arrays

Very often it is convenient to have a list of values all associated with the same variable. One way to do this is to use an array. For example, suppose you wish to place 5 x-values in a single variable called x and the corresponding 5 y-values in a single variable named y. How would you do this? Well, it's simple. Look at listing E.9

There are several points to note here. First of all, when you define an array, you need to specify its length. You can do this by typing an actual number inside of the square brackets when you declare the variable type or, as I have done here, declare an integer *constant* and use that to specify the array length. You can not use a variable to declare the array length; it must be a constant. Second, if you wish, you can assign the array values at the time of declaration by putting them in a curly

```cpp
1  #include <iostream>
2  #include <cmath> // need for sine function
3  using namespace std;
4
5  int main() {
6      const int length = 5;
7      int i;
8      double x[length] = {2.0, 4.0, 6.0,8.0, 10.0}, y[length];
9
10     for (i = 0; i < length; i++)
11     {
12         y[i] = sin(x[i]);
13     }
14     for (i = 0; i < length; i++)
15     {
16         cout << i << '\t' << x[i] << '\t' << y[i];
17     }
18     cout << endl;
19     return 0;
20 }
```

Listing E.9: `ArrayTst01.cpp`

```cpp
1  void printarray(double q[], int length);
2
3  int main(){
4      const int size = 10;
5      double x[size];
6      for (j = 0; j < size; j++)
7      {
8          x[j] = double(j);
9      }
10     printarray(x, size);
11 }
```

Listing E.10: Code snippet showing how to pass an array by value.

bracketed list or, if your prefer, you can defer assignment to some later time. Third, the array index always starts at 0. Thus, if the array has a length of 10, its indices run from 0 through 9. Suppose you want to use an array as the argument of a function. How would you do this? If you wish to pass just a single element of the array, you could do it as in listing E.9, where x[i] was passed as the argument of the sin function. If, on the other hand, you wished to pass the entire array of values you could do so as shown in the following code snippet (listing E.10):

Notice in this code snippet that when the function is declared (and also when it is defined) the array variable is so indicated with empty square brackets. Also take note that while it is not required that you pass the length of the array, it is common practice because, presumably, in order to make use of the array, the function will have to know its length.

Suppose you don't how long your array has to be at the time you write and compile the code? You have two options. The first is to choose a dimension that is guaranteed to be larger than anything you may possibly need. But this wastes memory. The second option is to use a *dynamic* array.

An array is actually a pointer variable that points to the location of the value of first (i.e. index 0) array element. We can use this fact to define arrays whose dimension can be assigned in real-time. This is called a dynamic array. Consider the following snippet (listing E.11):

```
int a[5] = {2,4,6,8,10};
int *p1, *p2;
p1 = a;
cout << p1[2] << endl;
```

Listing E.11: Code snippet demonstrating the equivalence between arrays and pointers.

```
1  void printarray(int *array, int size) {
2      for(int i=0; f < size; i++)
3          cout << array[i] << endl;
4  }
5
6  int main() {
7      int a[5] = {2,4,6,8,10};
8      printarray(a, 5);
9  }
```

Listing E.12: Code snippet showing how to pass an array by reference.

What you've actually done is to allow the pointer p1 to point to the value of the first element of the array. The output of this snippet would therefore be 6 because p1[2] = a[2] = 6. And since p1 *is* the array a you can use the square bracket notation not only for arrays, but for pointers that point to arrays since the two are nearly equivalent. Why only nearly? Well, you cannot assign a new address to a, so the statement a = p2 is not legal. In other words, you can have statements like pointer = array, but you cannot have array = pointer. The former allows the pointer to point to each member in the array; the latter illegally attempts to redefine where the array values are stored—a much more difficult operation for the computer—which is why it is illegal.

You create a dynamic array by applying the new operator to a pointer:

```
double *p;
int k = 10;
p = new double[k];
```

Now p is an array of length 10, and it can be used like any other array. But even better, its dimension was given as a variable, and therefore could be anything we want—even decided during runtime. Here we used the new operator with type double, but it works with any type, even types that you create yourself. When you are done with your array, it is a good idea to free that memory up again so it can be used by other elements of your program. You do this with the command:

```
delete [] p;
```

Because a pointer is, essentially, an array, you can pass it as a function argument like an array—and vice versa. Consider the code snippet in listing E.12:

Note that in the definition of the function printarray, I've defined the first argument as a pointer to an integer whereas in the calling routine I've passed an array. This works because the array in the main routine is really a pointer. Note also that I had to pass as an argument the length of the array. This is because the pointer just points to the first value of the array but has no idea of the array's length. Because we are just passing pointers, we are really 'passing by reference', as we've done before. Thus, if our function were to change values in the array, those values would also be changed in the calling program. This could potentially get us into trouble so C/C++ provides us with an optional safeguard: if we want the compiler to protect us against ourselves (at least so far as changing something we don't want to change) we can add the key word `const` in front of the pointer type in the function definition. Thus, the first line in the above snippet could be written:

```
void printarray(const int *array, int size)
```

E.6 Time to show some class

The major feature that distinguishes C++ from C is the existence of classes. A class is a type of structure that includes both member variables and member functions. (Member functions are usually called *methods*.) These class members can be either private (the default) or public. By private, we mean that the members can only be accessed by other class members, but not by any part of the program that is outside the class. Here is an outline of a user-created class:

The class 'silly' defined in listing E.13 is pretty bare-bones and really doesn't do anything useful, but at least shows how to create and use a class. First of all, notice that the class definition ends with a semicolon after its final curly bracket. From personal experience I can tell you that this is an easy detail to forget. Second, we have several class members, some variables, others methods. Some of these class members are 'public'. In this example, all of these happen to be methods. These are `silly()`, `silly(int, double)`, `getX()`, `getY()`, `createX()`, `createY()`. The first two, both having the same name as the class, are a special

```
1  class silly {
2  public:
3    silly(){}
4    silly(int goofY, double goofX)
5    {
6      x = goofX;
7      y = goofY;
8    }
9    int getX();
10   double getY();
11   void createX();
12   void createY();
13  private:
14    int x;
15    double y;
16    double f()
17    {
18      return x*x + y*y;
19    }
20  //etc
21  };
22
23  int silly::getX(){return x;} double silly::getY(){return y;} void
24  silly::createX() {
25    std::cout << 'Give me a value of x\n"'
26    std::cin >> x;
27  }
28  // etc
```

Listing E.13: Trivial example of a particularly useless class.

sort of method called a constructor. A constructor must have the same name as the class and it must not have a type (like int or double). A constructor is automatically called whenever you define a variable to be an object in that class. For example, in my main program I could write:

```
silly tweedleDum, tweedleDee(1.0, 2);
```

Here, I've declared two variables to be instances of the class silly. The first one, tweedleDum, had no arguments and so the constructor silly() was 'executed'. (In this case the constructor did nothing.) But the second variable, tweedleDee, had two arguments and so the compiler knows to use the second definition of silly(). In this case, the value of the first argument is given to the member variable y, and the value of the second argument is given to member variable x. Thus, if it exists, a constructor can be used to initialize member variables. A constructor must always be public and *it is good programming practice to always define a constructor*, even if it doesn't do anything.

The next two public methods, getX() and getY() are there so that the user can access the private variables x and y. A method that exists solely to access private member variables is called an *accessor*. Notice that, just for fun, I declared the accessors in the class definition, but I didn't define them there; I defined them outside the class' curly brackets. Just as in ordinary functions, you have the option of having just a method definition, or a combination of method declaration followed by a method definition located elsewhere in your listing. The choice is yours, but the *highly recommended* practice is to break up your class definition into two parts, the first containing just the declarations and the second containing just the definitions. If you do choose to separate your class definition into two parts, you must pre-pend the class' name to the function definition. Thus, in the above example, I wrote int silly::getX(). This is necessary when the method definition occurs outside the class definition; otherwise the compiler wouldn't know that getX() is a member of the class silly. Now, instead of using an accessor, we could simply have made x and y public variables. Then from our main program we could have written:

```
q = tweedleDum.x;
```

This is simple, and saves us the trouble of creating an accessor, but is considered poor programming practice. In general, you should keep the member variables private and only access their values with (usually trivial) accessor functions. Sometimes you need to give (or change) private member variables values. To do this you need a public function. These special purpose member functions are called *mutators*. In the above example, I have two mutator functions, createY() and createY(). Note that because these particular functions do not return values, I made them of type void. (This is not a requirement of mutators; you can also create

E-15

mutators that return a value.) I separately wrote the definition of createX(). If I expect the code to compile, I'd also need to create a definition of createY().

Among the private members, I declared the two member variables x and y, and a private method f(). With the class definition given, there is no way to use f(). But in a complete class definition, there is presumably some public or private member function that would use f().

That's pretty much all there is to it. Let's go on to an actual working example. I break up the following code into three separate files, two for the class definition, and one of the program that uses the class. The two class files are sphere.h and sphere.hxx. The first of these is the so-called *header file* and contains only the class declarations. The second contains just the class method definitions.

I compile the main program in the usual way:

```
g++ testSphere.cpp -o testSphere
```

Notice that in line 2 of testSphere.cpp I could not use the usual angle brackets, but had to write the actual filename in quotes. This is because the included file is one that I wrote; it is not part of the C++ library.

Now look at the first two lines in listing E.14 which is the sphere.h header file. The first line is a conditional that says 'if SPHERE_H has not been defined, then do everything until you encounter an #endif statement' (which is placed at the very end of the sphere.h listing). The second line defines SPHERE.H. The reason you often surround your header files with these compiler directives is so that you don't accidentally try to define your class more than once (which would cause a compiler error). The header listing ends with

```
#include 'sphere.hxx'
#endif    // SPHERE_H
```

The first of these lines includes the function definitions file sphere.hxx which is given in listing E.15. And, as mentioned, the last line ends the conditional compiling block. Study listings E.14–E.16 carefully. There should not be anything there that we have not, by now, talked about.

E.7 Is that all there is?

Not by a long shot! This is just the beginning of C++. But, hopefully, we have given you enough to get started. As in many things it is best to learn to program by doing. So start doing now! Here are some ideas of simple programs you can use to practice:

- Write a program that generates the first N prime numbers, where N is inputted from the keyboard.
- Write a program that generates the first N numbers in the Fibonacci series.

```
 1 #ifndef SPHERE_H
 2 #define SPHERE_H
 3
 4 class sphere {
 5  public:
 6   // constructors:
 7   sphere(); // default constructor
 8   sphere(double x, double y, double z);
 9   sphere(double mass);
10   sphere(double x, double y, double z, double mass);
11
12   // mutators:
13   void putRadius(double r);
14   void putRadius();
15
16   void putXYZ(double x, double y, double z);
17   void putXYZ();
18
19   void putMass(double newMass);
20   void putMass();
21
22   // accessors:
23   double getVolume();
24   double getArea();
25   double getDensity();
26
27  private:
28   // methods:
29   void calcVolume();  // return volume of sphere
30   void calcArea();    // return surface area of sphere
31   void calcDensity(); // return average density of sphere
32
33   // variables:
34   double xPosition;
35   double yPosition;
36   double zPosition;
37   double radius;
38   double mass;
39   double volume;
40   double area;
41   double density;
42   bool havePosition;
43   bool haveRadius;
44   bool haveMass;
45   bool haveVolume;
46   bool haveArea;
47   bool haveDensity;
48 };
49
50 #include "sphere.hxx"
51 #endif  // SPHERE_H
```

Listing E.14: sphere.h.

- Pick a number between 0 and 1000. Now have your program guess your number by asking you questions like 'Is it larger than x?'.
    - Hint: Use bisection.
- Use iteration to solve $x = 3\cos(x)$.
- Use the 'Monte Carlo' approach to compute π:
    - Note that the area of a quarter circle is $\pi r^2/4$; if $r = 1$, the area is $\pi/4$.
    - For a square having sides of length 1, the area is 1.
    - The ratio of the area of a quarter circle to that of the circumscribed square is therefore $\pi/4$.
    - Use a random number generator to produce pairs of numbers each having values between 0 and 1. Use these as coordinates. Note that all the points lie within a square having sides of length 1, but only some of them lie inside a quarter circle having radius 1.

```
 1  #include<cmath> //for sqrts etc
 2  #define PI_ 3.14159
 3
 4  // constructors:
 5  sphere::sphere() {
 6    havePosition = false;
 7    haveRadius = false;
 8    haveMass = false;
 9    haveVolume = false;
10    haveArea = false;
11    haveDensity = false;
12  }
13
14  sphere::sphere(double x, double y, double z) {
15    putXYZ(x, y, z);
16    havePosition = true;
17    haveRadius = false;
18    haveMass = false;
19    haveVolume = false;
20    haveArea = false;
21    haveDensity = false;
22  }
23
24  sphere::sphere(double mass) {
25    putMass(mass);
26    havePosition = false;
27    haveRadius = false;
28    haveMass = false;
29    haveVolume = false;
30    haveArea = false;
31    haveDensity = false;
32  }
33
34  sphere::sphere(double x, double y, double z, double mass) {
35    putMass(mass);
36    putXYZ(x, y, z);
37    havePosition = true;
38    haveRadius = false;
39    haveMass = true;
40    haveVolume = false;
41    haveArea = false;
42    haveDensity = false;
43  }
44
45  // mutators:
46  void sphere::putRadius(double r) {
47    radius = r;
48    haveRadius = true;
49    calcVolume();
50    haveVolume = true;
51  } void sphere::putRadius() {
52    std::cout << 'Give the radius\n';
53    std::cin >> radius;
54    haveRadius = true;
55  }
56
57  void sphere::putXYZ(double x, double y, double z) {
58    xPosition = x;
59    yPosition = y;
60    zPosition = z;
61    havePosition = true;
62  }
63
64  void sphere::putXYZ() {
65    std::cout << 'Give x, y, and z coordinates\n';
66    std::cin >> xPosition >> yPosition >> zPosition;
67    havePosition = true;
68  }
69
70  void sphere::putMass(double newMass) {
```

Listing E.15: sphere.hxx.

```
71    mass = newMass;
72    haveMass = true;
73  } void sphere::putMass() {
74    std::cout << 'Give the mass\n';
75    std::cin >> mass;
76    haveMass = true;
77  }
78
79  // accessors:
80  double sphere::getVolume() { if(!haveVolume)
81    {
82      calcVolume();
83      haveVolume = true;
84    }
85    return volume;
86  }
87
88  double sphere::getArea() { if(haveArea)
89    return area;
90    std::cout << 'The area has not been computed!\n';
91    return 0.0;
92  }
93
94  double sphere::getDensity() { if(!haveDensity)
95    {
96      calcDensity();
97      haveDensity = true;
98    }
99    return density;
100 }
101
102 // private methods:
103 void sphere::calcVolume()
104 // return volume of sphere
105 {
106   if(haveRadius)
107     volume = 4.0/3.0*PI_*radius*radius*radius;
108   else
109     std::cout << 'Can't compute volume without a radius!!\n';
110 }
111
112 void sphere::calcArea()
113 // return surface area of sphere
114 {
115   if(haveRadius)
116     area = 4.0*PI_*radius*radius;
117   else
118     std::cout << 'Can't compute volume without a radius!\n';
119 }
120
121 void sphere::calcDensity()
122 // return average density of sphere
123 {
124   if(!haveVolume)
125     calcVolume();
126   if(haveMass)
127     density = mass/volume;
128   else
129     std::cout << 'Can't compute a density without a mass!\n';
130 }
```

Listing E.15: (Continued.)

```
1  #include <iostream>
2  #include 'sphere.h'  // gotta have class!
3  using namespace std;
4
5  int main() {
6    sphere bigBall;
7
8    bigBall.putRadius(1.0);
9    cout << 'The volume = ' << bigBall.getVolume() << endl;
10   bigBall.putMass(2.0);
11   cout << 'The density = ' << bigBall.getDensity() << endl;
12   return 0;
13 }
```

Listing E.16: Program testSphere.cpp that uses the sphere class.

IOP Publishing

Practical Analog, Digital, and Embedded Electronics for Scientists

Brett D DePaola

Appendix F

Moving files onto and off of a Linux USB port

You may decide that you'd like to move files off of or onto the **BBB**. For example, perhaps you'd like to archive all the nice code you've written. Or perhaps you've taken data and would like to off-load it. Or perhaps you've developed some code on your laptop and you'd like to put it onto the **BBB**. You can easily move files to and from Linux machine using a thumb drive or USB hard drive. Let's suppose you'd like to use a thumb drive. Then, just follow these instructions:

- Create a directory on your Linux machine, named for example, `~/tempdir`.
- Insert thumb drive into the USB slot.
- Wait a moment for the computer to recognize that a device has been inserted.
- Look in `/dev`. You should see 'files' named `/dev/sda` and `/dev/sda#`, where '#' is some number. Let's suppose that number is '1'.
- type: `sudo mount /dev/sda1 tempdir`.
- You should now see the contents of the thumb drive in the `tempdir` directory. You can now write to or read from `tempdir` which is, essentially equivalent to the thumb drive.
- To unmount the drive, type: `sudo umount tempdir`.
- NOTE: it really is `umount`, *not* unmount!
- Remove the thumb drive.

doi:10.1088/978-0-7503-3491-4ch28 F-1

IOP Publishing

Practical Analog, Digital, and Embedded Electronics for Scientists

Brett D DePaola

Appendix G

Introduction to Gnuplot

It is often necessary to plot the data that your embedded device is taking, and to make these plots in real-time so that you can evaluate the quality of the data. This is an extremely brief introduction to the Gnuplot plotting package. Gnuplot is available for free download and runs on virtually all platforms. Gnuplot is extremely powerful and can make extremely high quality graphs of all kinds. It can be run from a command line or, if desired, those command line expressions can be collected and placed in a script. This script can be run from the command line or even from within a program. Gnuplot can plot functions, data, and even fit data to user-supplied functions. The **BBB** does not come with Gnuplot, but it is easily installed.

G.1 Plotting functions

You get into Gnuplot by typing its name:

```
gnuplot
```

which will give you information about the version number etc and the Gnuplot command line prompt:

```
gnuplot>
```

As a first example of using Gnuplot, we can plot 'known' functions:

```
plot sin(x)
```

Gnuplot will respond by opening up a graphics window and plotting the sine function. Whenever possible, Gnuplot will auto-scale the axes and even decide on ranges, in this case, x.

You can plot in 3D as well using the `splot` command:

```
R(x,y) = x*x + y*y
splot exp(-0.2*R(x,y))*cos(R(x,y)/1.5)
```

The resulting 3D surface plot can be tweaked through adjustment of wire mesh spacing etc.

G.2 Plotting data

Suppose you have taken data and it is saved in a file named `test01.dat`. Suppose the data consist of two-columns, the left one containing x-values and the right one containing the corresponding y-values. If you want Gnuplot to plot these, just type:

```
plot 'test01.dat' using 1:2 with lines
```

The `1:2` tells Gnuplot that the horizontal coordinate is in column 1 and the vertical coordinate is in column 2. If you leave out the expression `with lines`, the plot will default to being a point-plot.

The keywords `using` and `with` can be abbreviated to `u` and `w`, respectively; this shortening of keywords to a single character is typical of most commands in Gnuplot.

Now suppose you have a file `test02.dat` in which there are three columns. The first is the x-value and the second two are $y_1(x)$ and $y_2(x)$. And suppose you'd like to plot both of them. Here's what you'd do:

```
plot 'test02.dat' u 1:2 w 1 , '' u 1:3 w 1
```

Notice how if you use an empty set of quotes, Gnuplot will assume that you mean the same file as before. If you do not specify a color, Gnuplot will decide for you, automatically making each line a different color. Notice also that I made full use of shorthand (single-characters) for the keywords. (Well, nearly full use: I could have abbreviated `plot` by `p` but chose not to in the interest of clarity.) Table G.1 shows a partial list of commonly abbreviated Gnuplot commands and their abbreviations.

You can also include error bars on your data. Suppose you have a three-column data file, `test03.dat`. The first column is x, the second is $y(x)$, and the third is the absolute error in y, i.e. $\pm\Delta y$. You can plot this by typing

```
plot 'data03.dat' u 1:2 w 1, '' u 1:2:($2-$3):($2+$3) w yerrorbars
```

This looks a bit tricky, but it's pretty simple: We plotted the data in the usual way, and then plotted the error bars. The `yerrorbars` directive expects the error will be expressed as 'y', 'minimum y', 'maximum y'. We The $ means 'the value of the data in the indicated column'. So the second part of the statement says to plot the data in columns 1 & 2; the lower bound of the error is the value $y - \Delta y$; the upper bound of the error is $y + \Delta y$.

By the way, you can plot a graph on your screen and then plot a new graph without deleting the old one. From within Gnuplot, just follow the following protocol:

Table G.1. Commonly abbreviated Gnuplot commands.

Full command	Abbreviation
index	i
every	ev
using	u
smooth	s
smooth acsplines	s acs
title	t
with lines	w l
with linespoints	w linesp or w lp
with points	w p
set terminal	set t
set output	set o
set logscale	set logsc
plot	p

```
set term wxt 0 plot sin(x)  #(or whatever you wanted to plot)
set term wxt 1
plot cos(x)  # (or whatever else you wanted to plot.)
```

(Note that you can use # to indicate a comment in Gnuplot.) You can add as many plots as you wish by using this approach.

G.3 Saving your plots

You can save your plots as png, jpeg, and other standard graphics files. Suppose you choose png. After you've gotten the plot to look the way you like, type

```
set terminal png
set output 'myGraph.png' # or whatever you want to call the png file
replot
```

Note the use of replot. This just reproduces whatever you've most recently plotted without you having to retype everything. You can set the terminal back to what it was again by typing:

```
set terminal wxt
set output
```

G.4 Fitting the data

You can also fit the data. Suppose we know that the data in the file test03.dat should resemble a Gaussian distribution and we need to know the amplitude A, the center x_0, and the width w. To fit, you first define the function you wish to fit the data to; then give the fit command. Optionally, you can give starting values to the fit parameters (usually a good idea).

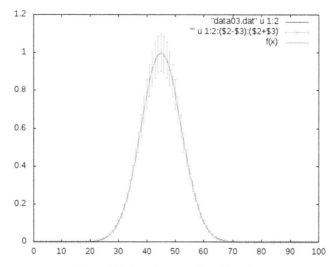

Figure G1. Sample output from Gnuplot.

Here is an example:

```
f(x) = A*exp(-(((x-x0)/w)**2)
A = 5; x0 = 15; w = 10
fit f(x) 'data03.dat' u 1:2 via A,x0,w
```

Notice how the fit command resembles the plot command. When you execute the fit command you will see text scrolling by as Gnuplot works on getting the best possible fit. Gnuplot will then show you what it thinks is the best fit (figure G1). You may see that the fit results are nonsense. In that case, make a better estimate of the fitting parameters and try again. Sometimes you might have data that follow two distinct functional forms For example, you may have $f(x) = mx + b$ for $x < $ xmin and $f(x) = c/x + d$ for $x > $ xmin. You can fit those two portions of the data separately by setting the xrange: just insert the command [xmin:ymin] fit and f(x), where the arguments of the command are the minimum and maximum values of x over which you wish to do the fit.

You can now plot the data, with the error bars, and with the fitted curve:

```
plot [xmin:xmax] 'data03.dat' u 1:2 w 1, '' u 1:2:($2-$3):($2+$3) w yerrorbars,
f(x)
```

Note the optional use of [xmin:ymin] to set the range in x over which the fit will be made. When plotting, you can set the xrange and/or yrange by putting that same command between plot and 'data03.dat'.

G.5 Writing a Gnuplot script

Very often you will have to plot similar data over and over again. Once you've figured out how to make the plots look the way you like, it can get very monotonous typing in all those Gnuplot commands every time. But you don't need to. Simply collect all the commands and put them in a file. You can then execute the script from

```
1  /*******************************************************
2   * Program: plotdata.cpp                              *
3   * Purpose: demo invoking gnuplot from inside a       *
4   *          program w/o a Gnuplot script file. Unlike *
5   *          plotfct, this example plots data with     *
6   *          error bars.                               *
7   *                                                    *
8   * Written  on 03/07/2016 by B. DePaola               *
9   * Last edit on 03/07/2016 by B. DePaola              *
10  *******************************************************/
11
12 #include <stdio.h>
13 #include <cstdlib>
14 #include <math.h>
15 #include <iostream>
16 #include <fstream>
17 #define GNUPLOT 'gnuplot -persist'
18
19 using namespace std;
20
21 struct params {
22   double amplitude ;
23   double width;
24   double center;
25 };
26
27 double gauss(params P, double x);
28
29 int main() {
30   double x, y, yerr, xMin = 0.0, xMax = 100.0, dx = 1.0;
31   double A = 1.0, W = 10.0, x0 = 45.0;
32   params gaussStuff;
33   ofstream dataout;
34   FILE *gp;
35
36   gaussStuff.amplitude = A;
37   gaussStuff.width = W;
38   gaussStuff.center = x0;
39
40   dataout.open('data03.dat');
41   for (x = xMin; x < xMax; x += dx)
42     {
43       y = gauss(gaussStuff, x);
44       yerr = 0.1*y;
45       dataout << x << '\t' << y << '\t' << yerr << endl;
46     }
47   dataout.close();
48
49   gp = popen(GNUPLOT,'w'); // 'gp' is the pipe descriptor
50   if (gp==NULL)
51     {
52       cout << 'Error opening pipe to GNU plot. Check if you have it!' << endl;
53       exit(0);
54     }
55
56   fprintf(gp, 'plot \"data03.dat\" u 1:2 w l, ');
57   fprintf(gp, ' \"\" u 1:2:($2-$3):($2+$3) w yerrorbars');
58   fprintf(gp, '\npause -1\n');
59   fclose(gp);
60
61   return 0;
62 }
63
64 double gauss(params P, double x) {
65   double x2, w2;
66
67   x2 = (x - P.center)*(x - P.center);
68   w2 = P.width * P.width;
69   return P.amplitude*exp(-x2/w2);
70 }
```

Listing G.1: Using Gnuplot to plot data from within a C++ program.

the Linux command line. For example, if we put the commands in a file called plotData.gp (the extension can be whatever you like, but standard is gp) then you can execute the script by typing:

```
gnuplot plotData.gp
```

Most likely if you do this, you'll see the plot come and go in a flash. This is because once the script has been executed, you are returned to the Linux command prompt. To fix this, just make the last line of your script:

```
pause -1
```

The number following the pause command is the number of seconds that Gnuplot will wait before returning to the Linux command line. A negative number tells Gnuplot to wait until you type enter before it quits.

G.6 Plotting data from within a program

Here's the listing of a simple program that generates a curve, with 'errors', and calls Gnuplot to plot it (listing G.1).

There is a great deal of information about gnuplot out on the web and you really should look into it so you can get the most out of this free and very powerful plotting and fitting package.

IOP Publishing

Practical Analog, Digital, and Embedded Electronics for Scientists

Brett D DePaola

Appendix H

spidev.c Listing

```
1  /*
2   * SPI testing utility (using spidev driver)
3   *
4   * Copyright (c) 2007  MontaVista Software, Inc.
5   * Copyright (c) 2007  Anton Vorontsov <avorontsov@ru.mvista.com>
6   *
7   * This program is free software; you can redistribute it and/or modify
8   * it under the terms of the GNU General Public License as published by
9   * the Free Software Foundation; either version 2 of the License.
10  *
11  * Cross-compile with cross-gcc -I/path/to/cross-kernel/include
12  */
13
14 #include <stdint.h>
15 #include <unistd.h>
16 #include <stdio.h>
17 #include <stdlib.h>
18 #include <getopt.h>
19 #include <fcntl.h>
20 #include <sys/ioctl.h>
21 #include <linux/types.h>
22 #include <linux/spi/spidev.h>
23
24 #define ARRAY_SIZE(a) (sizeof(a) / sizeof((a)[0]))
25
26 static void pabort(const char *s) {
27     perror(s);
28     abort();
29 }
30
31 static const char *device = "/dev/spidev1.0"; static uint8_t mode; static
32 uint8_t bits = 8; static uint32_t speed = 500000; static uint16_t delay;
33
34 static void transfer(int fd) {
35     int ret;
36     uint8_t tx[] = {
37         0xFF, 0xFF, 0xFF, 0xFF, 0xFF, 0xFF,
38         0x40, 0x00, 0x00, 0x00, 0x00, 0x95,
39         0xFF, 0xFF, 0xFF, 0xFF, 0xFF, 0xFF,
40         0xFF, 0xFF, 0xFF, 0xFF, 0xFF, 0xFF,
41         0xFF, 0xFF, 0xFF, 0xFF, 0xFF, 0xFF,
42         0xDE, 0xAD, 0xBE, 0xEF, 0xBA, 0xAD,
```

```
43          0xF0, 0x0D,
44      };
45      uint8_t rx[ARRAY_SIZE(tx)] = {0, };
46      struct spi_ioc_transfer tr = {
47          .tx_buf = (unsigned long)tx,
48          .rx_buf = (unsigned long)rx,
49          .len = ARRAY_SIZE(tx),
50          .delay_usecs = delay,
51          .speed_hz = speed,
52          .bits_per_word = bits,
53      };
54
55      ret = ioctl(fd, SPI_IOC_MESSAGE(1), &tr);
56      if (ret < 1)
57          pabort("can't send spi message");
58
59      for (ret = 0; ret < ARRAY_SIZE(tx); ret++) {
60          if (!(ret % 6))
61              puts("");
62          printf("%.2X ", rx[ret]);
63      }
64      puts("");
65  }
66
67  static void print_usage(const char *prog) {
68      printf("Usage: %s [-DsbdlHOLC3]\n", prog);
69      puts("  -D --device   device to use (default /dev/spidev1.1)\n"
70           "  -s --speed    max speed (Hz)\n"
71           "  -d --delay    delay (usec)\n"
72           "  -b --bpw      bits per word \n"
73           "  -l --loop     loopback\n"
74           "  -H --cpha     clock phase\n"
75           "  -O --cpol     clock polarity\n"
76           "  -L --lsb      least significant bit first\n"
77           "  -C --cs-high  chip select active high\n"
78           "  -3 --3wire    SI/SO signals shared\n");
79      exit(1);
80  }
81
82  static void parse_opts(int argc, char *argv[]) {
83      while (1) {
84          static const struct option lopts[] = {
85              { "device",  1, 0, 'D' },
86              { "speed",   1, 0, 's' },
87              { "delay",   1, 0, 'd' },
88              { "bpw",     1, 0, 'b' },
89              { "loop",    0, 0, 'l' },
90              { "cpha",    0, 0, 'H' },
91              { "cpol",    0, 0, 'O' },
92              { "lsb",     0, 0, 'L' },
93              { "cs-high", 0, 0, 'C' },
94              { "3wire",   0, 0, '3' },
95              { "no-cs",   0, 0, 'N' },
96              { "ready",   0, 0, 'R' },
97              { NULL, 0, 0, 0 },
98          };
99          int c;
100
101         c = getopt_long(argc, argv, "D:s:d:b:lHOLC3NR", lopts, NULL);
102
103         if (c == -1)
104             break;
105
```

```
106            switch (c) {
107            case 'D':
108                device = optarg;
109                break;
110            case 's':
111                speed = atoi(optarg);
112                break;
113            case 'd':
114                delay = atoi(optarg);
115                break;
116            case 'b':
117                bits = atoi(optarg);
118                break;
119            case 'l':
120                mode |= SPI_LOOP;
121                break;
122            case 'H':
123                mode |= SPI_CPHA;
124                break;
125            case 'O':
126                mode |= SPI_CPOL;
127                break;
128            case 'L':
129                mode |= SPI_LSB_FIRST;
130                break;
131            case 'C':
132                mode |= SPI_CS_HIGH;
133                break;
134            case '3':
135                mode |= SPI_3WIRE;
136                break;
137            case 'N':
138                mode |= SPI_NO_CS;
139                break;
140            case 'R':
141                mode |= SPI_READY;
142                break;
143            default:
144                print_usage(argv[0]);
145                break;
146            }
147    }
148 }
149
150 int main(int argc, char *argv[]) {
151    int ret = 0;
152    int fd;
153
154    parse_opts(argc, argv);
155
156    fd = open(device, O_RDWR);
157    if (fd < 0)
158        pabort("can't open device");
159
160    /*
161     * spi mode
162     */
163    ret = ioctl(fd, SPI_IOC_WR_MODE, &mode);
164    if (ret == -1)
165        pabort("can't set spi mode");
166
167    ret = ioctl(fd, SPI_IOC_RD_MODE, &mode);
168    if (ret == -1)
```

```
169        pabort("can't get spi mode");
170
171    /*
172     * bits per word
173     */
174    ret = ioctl(fd, SPI_IOC_WR_BITS_PER_WORD, &bits);
175    if (ret == -1)
176        pabort("can't set bits per word");
177
178    ret = ioctl(fd, SPI_IOC_RD_BITS_PER_WORD, &bits);
179    if (ret == -1)
180        pabort("can't get bits per word");
181
182    /*
183     * max speed hz
184     */
185    ret = ioctl(fd, SPI_IOC_WR_MAX_SPEED_HZ, &speed);
186    if (ret == -1)
187        pabort("can't set max speed hz");
188
189    ret = ioctl(fd, SPI_IOC_RD_MAX_SPEED_HZ, &speed);
190    if (ret == -1)
191        pabort("can't get max speed hz");
192
193    printf('spi mode: %d\n', mode);
194    printf('bits per word: %d\n', bits);
195    printf("max speed: %d Hz (%d KHz)\n", speed, speed/1000);
196
197    transfer(fd);
198
199    close(fd);
200
201    return ret;
202 }
```

IOP Publishing

Practical Analog, Digital, and Embedded Electronics for Scientists

Brett D DePaola

Appendix I

Pinouts of selected components

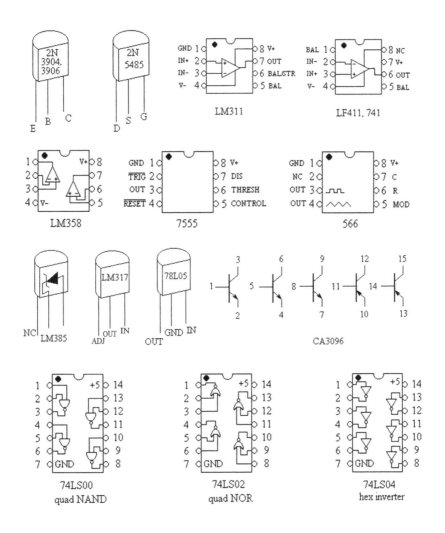

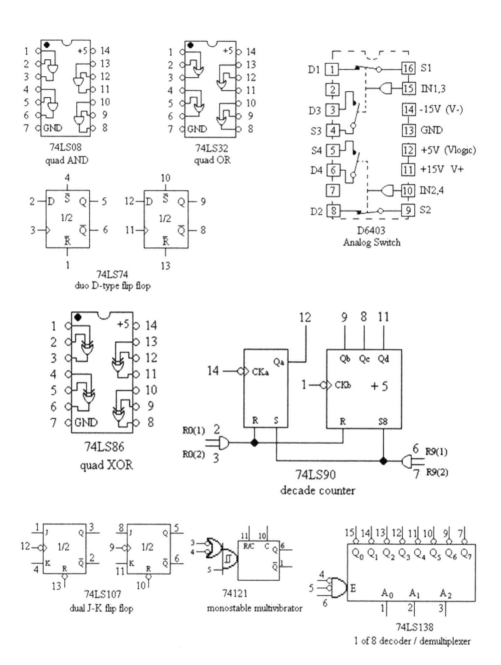

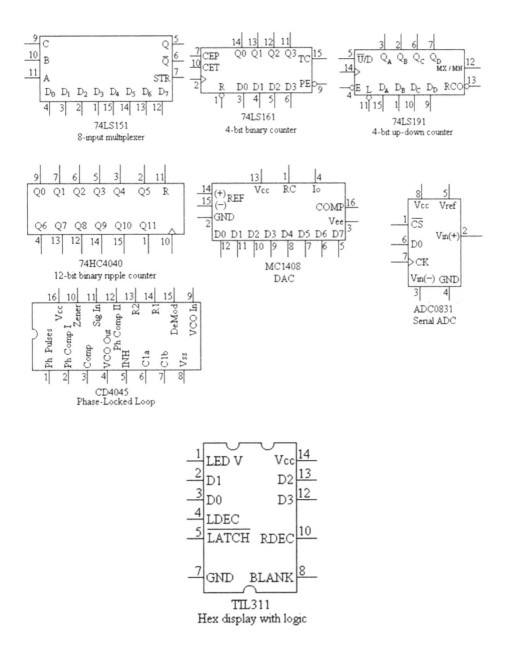

74LS151
8-input multiplexer

74LS161
4-bit binary counter

74LS191
4-bit up-down counter

74HC4040
12-bit binary ripple counter

MC1408
DAC

ADC0831
Serial ADC

CD4045
Phase-Locked Loop

TIL311
Hex display with logic

IOP Publishing

Practical Analog, Digital, and Embedded Electronics for Scientists

Brett D DePaola

Appendix J

Setting up the Beaglebone Black

If you are running Debian, then you can easily make a flash backup on a micro SD card by following the following steps:
1. Boot master BBB without the SD card inserted.
2. Insert SD card.
3. Log in (e.g. with serial terminal, SSH etc) and run

```
sudo /opt/scripts/tools/eMMC/beaglebone-black-make-microSD-flasher-from-eMMC.sh
```

The LEDs will flash in sequence whilst SD card is being written. This will take about 20 min.
4. When the LEDs stop and the script terminates, unpower the board. (A sudo reboot is not enough.)
5. Remove the SD card.

To flash a system from an SD card to a Beaglebone:
1. Insert SD card into new BBB then insert the external power jack (not the USB) while holding down the boot button (the button above the SD card).
2. Keep holding the boot button until the LEDs start blinking.
3. Let go of the boot button and wait until the LEDs are all lit up (success) or all off (failure). This could take up to about an hour.
4. Disconnect the power and remove the SD card.
5. The new system should now be on the BBB and you should be able to boot and log on in the usual manner.

doi:10.1088/978-0-7503-3491-4ch32

IOP Publishing

Practical Analog, Digital, and Embedded Electronics for Scientists

Brett D DePaola

Appendix K

Parts lists

K.1 Total parts

Component values are followed by the lab in which they are used. Numbers in brackets indicate the minimum number of components required (if greater than 1) (tables K1–K8).

Table K1. Resistors sorted, by lab chapter number. Bracketed number indicates the minimum number required for that lab.

Resistors, 5%

100	10	**120**	16	**180**	12
330	11	**390**	12	**470**	11
560	13	**680**	11	**820**	11
1k	11, 12, 13, 14[2], 15[3]	**2k**	13, 15	**2.2k**	11
2.7k	13, 15	**3.3k**	11, 12	**4.7k**	13
6.2k	11, 15	**6.8k**	11	**7.5k**	11, 15
10k	10, 11, 12[2], 13[2], 15, 16	**15k**	10, 12	**68k**	11
75k	11	**100k**	12, 13[2], 15	**110k**	11
150k	11	**1.8M**	15[2]	**10M**	12, 15

Table K2. Capacitors sorted, by lab chapter number. Bracketed number indicates the minimum number required for that lab.

Capacitors

100 pF	10, 12	**270 pF**	15	**0.001 μF**	13, 15
0.01 μF	10, 12, 13[2], 15	**0.1 μF**	11, 13, 15	**0.33 μF**	11
1.0 μF	11, 16	**4.7 μF**	11	**15 μF**	11

Table K3. Potentiometers, sorted by lab chapter number.

Potentiometers						
2.5k	15	**10k**	11, 12, 16	**25k**	16	**50k**	12, 13

Table K4. Diodes, sorted by lab chapter number.

Diodes					
1N4148	12, 15	**LED**	14, 15, 16	**PIN125**	15

Table K5. Transistors, sorted by lab chapter number.

Transistors			
2N3904	11, 12, 16	**2N3906**	11, 12, 13

Table K6. Linear Devices, sorted by lab chapter number. Bracketed number indicates the minimum number required for that lab.

Linear					
LF411	12, 13, 15[2]	**LM311**	13, 15	**7555**	13

Table K7. Digital devices, sorted by lab chapter number. Bracketed number indicates the minimum number required for that lab.

Digital					
74LS00	14	**74LS02**	14	**74LS04**	14
74LS74	14, 15	**74LS121**	15	**74LS151**	14
74LS161	14	**74LS191**	15[2]	**74HC595**	16
TIL311	14, 15	**AD630**	15	**MC1408**	15
2Y0A21	16	**ADXL345**	16		

Table K8. Other parts, sorted by lab chapter number.

Other					
Ammeter	11, 12	**#1869 lamp**	13	**switch (SPDT)**	14, 15
switch (pushbutton)	16	**Beaglebone Black**	16	**HS422**	16

K.2 Parts listed by lab

[Number in bracket indicates the minimum required quantity of that component.]

Chapter 10

    Resistors: **100, 10k, 15k**

    Capacitors: **100 pF, 0.01 μF**

Chapter 11

    Resistors: **330, 470, 680, 820, 1k, 2.2k, 3.3k, 6.2k, 6.8k, 7.5k, 10k, 68k, 75k, 110k, 150k**

    Capacitors: **0.1 μF, 0.33 μF, 1.0 μF, 4.7 μF, 15 μF**

    Pots: **10k**

    Transistors: **2N3904, 2N3906**

    Other: **ammeter**

Chapter 12

    Resistors: **180, 390, 1k, 3.3k, 10k[2], 15k, 100k, 10M**

    Capacitors: **100 pF, 0.01 μF**

    Pots: **10k, 50k**

    diodes: **1N4148[2]**

    Transistors: **2N3904, 2N3906**

    Linear: **LF411**

    Other: **ammeter**

Chapter 13

    Resistors: **560, 1k, 2k, 2.7k, 4.7k, 10k[2], 100k[2]**

    Capacitors: **0.001 μF, 0.01 μF[2], 0.1 μF**

    Pots: **50k**

    Transistors: **2N3906**

    Linear: **LM311, LF411, 7555**

    Other: **#1869 lamp**

Chapter 14

    Resistors: **1k[2]**

    Diodes: **LED**

    Digital: **74LS00, 74LS02, 74LS04, 74LS74, 74LS151, 74LS161, TIL311**

    Other: **SPDT switch**

Chapter 15

    Resistors: **1k[3], 2k, 2.7k, 6.2k, 7.5k, 10k, 100k, 1.8M[2], 10M**

    Capacitors: **270 pF, 0.001 μF, 0.01μF, 0.1 μF**

    Pots: **2.5k**

    Diodes: **1N4148, PIN125, LED**

    Linear: **LF411[2], LM311**

    Digital: **74LS74, 74LS121, 74LS191[2], MC1408, TIL311, AD630**

Other: **SPST switch**

Chapter 16

Resistors: **120, 10k**
Capacitors: **1 μF**
Pots: **10k, 25k**
Diodes: **LED**
Transistors: **2N3904**
Digital: **2Y0A21, ADXL345, 74HC595**
Other: **Pushbutton switch, HS422, Beaglebone Black**